W9-COY-099

NATIONAL
GEOGRAPHIC

COMPLETE GUIDE TO
BRAIN
HEALTH

NATIONAL
GEOGRAPHIC

COMPLETE GUIDE TO
BRAIN
HEALTH

How to Stay Sharp, Improve Memory, and Boost Creativity

Michael S. Sweeney
Including "Brain Boosters" by Cynthia R. Green, Ph.D.

NATIONAL GEOGRAPHIC
WASHINGTON D.C.

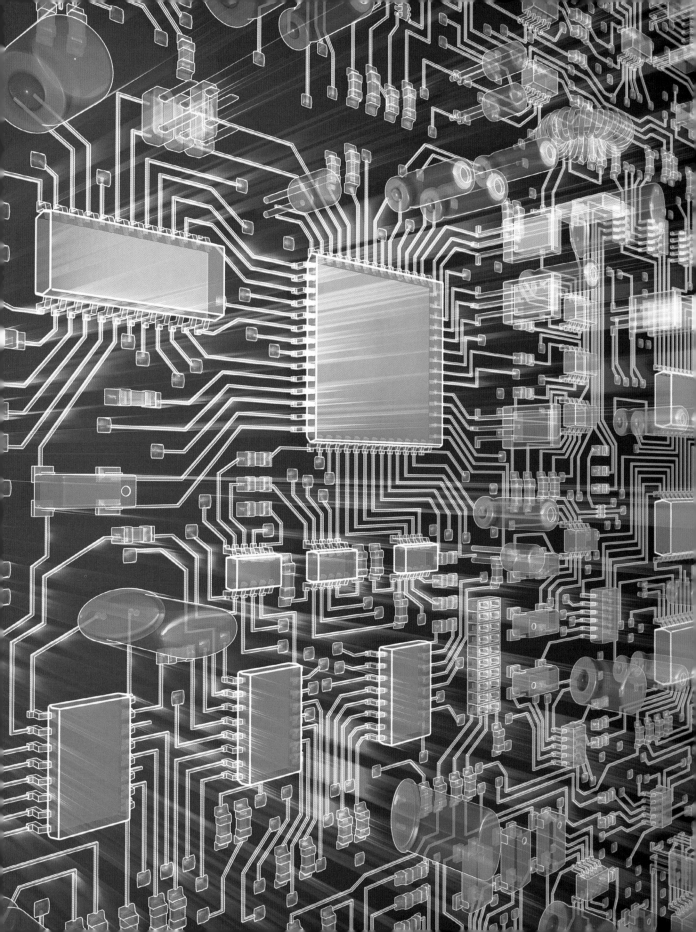

CONTENTS

INTRODUCTION

The Nuns of Mankato

By all accounts, Sister Nicolette Welter was born to teach, but like the rest of her 1927 vows class, the nun from Mankato, Minnesota, may be giving her best lessons posthumously. Though she died in 2010 at age 102, she left her brain behind.

Affectionately nicknamed the Last Nun Standing because she outlived the rest of her class, and because she remained an upright fixture in every reunion photo, Sister Nicolette was one of the original School Sisters of Notre Dame who volunteered for perhaps the most seminal inquiry on aging and brain health to date. Eventually, 678 participants would consent to donate their brains to what would become known as simply the Nun Study.

In 1986, Dr. David Snowdon, an epidemiologist seeking to unravel the mysteries of aging, identified nuns as a textbook control group for a pilot project he began while completing his doctorate. Nuns are well educated and lead healthy, similar lives. But above all, most seem to enjoy a long, vigorous life, staying sharp through their ninth or tenth decades.

How? Was it as simple as refraining from tobacco and alcohol?

Snowdon discovered a remarkable clue in the Mankato archive. Eighty years ago, before a young postulant could take her first vows, she had to submit an informal autobiographical essay. Decades later, Snowdon found a meticulously maintained archive awaiting him, which he and colleagues used to supplement their mental and physical evaluations of living subjects.

Upon convening to share data, the team found their results mostly agreed. If the psychological evaluation turned up an Alzheimer's diagnosis, the brain examinations usually followed suit, with an abundance of plaques and tangles in brain cells. But the good stuff came when their diagnoses differed. How to account for a psychological score of 1 or 2—the severity of Alzheimer's is traditionally measured on a 7-point scale—when, upon dissection, the sister's brain practically had "Alzheimer's!" inscribed across the prefrontal lobe?

Perhaps, Snowdon guessed, a sister who had established a thicket of neural connections in her youth might avoid the diminishing effect of Alzheimer's even if her aged brain displayed the notorious cellular lesions. To test this hypothesis, he commissioned a linguist to scrutinize those decades-old essays, analyzing them primarily for idea density—the number of propositions per sentence, for example—which might reflect a similar density of neural connections in the writer's brain.

What they discovered astonished them. Ninety percent of those writers who rated in the lowest percentile for idea density would later show symptoms of Alzheimer's, while only 13 percent of healthy individuals had low idea density.

Snowdon directed the Nun Study until his recent retirement, unearthing mountains of data that correlate brain health and longevity to even such abstract factors as emotional outlook and communal living. In the spirit of Sister Nicolette, this book aims to pass on science's understanding of how to maintain your brain health today, and venture a guess as to how the brain of the future will look.

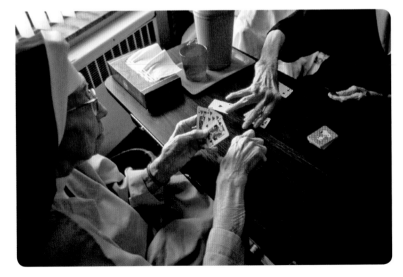

PLAYING THEIR CARDS RIGHT
Nuns at the Mankato convent showed the long-term benefits of staying mentally engaged.

About This Book

From the details of brain structure through descriptions of how your brain senses and remembers the world, and on to the startling future of brain research, the *National Geographic Complete Guide to Brain Health* not only explains the workings of your body's most complex organ, but also gives you a daily plan for keeping it sharp. In three parts and 17 chapters, you will learn how the brain works, how you can nurture its many functions, and how advances in biology and computer science may transform your life.

In addition to "Brain Insight" sidebars that highlight fascinating aspects of the text, illustrated "Brain Booster" sidebars created

Section header ·········

Brain Booster sidebar ········

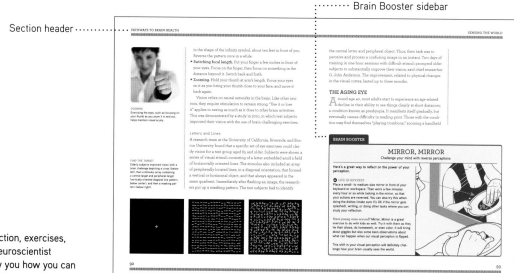

BRAIN BOOSTERS
In the book's central section, exercises, games, and tips from neuroscientist Dr. Cynthia Green show you how you can boost your brain health in enjoyable ways.

by brain fitness expert Dr. Cynthia Green will give you dozens of easy and practical techniques and tips for boosting your memory, building your language skills, improving creativity, and generally strengthening your brain to stave off the effects of aging. Fascinating brain facts and extensive photography and art will help you understand the extraordinary abilities of your own extraordinary brain.

Photos throughout illustrate key concepts.

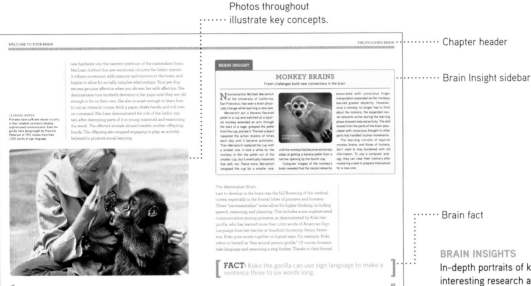

Chapter header

Brain Insight sidebar

Brain fact

BRAIN INSIGHTS
In-depth portraits of key personalities and interesting research are found in "Brain Insight" sidebars throughout the book.

Seventeen chapters range from brain anatomy to brain futures.

CHAPTERS
Each chapter highlights a different aspect of the brain, its interconnected parts, and its abilities.

PART 1

Welcome to

Your Brain

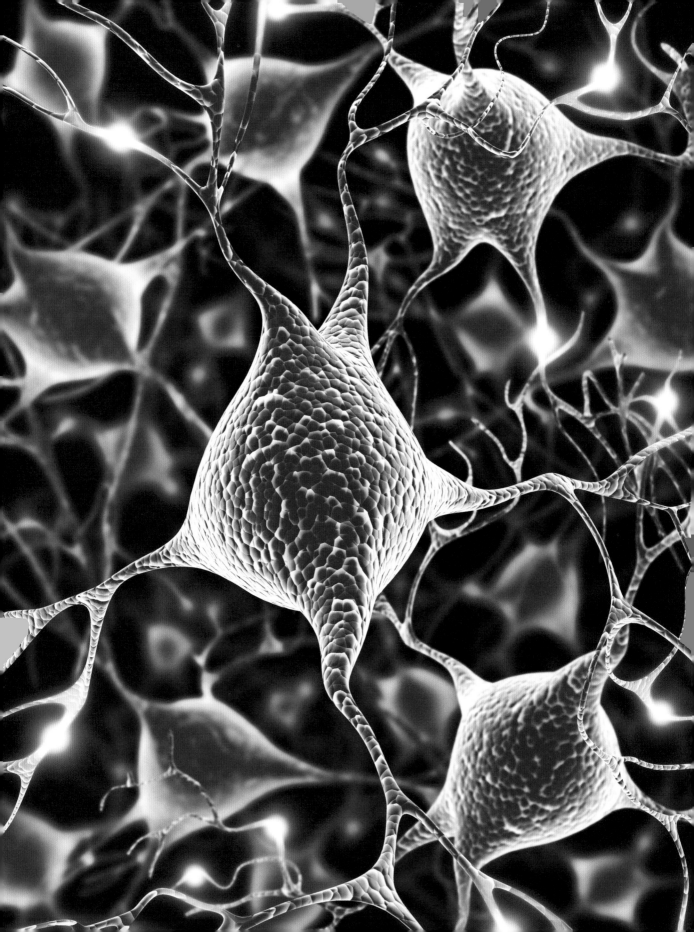

> *"The Brain—is wider than the Sky—*
> *For—put them side by side—*
> *The one the other will contain*
> *With ease—and You—beside"*
> EMILY DICKINSON

AN INTRICATE STRUCTURE
You can change your brain

In your brain, billions of cells called neurons connect without touching. This allows them to change how they work together, reconfiguring your brain as you have new experiences and thoughts. Large structures remain relatively intact, keeping your organs functioning, your muscles contracting, and your senses collecting and processing information. But as you think and learn, your brain forges new neural circuits. Changes are particularly evident in your uniquely human cerebral cortex. Your brain today is not the same as the one you had yesterday. That means it's never too early or too late to change your life to improve the health of your brain. And if you do that—if you pamper your billions of neurons through diet, physical and mental exercise, and precautions to minimize risk of injury or illness—you'll take the best steps to increase your chances of having a rich, long life.

CHAPTER 1

Healthy Brains Mean Long Lives

CHANGEABLE CELLS
(Preceding pages) The brain's web of neurons is constantly being rewired.

NEVER TOO LATE
(Opposite) You can take steps at any age, like the joggers at right, to improve your brain.

Your brain's health may be the most powerful indicator of how long you will live. It is crucial to whether that life will be rich and satisfying from youth well into old age, or something substantially less rewarding, and for less time.

A car driven wisely, fueled with high-quality gasoline, given regular oil changes, and repaired with new parts as old ones wear out is likely to last longer than one that's abused or neglected. Likewise, the easiest way to have a healthy brain in middle age and beyond is to start with one as a youth and to follow good physical and mental habits. Exercise it. Feed it. Challenge it. Then enjoy the rewards.

But what of the person who comes late to repairs, like the owner of a car that rusts for years on blocks or runs too long on dirty oil? The car owner can always swap out the engine. You, on the other hand, have only one brain, basically composed of the same neurons you were born with, plus a few added to some narrowly specific areas. Once they've begun to deteriorate, can they be saved—or even made stronger?

Brain researcher Marian Diamond is certain they can.

In the 1960s, Diamond compared two groups of lab rats. The first group was confined to the equivalent of a gray isolation cell

STAY YOUTHFUL
Enriching experiences, such as the joy of playing with others and learning new things, spread new connections throughout the circuits of the brain, increasing its complexity.

in a maximum-security prison. They ate simple rations to keep them alive from day to day, but their brains received little stimulation. No rat games, no rat puzzles, no rat get-togethers to break the boredom. She enrolled the second group in a version of rat school, complete with recess. They had toys and balls for play, challenging mazes to explore, exercise equipment to get blood pumping to their muscles and their neurons, and best of all, other rats to share their experiences. When she pitted the two in timed contests in which they ran the same mazes, the rats that had lived in the mentally and physically invigorating environment performed much better.

[FACT: Most babies learn to walk about a year after birth, but they are born with the neural program already hardwired. **]**

MAKING STRONGER BRAINS

Diamond then did what she could not do to humans in a similar experiment. She put both winners and losers under the knife to examine their brains. (Life's not fair, especially for a rodent.) Rats that had enjoyed the richer learning environment and had won the maze races exhibited markedly different brains from those in the control group. Their cerebral cortices—the outer, wrinkled shells that are home to neural pathways that make sense of the world—were thicker than those of the unstimulated rats. The enriched-brain rats had more neural connections, a sign of greater mental activity. And they had more blood vessels to carry vital oxygen to keep those connections firing at peak efficiency. Diamond had gathered concrete evidence that what goes on in the mind manifests itself in the physical state of the brain. Learning strengthens the organ of the brain just as exercise strengthens muscles in the legs, arms, and abdomen.

BRAIN INSIGHT

THE RECORD HOLDER

Jeanne Calment lived for 122 years on chocolate, exercise, and equanimity

The oldest person of verifiable age was a good example of the lifelong benefits of staying mentally and physically active.

Official records have confirmed Jeanne Calment's birth on February 21, 1875, in Arles, France. From that day until 1997, she spent many of her 122 years and 164 days staying fit by playing tennis, hunting, skating, and swimming. She rode a bicycle until she turned 100, and spent her centennial birthday walking to neighbors' homes.

Calment stimulated her mind with opera and piano. Although her vision and hearing deteriorated in her final

years, she remained remarkably healthy nearly until the end.

As for her diet, she enjoyed chocolate and red wine, a combination linked in scientific studies to lowered blood

pressure, reduced risk of heart disease, and delayed progression of dementia. On the other hand, she smoked cigarettes nearly all her life.

Significantly, Calment stayed unflappable. Jean-Marie Robine, a demographer who interviewed her, called Calment "immune to stress. She once said, 'If you can't do anything about it, don't worry about it.' "

Calment even found it difficult to stay upset at the notoriously irascible Vincent van Gogh, whom she knew when he painted in Arles. She later called him "very ugly, ungracious, impolite, sick," but added, "I forgive him."

As revealing as Diamond's research was, it had a twist: She didn't experiment on young rats. She chose to work with rats in middle age and older, equal to ages between 60 and 90 in humans. Old rats had brains they could reshape in response to new experiences, a condition known as plasticity.

That's good news, and not just for rats. The structure of the brain remains remarkably similar for all mammals. What works for mice, dogs, horses, and monkeys works for humans as well. Diamond took comfort in her findings that the brain can change at any age. Older brains take longer to respond to healthy living, but they do respond. "We're saying that if you use your brain, you can change it as much as a younger brain," she said.

GOODBYE TO THE MYTHS

That revelation changed widespread beliefs about the plasticity of older brains. Studies with young rats, cats, and other mammals had suggested that the brain opened a crucial window for learning during youth, and then closed it.

For instance, in a series of famous experiments in the 1960s, neurobiologists David Hubel and Torsten Wiesel took a group of kittens and sewed one of each pair of eyes shut at birth but left the other untouched. At six months, they opened the closed eye. Although the eye was physically sound, the kitten never learned to see through it.

The experiment demonstrated that the kitten's brain had been wired to expect, and process, visual information at a crucial time in development. When that time passed, those abilities were gone forever. Scientists call this type of brain development "experience-expectant," meaning the brain awaits the stimulus of a particular experience, such as sight or sound, to develop the means to process that information.

EYES LIKE A CAT
Hunter and Wiesel used kittens, like the one below, to demonstrate the brain's extreme sensitivity to developing functions such as vision at an early age.

Shaped by Your Surroundings

But there's a second category of brain-developing experiences. These are called "experience-dependent." They prompt brain growth in response not to stimuli common to the species, such as light and sound, but rather to the individual's unique environment. A child raised in the Amazon jungle learns a lot about plants and animals of the rain forest. A child growing up in the suburbs figures out how to play on the jungle gym and swings, or to swim in a pool or kick a soccer ball. This second type of brain development can occur at any time. Some types of learning, such as mastery of a second language, are easier before the age of puberty, but on the other hand, vocabulary building occurs throughout life. In general, there is no single, crucial time window for this kind of learning. Your brain can learn experience-dependent knowledge at any time.

YOUR OWN WORLD
Your environment triggers patterns of brain development. Children adapt to their local surroundings, whether rain forest, arctic tundra, or city playground.

This means it doesn't make much sense to immerse your child in the world of Mozart in hopes of stimulating intelligence—musical or otherwise. Literacy for children who come relatively late to reading sometimes outdistances that of children taught to read at the earliest possible moment. Experts such as William Greenough at the University of Illinois suggest parents should stop worrying so much about enriching a child's environment. The "rich" environment of lab rat studies closely matches the normal environment of a child. Even if a child doesn't have toys, he or she has a complex world of grass, sidewalks, furniture, carpets, clothes, and so on to navigate, and thus learn how to engage with the world.

EXERCISING NEURONS
People practice tai chi in Shanghai, China. All brain regions, including those associated with movement and balance, improve when challenged.

THE VALUE OF AGE

All parts of the brain, not just the ones related to higher forms of thinking, can be improved through stimulating challenges—at any age. Someone who wants to improve balance can take up tai chi at age 30 or 90. Wii bowling improves eye–hand coordination and the ability to focus attention just as well for senior citizens as for teenagers.

The brain's plasticity reveals much about its amazing structure. It is the most complicated object in the universe, composed of billions of independent units that work together in remarkably complex symphonies that manage to comprehend the world; process, store, and retrieve information; and use that information to decide how to interact with the world. Each new experience changes the brain's physical makeup, so that by the time you finish reading this page, your brain will be slightly different from your brain at the time you began with the page's first word.

> Each new **EXPERIENCE** changes the brain's physical makeup.

BRAIN INSIGHT

FOOLING MOTHER NATURE

Leonard Hayflick explains that you weren't meant to live that long, anyway

Aging is an artifact of civilization. So says Leonard Hayflick, a founding member of the National Institute on Aging and leading expert on how and why people grow old. It was Hayflick who, in the 1960s, discovered the so-called "Hayflick limit," the maximum number of times a species' cells can divide before growing senescent. For humans, it's about 50. For the Galápagos turtle, which can live up to 200 years, it's 90.

Wild animals seldom get to test the Hayflick limit. Illness, injury, starvation, and predation take their toll long before an animal has the chance to die of old age. Your pet dog or cat would never grow long in the tooth if you weren't around to take care of it. Similarly, you would have a much, much smaller chance of growing old if not for the gifts of modern medicine, food, clothing, and shelter.

"Nature planned things so that we would die well before we became old," Hayflick wrote. "If you believe that nature does things with a purpose, then aging is a phenomenon that nature never intended us to experience."

Such a view turns efforts to enjoy a long, healthy life into attempts to fool Mother Nature.

ALDABRA GIANT TORTOISE

The Virtues of Novelty

Repeating familiar experiences is good, up to a point. Practicing an old favorite on the guitar changes the brain in ways that improve future performances; practicing the lyrics to the Italian folk song your mother sang as a child will help keep the words and melody fresh long after she is gone. But the best stimulation for the brain, young or old, is novelty.

Even rats given a nest full of colorful toys find them boring after a while, as playing with them fires the same well-worn neural pathways and takes less and less mental effort. New experiences—new ways to learn—keep the brain more robust at any age because they grow new connections among the brain's neural circuitry. And the more connections the brain has, the better able it will be to stand up to the changes brought about by normal aging and disease.

LEARNING AT ANY AGE
An elderly brain can learn anything, such as the latest computer technology, albeit a bit slower than a youthful one.

The Effects of Time

Time works against the brain in three ways. When the brain reacts negatively to aging, it does so through disease, disuse, and physical changes associated with aging itself. Diseases become more common with age, and many attack the brain. They range from strokes, which kill brain cells by cutting off the blood supply, to cancerous tumors and dementia. Disuse causes neglected neural connections to fade, eventually severing connections entirely. Who, in middle or old age, hasn't forgotten vast chunks of high school trigonometry, if never used since age 18, or become rusty at chess after years without a challenging opponent?

Finally, aging itself prunes some of the brain's neural thickets, eliminating some neurons and leaving the remaining ones

BRAIN INSIGHT

LEARNING IN RETIREMENT

Virtual games can produce real results for the elderly

Who needs a ball?

Among the senior set, virtual bowling using handheld Wii motion-sensing controllers and consoles has caught on as a low-impact way to enhance cardiovascular function, mobility, mental focus, and the invigorating social connections of old-time bowling leagues. In 2007, Erickson Retirement Communities began a national Wii bowling championship, complete with trophies and funky-colored team shirts.

"It's a very social thing and it's good exercise . . . and you don't have to throw a 16-pound bowling ball to get results," retirement center Wii bowler

Flora Dierbach, in her 70s, told a television interviewer. "We just had a ball with it."

WII SPORTS

Exercise by the elderly has been shown to diminish the risk of falls, increase mobility, and possibly fight dementia. Yet only about one in eight Americans between ages 65 and 74, and one in 16 over age 75, reports performing robust physical activity for at least 20 minutes three times a week.

For many, it's a big step just to get outside and walk, much less do something more vigorous. For some, reliance on a wheelchair makes many exercises impossible.

But thanks to virtual games such as Wii bowling, thousands of seniors are getting exercise to spare.

susceptible to the cumulative effects of a lifetime of exposure to toxins and other natural chemical agents.

And yet, practically everyone knows a person who has lived to 80, 90, or beyond while remaining mentally healthy. The brain of a healthy senior citizen processes information more slowly than a youthful one, but once it has learned something, it keeps it as treasure to be used again and again. A mature or elderly brain is an experienced one. It calls upon a lifetime of memories to analyze a problem, and chooses a response with reasoned care. Old lawyers, doctors, and pilots may be wiser about their professions than younger peers because they have had more experiences that have enriched the neural connections dealing with their craft.

[FACT: Brain scans confirm that adults have greater control over their emotions than adolescents. **]**

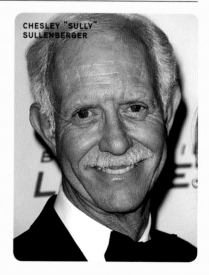

THE WISDOM OF AGE AND EXPERIENCE

MALE OR FEMALE?
The brain has extremely fine perceptive skills, which can be cultivated. So-called "chicken sexers" sort male and female chicks based on indescribably fine details that are indistinguishable to nonexperts.

This is the quality of wisdom that leads many cultures to revere elders. Japanese people, for example, associate wrinkles and gray hair with wisdom. Japan also provides an excellent example of experience-dependent wisdom at any age. In his book *Incognito*, Baylor University neuroscientist David Eagleman describes the way experienced Japanese chicken experts teach students how to tell the sex of a chick. The poultry industry wants female chickens. Males cannot lay eggs and they have stringy meat, so they're not economically desirable. Therefore, the industry's business plan calls for investment in feeding and raising female chicks, while culling most male chicks as soon as possible, rather than spending money to raise them without hope of financial return.

BRAIN INSIGHT

THE WISE, OLD BRAIN

A flawless emergency landing shows there's no substitute for experience

Landing a powerless passenger plane safely on the Hudson River was "the ultimate challenge of a lifetime," said U.S. Airways Captain Chesley "Sully" Sullenberger.

Good thing he had spent a lifetime preparing his brain for just that moment.

Not that Sullenberger had drilled for the specific scenario of January 2009, when his plane encountered birds shortly after takeoff from LaGuardia Airport and his engines cut out. Instead, his four decades of flying experience had built up the skills, judgment, and knowledge to make decisions that saved all 155 aboard.

Older brains don't manipulate information or reach conclusions as swiftly as younger ones. But their maturity—memories filtered by wise judgment—often leads them to the best conclusion.

"Never in the most demanding flight simulator training session had we practiced the entirety of those challenges, at such a low altitude, at such a low speed, in such a short time frame," Sullenberger told an interviewer. What he could do, however, was synthesize portions of the airborne emergencies he had practiced and find a way, in 208 seconds, to solve a problem he had never before encountered.

CHESLEY "SULLY" SULLENBERGER

The problem is that male and female chicks are extremely difficult to tell apart after they emerge from their shells. A chicken sexer—yes, that's a job, and a high-paying one at that—picks up the chick, examines a crevice in its backside, and searches for nearly invisible clues that point toward the chick being a male or female. The pressure is on to get the call right. In the 1960s, one hatchery paid a penny for each correctly sexed chick, but deducted 35 cents for every error. The process is so maddeningly complicated that chicken sexers cannot explain in words what makes them get the calls right. However, Japanese chicken sexers nevertheless have found ways to develop the brain's chicken-sexing neural circuitry in their students. They watch as their students grab a chick, examine its rear, and make their call. The masters just say yes or no. Within weeks, the students' brains begin to figure out the inexplicable science.

WISDOM OF AGE
Elderly brains have more experience to draw upon when making decisions, such as the best ways to shape the growth of a bonsai tree.

CHAPTER 2

How Brain Cells Work

T he ability to land a plane on the Hudson, tell one baby chick from another, or even to speak, read, or write depends upon the brain's unique structure.

At the cellular level, the human brain is a collection of as many as 100 billion nerve cells called neurons and about 50 trillion neuroglia cells. The latter sometimes are simply called "glial" cells, from the Greek word for glue. Their role is similar to that of hordes of servants in a castle: They serve their comparatively few masters, the neurons. Glial cells help neurons make connections and promote their health and steady functioning. Some take an active role in physical health by attacking microbes. Others, called oligo-dendrocytes, produce an insulating substance called myelin that speeds communication from neuron to neuron.

A WEB OF CONNECTIONS

N eurons are the brain's key players. Each begins as its own little orb. Once the neuron has fixed itself into its particular cubbyhole in the brain during fetal development, two types of projections sprout from its central core: a single, whiplike axon, some as short as a fraction of an inch and others several feet long, and from one to as many as 100,000 dendrites branching out like the knobby ends of a cat-o'-nine-tails. Dendrites reach out to other neurons, some near and some far. They receive information from the axons of their neighbors and pass it to their neuron for processing; their

TANGLED TISSUE
(Opposite) A confocal light micrograph of the cerebellum reveals Purkinje cells, a type of neuron, in red. Glial cells are green, and cell nuclei are blue. Purkinje cells have a flask-shaped body with many branching dendrites.

A LOOK INSIDE
(Below) A cross-section reveals the inner structure of the cerebellum, the brain region that controls balance and muscle coordination.

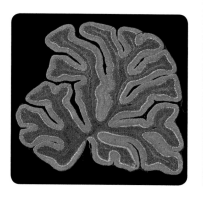

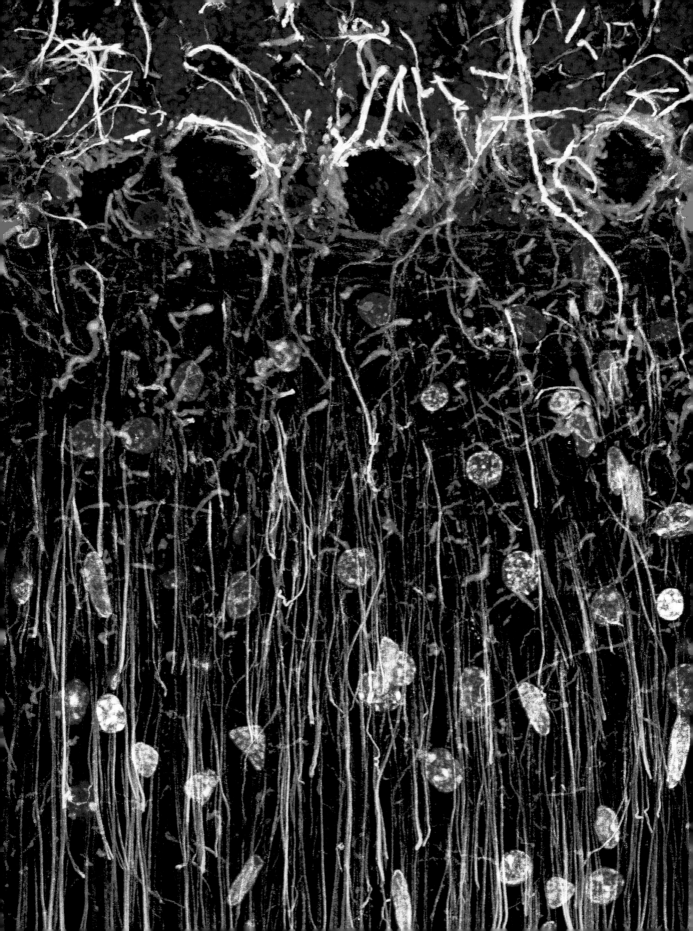

input allows a neuron to gather data—to learn. The neuron initiates or passes information via its axon to the dendrites of other neurons, like a teacher speaking to a classroom of students, with each of those students channeling the information to other students, parents, and friends. The web of axons and dendrites pointing in every direction makes the brain's interior wiring resemble the chaos of a mangrove swamp. Except, the neurons' color is gray, not leafy green. Scientists call the collection of neural cells "gray matter," a description that lives on whenever Agatha Christie's fictional detective Hercule Poirot taps his head and consults his "little gray cells." Poirot insisted on neatness, so the messy organization of neurons no doubt would displease him. Gray matter in the cerebrum, the brain's outermost cover, folds upon itself in creases and wrinkles that boost surface area, maximizing information for storage and processing.

CONNECTED, YET NOT
Like flocks of birds, communicating without touching, neurons send signals almost instantaneously across tiny gaps.

BRAIN INSIGHT

SOME KEY NEUROTRANSMITTERS

These chemicals are some of the most important messengers in the brain

ACETYLCHOLINE

Causes muscles to contract; also linked to memory, sleep, and attention.

DOPAMINE

Crucial for movement of the body, as well as the brain's reward system, associated both with pleasure and addiction. Patients with Parkinson's disease have lowered dopamine levels, causing characteristic shaking of limbs and head.

ENDORPHIN

Released following stress or pain, acting like a natural opiate by binding to opiate receptors on neurons.

GAMMA-AMINOBUTYRIC ACID, OR GABA

Quiets, rather than excites, neurons, because the brain needs to decelerate as well as accelerate a multitude of functions.

GLUTAMINE

Excites neurons, except in high concentrations fatal to neurons; required for learning and memory.

NOREPINEPHRINE

Plays a key role in regulating mood, as well as blood pressure, heartbeat, and arousal.

ENKEPHALIN CRYSTALS, AN ENDORPHIN

SEROTONIN

Prompts sleep and appetite; also plays a role in mood, related to everything from depression to anxiety to sexual arousal.

SYNAPSES

If only you could watch as information passes along circuits of neurons, it might look like flocks of birds darting, converging, and scattering against the sky. Like birds in flight, reeling and turning as if by magic, neurons communicate without the need to touch one another. A tiny space, called a synapse, separates the would-be embrace of axons and dendrites.

The neuron's language of communication within its own cell body is electricity. A spark received via a dendrite travels as electric energy until it reaches the end of the neuron's axon. There, the information it contains is translated into a variety

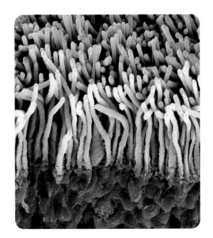

VISION NEURONS
A colored scanning electron micrograph reveals tightly packed neurons in the retina, a light-sensitive region at the back of the eyeball that actually is an extension of the brain.

STIMULUS, RESPONSE
A neuron fires to start a chain reaction when stimulation reaches a threshold. Laughter circuits in the brain of Garnet Schneider of West Bend, Wisconsin, top that threshold as she talks with friends at the Wisconsin State Polka Festival.

of chemicals known as neurotransmitters. Each neurotransmitter has its own particular job, ranging from energizing the receiving neuron to fostering positive feelings of rewarding behaviors to suppressing particular actions. The neurotransmitters traverse the synaptic gap and dock in matching receptor sites like keys in a lock. Their joining with the cell wall of the receptor neuron initiates a new electrical charge, which travels the length of *that* neuron until it is converted to chemical energy at the far side.

A neuron requires stimulation to fire. That stimulus could begin outside the body, as when you look at the sea and electromagnetic waves reflecting off the surface activate the light-sensitive rod and

[FACT: Neurons can live more than a hundred years. Many of the ones you have at birth function until you die. **]**

cone cells in your eyes' retinas. That sensation—blue or green, flat, rolling, or choppy—knocks down the first domino in the line. From the retina, the signal passes along a neural chain to the visual cortex at the back of the brain and then back to the front for further processing. A stimulus could also originate internally, as when you feel hungry, or when your conscious mind remembers the face of your fifth-grade teacher and activates the first neuron in another domino-like pattern. Some neurons fire consciously, and some fire below the level of conscious thought. Some even fire in ways to mimic the world outside.

Mirror Neurons

Italian scientists accidentally discovered so-called mirror neurons in the 1990s. To monitor brain regions as neural circuits became active, they implanted electrodes in a monkey's brain. When a monkey reached for a nut, the neurons associated with moving the arm and closing the fingers dutifully registered on their equipment. The surprise came when a monkey merely *witnessed* another monkey reaching for and grabbing a nut. The same neural circuit, linked to movement, began firing even though the monkey hadn't moved.

Some
NEURONS
fire consciously,
and some fire
below the level
of conscious
thought.

MOVEMENT AND EMOTION
Multiple stimuli of vision and movement connect with the emotion centers of the brain to create the excitement of a roller-coaster ride.

Their discovery was more than monkey see, monkey do. The Italians opened the door to a host of subsequent studies of mirror neurons, which fire not only for movement but also for emotion. The discovery explains why laughter and tears can be contagious. Seeing someone lean back and roar in response to a good joke makes the witness's laughter circuit fire in concert. Watching a romantic kiss stirs mushy feelings. And when the teenage heroine tries to hide from the slasher in the B-grade horror movie, the audience pants with vicarious, but amazingly real, terror. Mirror neurons even explain how newborns can mimic the goofy faces of adoring parents.

When a particular bit of information travels throughout a circuit of neurons, it changes from electrical to chemical, back and forth, propagating a signal at speeds that can reach more than two

DO AS I DO
Mirror neurons prompt babies to try to mimic facial expressions they see. They also tend to make laughter and tears contagious in a crowd.

BRAIN INSIGHT

BRAIN VERSUS COMPUTER

Computers are fast, but human brains are far more flexible

"I for one welcome our new computer overlords," wrote *Jeopardy!* wizard Ken Jennings, quoting an episode of *The Simpsons,* after losing to a supercomputer in a 2011 game-show showdown.

Not to worry. "Watson," the IBM supercomputer that bested Jennings and fellow human competitor Brad Rutter, won't govern us any time soon. It's just not capable of doing so.

Watson defeated its human competitors because its programmers took advantage of the rules of the game. Given an answer—remember, *Jeopardy!*

provides answers for which contestants must give the question—as a string of typed words, Watson rapidly searched its memory banks for those words and common themes. It then constructed an answer based on software programs that calculated probabilities. It could only find what it was searching for. Like a train, it could only go where its programmers had laid track.

Watson's human competitors often knew the response and even beat the computer to the correct question several times. But human brains have the powers of association, creativity, adaptability, self-awareness (Watson did not know it had won), and other advantages. The brain may be slower than a computer, but it's smart enough to build a computer. Vice versa has yet to occur.

---

hundred miles an hour. As it travels, it may prompt the addition or subtraction of more information, or set off a flood of new signals with new information. All this motion requires energy. The brain accounts for only about 2 percent of a body's weight, but it uses about 25 percent of the body's blood sugar and oxygen.

Because neurons aren't bound to each other like bricks in a wall, they remain free to make new connections and break old ones. That's exactly what happens when the brain learns something new: The information physically alters the connections.

NOT A COMPUTER

It is an artifact of history that much of the vocabulary that describes the brain is borrowed from computers. We may speak, for instance, of information being stored in the brain's complex circuits. Human understanding of both neurology and computer science blossomed at the same time, suggesting the easy transfer of computer metaphors—hardware, software, stored memory, and so on—to the human brain. But the brain is nothing like the computer that sits on your desktop, nor even the IBM supercomputer named Watson that defeated the best players in the history of the television game show *Jeopardy!* in 2011.

Analog Versus Digital

Consider the differences between human and computer in perception and knowledge. Computers can capture images and sounds from the world and represent versions of them using strings of zeros and ones. They can also store arrangements of words in similar digital patterns. In contrast, the brain is analog, not digital. It stores images and information among neural maps, or arrangements of electrochemical connections, that represent entire objects, both real and imagined/constructed in the mind. The images and thoughts you associate with the words *strawberry* and *dessert* don't get stored in a single neuron, or a group of neurons, the way a computer stores its strawberry data on a particular chip.

> The brain teaches itself new things, and then **CHANGES** its circuitry in response.

Instead, the qualities of the strawberry, including color, shape, taste, whether they are fresh or frozen, whole or sliced, woody or juicy, in jam or a pie, are dispersed among the neural maps. So, too, are any related thoughts. Strawberry shortcake. Strawberry blondes. "Strawberry Fields Forever." It is only when you imagine a strawberry that your brain pulls together its attributes for that moment, before dispersing them again when your brain drops the idea and you settle for some cheese and white wine instead. As neuropsychologist Rick Hanson writes in *Buddha's Brain,* "Conscious mental events are based on temporary coalitions of synapses that form and disperse—usually within seconds—like eddies in a stream." Some pass from a moment's thought into long-term memory. When they do, they make long-lasting circuit connections, like rivers that flow for ages through the same channels.

ZEROS AND ONES
(Left) Binary code stringing zeros and ones depicts the way computers store information. Thoughts in the human brain, such as retrieving a particular memory, converge streams of analog data and then disperse them.

WHICH IS WHICH?
(Below) Human brains have evolved to excel at finding patterns, such as what distinguishes a dog from a cat. Computers struggle with such seemingly simple pattern-recognition tasks.

The Pattern Finder

The analogy atlas that is the brain calls up myriad metaphors and connections, arriving at ideas that a hardwired computer never would discover. The brain finds patterns, relating entire ideas, one to another, and seeking similarities, differences, and relationships. Out of this analog richness comes the creativity of literature, art, and science, as well as a richness of perception that far surpasses the computer. A computer has great difficulty telling a cat from a dog, for example, but human brains find it easy to pick out the most important catlike and doglike patterns in Siamese and schnauzers.

Other major differences separate the brain from the computer. The brain teaches itself new things, and then changes its circuitry in response. Scientists encapsulate this idea with the adage, "Neurons that fire together, wire together." Actions in the ethereal construct that is your mind physically change your brain. Computers neither create their own software nor function well, if at all, when they lose a component.

FACT: Nerve impulses travel at between 9 and 400 feet a second. Pain signals are among the slowest travelers.

CHAPTER 3

Form and Function

A t the micro level, neurons in the billions form an intricate electrical net. At the macro level, they are organized into the discrete structures of the brain, with four main parts: cerebrum, diencephalon, cerebellum, and brain stem.

The outer surface of the cerebrum, nearest the skull, is the cerebral cortex. It's the wrinkly, gray, walnut-shaped covering that most people think of when they visualize the brain. The cerebral cortex is home to the functions of information processing that separate humans from other animals. In general, the larger a mammal's brain in relation to its body, the longer it lives, and the greater the amount of its brain devoted to the cerebral cortex, the more intelligent the animal.

Homo sapiens tops the chart with 76 percent of its brain in the cerebral cortex, followed by chimpanzees, other primates, and dolphins. The cerebrum exists in two hemispheres, the left and right, connected by a band of neural tissue called the corpus callosum, which allows information to pass between the two. The left hemisphere has long been considered dominant because it typically is the site of language processing. Strokes in the left hemisphere sometimes impair speech. Injuries to the right hemisphere, on the other hand, sometimes result in reductions in or loss of the ability to integrate information—to see the forest for the trees. The right hemisphere apparently plays a crucial role in emotional and spatial recognition, such as seeing raised eyebrows and upturned corners

BRAINS AND BEAUTY
(Opposite) After primates, dolphins have the largest cerebral cortex in the animal world.

NETWORKS AFIRE
(Below) A computer-generated conceptual image illustrates neural pathways in a human brain.

THE "HUMAN" PART

THE "HUMAN" PART
Wrinkles and folds appear prominently in an overhead view of the cerebrum, outermost layer of the human brain. The cerebrum is home to many of the brain's higher functions, including speech and reason.

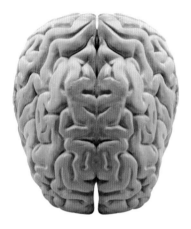

of the mouth and realizing that a face expresses joy. (Because it would be unethical to experiment on a living brain by deliberately destroying parts of it to gauge the result, much of what science learns of the brain comes by accident or from observing people who have suffered a brain injury.)

The Independent Arms Theory

One theory about the separation of functions in mirror-image hemispheres suggests links to humans' apelike ancestors, who lived in trees. Swinging from branch to branch requires independent action in each limb. Some scientists postulate that humans' primate forebears emphasized the use of one arm more than the other, which would have promoted extra neural development in the brain networks controlling that limb.

The two hemispheres duplicate many anatomical structures. Brain experts speak of folds and fissures dividing the hemispheres

BRAIN INSIGHT

AMAZING COMPLEXITY
Out of billions of neurons arises human consciousness

Your brain is astonishingly, incomprehensibly, jaw-droppingly complicated.

Assume that each of your brain's roughly 100 billion neurons (nobody has counted them, but that's a pretty good estimate) has the capability to connect with one to as many as 10,000 other neurons, thanks to its arrangement of axons and dendrites. If that's the case, then the number of theoretical connection patterns in your brain is 40 quadrillion: 40,000,000,000,000,000. If you factor in the variable power of how strongly neurotransmitters send a signal from one neuron to the next, hypothesizing that each neuron has ten different signal strengths, then the number of electrochemical

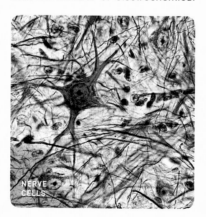

NERVE CELLS

configurations in the brain runs to ten to the one-trillionth power. That's the number 1, followed by a trillion zeros. Compare this with the estimates of the number of atoms in the observable universe: 10 to the 80th power, or 1 followed by 80 zeros.

Out of this mind-blowingly vast maze of neural connections of varying intensities comes the ability to comprehend and interact with the universe. At some point in the brain's development, consciousness arises within a three-pound, tofu-like mass of wrinkled matter. The universe becomes aware of itself—and can marvel at its own complexity.

into four lobes, but each lobe has a separate left and right half. As a result, neurologists sometimes refer to a particular lobe in the singular or plural, but may be talking about the same thing.

FRONT TO BACK

In general, the back portion of the brain takes in information about the world and begins to process it. The front portion decides what to do with that information.

The foremost part of the brain, appropriately enough, is called the frontal lobe. It lies in front of a major divide called the central fissure. A frontal lobe region called the precentral gyrus controls movement. A quirk of evolution has caused the left half of the frontal lobe to control the right side of the body, and vice versa. Gustav Theodor Fritsch, a German doctor, noted this oddity in

LEFT, RIGHT
Some scientists believe that localization of brain functions in left and right hemispheres evolved with primates, such as these orangutans, emphasizing one limb over another while moving through trees.

A PLACE FOR HAPPINESS
Emotions associated with experiences, such as the joy of blowing bubbles, are processed in the brain's temporal lobe.

1864, while treating wounded soldiers. As he dressed a head wound and touched the frontal lobe, the patient's body twitched on the opposite side. Related areas of the frontal lobe oversee complex motion and inhibit motion, giving the brain the power to override the desire to run away from danger or shout with happiness. In the very foremost part of the frontal lobe, right behind the forehead and eyes, lies the prefrontal cortex. This part of the brain developed last on the evolutionary time line, and is the last to become fully myelinated. It is the home to decision making and thus is sometimes called the brain's seat of "executive function."

Sensation, Speech, and Memory

Behind the frontal lobe lie the parietal and temporal lobes. The parietal lobe processes sensations from the body, including pain and the pressure of touch. The temporal lobe processes sounds, including speech. It is also associated with memory and the emotional content of experiences. Each half of the temporal lobe includes a small,

[FACT: Your brain uses about 12 watts of power—a fraction of the energy of a household lightbulb. **]**

seahorse-shaped form called the hippocampus, which comes from the Greek words for horse and sea monster. The hippocampus is part of the limbic system, a collection of structures on the inside of the cerebral cortex associated with emotions, motivation, and behavior.

LIMBIC SYSTEM
The oval thalamus, in red, receives sensory stimuli. In front and above is the corpus striatum, green, and its two basal ganglia. The limbic system processes expressions of instinct and mood, including fear, rage, and pleasure.

THE SEAT OF MEMORY

Neuroscientists once believed that the mature brain was incapable of producing new neurons—that the neurons you had at birth, or shortly afterward, were the only ones you would have for your entire life. Research in the 1990s laid that idea to rest. New neurons have been found growing in the hippocampus, a region that is crucial in the formation and storage of memories. In a famous study in 2000, University College London neuroscientist Eleanor Maguire demonstrated enlarged hippocampi

BRAIN INSIGHT

THE MAN WHO FORGOT

In 1953, time stopped passing for Henry Molaison, known to history as HM

SHORT-TERM MEMORIES NEED TO TRANSFER TO LONG-TERM STORAGE.

Henry Molaison's troubles began early. He began having epileptic seizures as a child after a being hit by a bicycle in his native Connecticut. Whole-brain seizures increased in frequency until, by age 27, in 1953, he suffered nearly a dozen a week.

His doctor reasoned they would stop if he eliminated their point of origin, so he surgically removed much of Molaison's temporal lobes, including the left and right hippocampus. The operation indeed halted the seizures. But Molaison awoke without the ability to make new memories. The hippocampus turns out to be crucial to the transference of short-term memories into long-term storage.

For the next 55 years, until he died in 2008, Molaison had the most-studied brain on the planet. Researchers repeatedly tested aspects of his memory, including the conscious and unconscious, the short and long term. Academic papers referred only to patient "HM" to preserve Molaison's privacy while he lived.

Molaison cheerfully submitted to every test; he never realized their endless repetition and could never get bored. If someone erased a crossword puzzle after he completed it, he happily did it—again and again. He lived in a permanent "now," thinking he was still 27, until the day he died.

in the brains of London cabdrivers. Cabbies spend two to four years memorizing London's intricate street grids, including the shortest distance between any two points. Using a magnetic resonance imaging (MRI) scanner, Maguire found that cabbies' right posterior hippocampus, a region devoted to spatial navigation, measured 7 percent larger than the norm. Evidently, neuroplasticity had reshaped the cabbies' brains as they learned more and more about navigating through London.

Conversely, damage to the hippocampus impairs memory. A patient known to science as HM had his hippocampi surgically removed to eliminate his severe epileptic seizures. HM survived, without seizures, for more than five decades. But the surgery had an unforeseen side effect: It permanently erased HM's ability to form new memories.

BIG MENTAL MAPS
Drivers of London cabs, such as this one on Shaftesbury Avenue, have developed larger hippocampi than the norm, thanks to memorizing details of the city's complex traffic grid.

THE SELF-CORRECTING BRAIN

Brain cells can make new pathways when the old ones are lost

Brain cells die when deprived of oxygen by a stroke. When those affected neural circuits play a key role in moving an arm or leg, the stroke patient loses some or all control of that limb.

However, brains can rewire themselves to regain lost movement. Psychologist Edward Taub of the University of Alabama at Birmingham has gotten impressive results restoring movement by enrolling stroke patients in "constraint induced movement therapy." He has stroke patients selectively try to use their affected arm or leg while deliberately avoiding use of their unaffected partners. Taub found that, in just two weeks, the patients' neural circuitry had rewired itself, a process known as cortical reorganization, to bypass dead neural arrays. Professional musicians who had lost some control of their arms were able to return to work.

The mere act of thinking about moving a stroke-affected limb can help rewire the brain. Researchers at the Drake Center/University of Cincinnati put subjects affected by stroke through visualization exercises that included listening to a CD while mentally orchestrating physical therapy exercises. Years later, those who added visualization exercises to their therapy improved more than those with therapy alone.

A STROKE PATIENT UNDERGOES THERAPY.

Mapping the Brain

Neurosurgeon Wilder Penfield stumbled upon the temporal lobes' role in memory when he tried to control epileptic seizures in the 1950s by destroying clusters of nerve cells where the seizures began. When he electrically stimulated temporal neurons, his patients reported reliving memories with vivid details of color, movement, and sound. Stimulating the same place, again and again, touched off the same memories, such as the view from the window of a childhood home. After much experimenting, he created two maps of the brain called the motor homunculus and sensory homunculus. Each one exaggerates the size of body areas in relation to the amount of their neural circuitry. Each map enlarges the fingers, lips, and eyes in relation to arms and legs because fine distinctions of touch, taste, and vision were crucial to survival during the early stages of human development.

At the back of the brain is the occipital lobe. Although it is at the opposite end of the brain from the eyeballs, the occipital lobe processes visual information. Much of the lobe interprets shape, color, motion, and other qualities of objects.

DIENCEPHALON, CEREBELLUM, AND BRAIN STEM

Moving out of the cerebrum, the diencephalon lies between the left and right hemispheres. Its structures regulate body rhythms such as sleeping and wakefulness, as well as body temperature, digestion, perspiration, and other body functions that usually occur below the level of consciousness. A portion of the diencephalon known as the thalamus relays sensory information from other brain regions and plays a role in emotion and memory.

The Balancing Act

Below the occipital lobe is the cerebellum. Although it contributes to emotional life and action, the cerebellum's most obvious task is to coordinate movement and balance. The cerebellum automatically processes the neural signals required to perform practiced tasks. For example, when you learn to type, you concentrate to find the right keys. That action, which initially requires focused attention and choices, takes place mostly in your frontal lobes. But eventually you type without consciously thinking of where to find each key. Your cerebellum houses the autopilot that keeps the right keys clicking.

The fourth major brain region is the brain stem. It comprises the area where the brain meets the spinal cord, which is merely an extension of neurons into the body. Key brain stem regions include the medulla oblongata, which controls heartbeat and respiration, and the pons, which controls reflexes such as the startled jump you make when a door slams shut.

PERFECTED MOTION
When a dancer first tries a difficult move, she thinks hard about it with her forebrain. As she masters it, her brain moves the required neural circuitry of motion to the cerebellum, and the movement becomes almost second nature.

[**FACT:** Infants who have one brain hemisphere removed generally grow up with normal brain function.]

CHAPTER 4

The Evolving Brain

NO LOVE, NO TEARS
(Opposite) Reptiles, such as the Nile crocodile, lack brain regions not only for reason but also for emotion. Their very basic brains are all they need to eat, sleep, and breed.

BRAIN STEM
(Below) At the base of the brain, the brain stem controls vital functions such as breathing and heartbeat, while the attached cerebellum directs fine motor skills and balance, among other tasks.

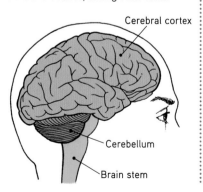

Cerebral cortex

Cerebellum

Brain stem

The specialized regions of the human brain evolved over eons of time. As animals became more complex, their brains did too. From fish to reptiles, to mammals and humans, the brain has not only gotten bigger in relation to the body, but also vastly more complex. Greater complexity of the brain's circuitry created the possibility of more sophisticated behavior.

In 1967, American neuroscientist Paul MacLean proposed a theory of brain evolution that suggested that the new layers developed on top of old ones. In other words, the oldest parts of the brain, on an evolutionary scale, are the lowest, including the brain stem and cerebellum.

THE OLDER BRAIN

This base of the brain acts as a simple command center for early evolving animals, such as reptiles. This area controls everything a crocodile needs to survive and make baby crocs: heartbeat, respiration, movement, sleep, alertness, temperature regulation, aggression, and sexual activity. As mammals evolved, they kept the reptilian brain as their core, but developed structures proving useful for survival of animals that, unlike reptiles, nurture their young and live in groups. Natural selection did the rest, cementing

new hardware into the nascent cerebrum of the mammalian brain. MacLean dubbed this new emotional circuitry the limbic system. It refines movement; adds memory and emotion to the brain; and begins to allow for socially complex relationships. Your pet dog returns genuine affection when you shower her with affection. She demonstrates true motherly devotion to her pups until they are old enough to be on their own. She also is smart enough to learn how to run an obstacle course, fetch a paper, shake hands, and roll over on command. MacLean demonstrated the role of the limbic system after destroying parts of it in young mammals and examining the result. The affected animals showed weaker mother–offspring bonds. The offspring also stopped engaging in play, an activity believed to promote social learning.

LEARNING WORDS
Primates have sufficient neural circuitry in their cerebral cortices to develop sophisticated communication. Koko the gorilla, here being taught by Francine Patterson in 1972, knows more than 1,000 words of sign language.

BRAIN INSIGHT

MONKEY BRAINS

Fresh challenges build new connections in the brain

Neuroscientist Michael Merzenich at the University of California, San Francisco, has seen a brain physically change while learning a new task.

Merzenich put a banana-flavored pellet in a cup and watched as a squirrel monkey extended an arm through the bars of a cage, grasped the pellet from the cup, and ate it. The test subject repeated the action dozens of times each day until it became automatic. Then Merzenich replaced the cup with a smaller one. It took a while for the monkey to fish the pellet out of the smaller cup, but it eventually mastered that skill, too. Twice more, Merzenich swapped the cup for a smaller one,

COMMON SQUIRREL MONKEY

until the monkey had become extremely adept at getting a banana pellet from a narrow opening by the fourth cup.

Computer images of the monkey's brain revealed that the neural networks associated with conscious finger manipulation expanded as the monkeys learned greater dexterity. However, once a monkey no longer had to think about the motions, the expanded neural networks active during the learning phase showed reduced activity. The skill moved from the parts of the brain associated with conscious thought to other parts that handled routine movements.

The learning circuits of squirrel monkey brains, and those of humans, don't need to stay burdened with old information. To use a computer analogy, they can clear their memory after mastering a task to prepare themselves for a new one.

The Mammalian Brain

Last to develop in the brain was the full flowering of the cerebral cortex, especially in the frontal lobes of primates and humans. These "neomammalian" areas allow for higher thinking, including speech, reasoning, and planning. This includes some sophisticated communication among primates, as demonstrated by Koko the gorilla, who has learned more than 1,000 words of American Sign Language from her teacher at Stanford University, Penny Patterson. Koko puts words together in logical ways. For example, Koko refers to herself as "fine animal person gorilla." Of course, humans take language and reasoning a step further. Thanks to their frontal

FACT: Koko the gorilla can use sign language to make a sentence three to six words long.

lobes, the most recent evolutionary structures, they can do calculus, write music, and plan for the future. Humans alone have science and religion.

> The prefrontal **CORTEX** is the region that most separates humans from all other animals.

Evolution doesn't discard the oldest regions. All remain active. For example, the "reptilian" portion of your brain reacts negatively when a loved one points out one of your faults. The "mammalian portion" stirs memories and emotions as you react. And the frontal lobes allow you to choose how to act—wisely, perhaps, if you opt not to escalate the episode into a verbal or physical confrontation.

MacLean's theory remains controversial, with some critics saying it lies outside conventional science. Others feel squeamish at the idea that human brains possess a core that resembles those of animals lower on the evolutionary ladder. For

BRAIN INSIGHT

PHINEAS GAGE

A famous accident illustrated the connections between personality and parts of the brain

A gruesome accident in 1848 linked the prefrontal cortex to moral behavior. Vermont railroad worker Phineas Gage was jamming a tamping iron into a hole to pack gunpowder and sand when the iron sparked on a rock. The powder exploded, sending the 13-pound rod through Gage's cheek, prefrontal cortex, and skull crown. Gage initially seemed barely fazed. "Here is business enough for you," he told a doctor.

Before the accident, co-workers liked Gage and considered him reliable and temperate. After the accident, he became rude, impatient, profane, and

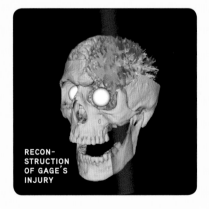

RECON-
STRUCTION
OF GAGE'S
INJURY

unable to stick to plans. Gage drifted from job to job and died 12 years later, at 36, after a series of seizures.

In 2012, a team of researchers at UCLA's Laboratory of Neuro Imaging (LONI) published a paper tracing the path of the tamping iron through Gage's brain. They managed to produce a striking new image of the damage, while tracing the probable severed connections to other parts of his brain. They concluded that Gage's behavioral changes came not only from harm to his prefrontal cortex, but also from the disrupted pathways to other areas that involve emotional response—showing once again that the brain is an immensely interconnected organ.

his own part, MacLean thought humanity would benefit if people could get in touch with the neural circuitry of their evolutionary forebears buried deep in their brains. Assessing violence in the world in 1971, MacLean told the *New York Times* that language barriers throw huge obstacles in the way of international understanding. "But," he said, "the greatest language barrier lies between man and his animal brains; the neural machinery does not exist for intercommunication in verbal terms."

THE PREFRONTAL CORTEX

The foremost part of the forebrain, the prefrontal cortex, or PFC, is the region that most separates humans from all other animals, including apes. The PFC comprises 30 percent of the human brain, compared with only 11 percent for a chimpanzee and 3 percent for a cat. As home to the brain's executive function, it acts as boss.

The Voice of Conscience

Clinical neuroscientist Daniel G. Amen considers the boss metaphor apt. When the boss is absent in an office or factory, sometimes little serious work gets done, Amen says. And when the PFC boss works very hard, micromanaging the rest of the conscious brain, it sometimes promotes anxiety and worry—and again, little useful work gets done. Amen also likens the PFC to the Disney cartoon character Jiminy Cricket, who acted as the conscience of the puppet-boy Pinocchio. The cricket's still, small voice suggested the best ways to behave. When the guiding voice grows too quiet, the result is what Amen calls "Jiminy Cricket deficiency syndrome." A barrel of negative behaviors blooms, including impulsive action, confusion, short attention span, bad judgment, low empathy, poor time management, and diminished conscience. For instance, 19th-century railroad worker Phineas Gage, so famous in medical circles that he was referenced in an episode of *House, MD*,

JIMINY CRICKET!
When the prefrontal cortex is insufficiently active, negative, impulsive behaviors flourish. Neuroscientist Daniel G. Amen calls this disorder "Jiminy Cricket deficiency syndrome," for the cartoon character who acted as Pinocchio's conscience.

BRAIN INSIGHT

WIRED TO BE NEGATIVE

You can consciously use positive thinking to lift the burden of bad memories

Thanks to evolution, your brain has a negativity bias. Bad experiences hit you much harder than good ones. That's your brain's way of getting you to change risky behavior. For instance,

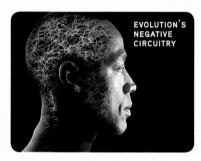

EVOLUTION'S NEGATIVE CIRCUITRY

if you approached a wild animal as a child and it bit you, the experience likely remains strong enough in your memory to prevent any repeat.

Negative experiences have their place. They may promote compassion or make you angry enough about something unpleasant to demand changes. But too much negativity can harm your emotional health.

Neuropsychologist Rick Hanson argues that the brain's plasticity can reshape emotionally negative memories into more positive ones. In his book *Buddha's Brain*, Hanson suggests not

only emphasizing positive experiences in everyday life, but also associating positive feelings with negative experiences when you recall them. As a memory leaves your awareness, your brain returns it to storage along with other memory strings associated with it. If you dwell on the humiliation of a particular failure, your brain stores those two things together and recalls them together. But if you can link your failure with more positive associations, such as a pathway to a rewarding new job or relationship, then you begin to shift the emotional balance of your brain.

underwent a radical change in his personality when his PFC suffered extensive damage in an accident. Although Gage was popular and showed good judgment before the accident, virtually every item on Amen's Jiminy Cricket checklist appeared in Gage's personality afterward.

IMPAIRMENTS

Low activity levels in the PFC have been associated with attention deficit/hyperactivity disorder, schizophrenia, some forms of depression, antisocial personalities, and some forms of dementia. Treatments include medications such as the attention-enhancing drug Adderall, a high-protein diet, exercise to get more oxygen-rich blood flowing, and therapy.

FACT: Sixty percent of a dolphin's brain is devoted to the cerebral cortex, the site of higher thinking.

Damage to the PFC

However, when the neurons in the prefrontal cortex fail or die, there's little that currently can be done. Alzheimer's can affect many brain regions, prompting many different results. It builds up plaques and tangles in neurons, which are believed to interfere with neural functioning and communication. In the brain stem, Alzheimer's can interrupt sleep patterns and interfere with swallowing and breathing. In the amygdala, Alzheimer's can lead to emotional roller coasters, including outbursts of temper and strong anxiety. In the parietal lobe, the disease can rob a person of the ability to locate objects in three-dimensional space, as well as interfere with reading and writing.

Development of the disease often first becomes apparent in the temporal lobe, including the hippocampus, as the patient's memory slips away. But some of the most dramatic symptoms of Alzheimer's arise when it strikes at the frontal lobe, and particularly the PFC. There, the disease gradually takes away many of the qualities we think of as uniquely human. Complex tasks requiring logic, concentration, memory, and planning evaporate. Patients with Alzheimer's may find themselves severely impaired in their ability to plan a trip, drive a car, or cook a meal.

Some of the most dramatic **SYMPTOMS** of Alzheimer's arise when it strikes at the frontal lobe.

OLD, SWEET SONG
Dementia patients may retain motor skills such as dancing.

Still Dancing

Yet the brain's plasticity may adapt and keep many parts working. The cerebellum appears to be less affected by Alzheimer's than other regions. As the cerebellum plays a central role in coordinating movement, and rehearsed movements in particular, a patient with Alzheimer's in the cerebrum would still be able to execute dance steps he learned long ago.

CHAPTER 5

The Maturing Brain

BLOSSOMING BRAIN
(Opposite) Blood vessels bringing precious oxygen to the brain are clearly visible in a human embryo in the seventh week after conception. Hundreds of thousands of neurons form every minute at peak development.

MIGRATING BRAIN CELLS
(Below) A scanning electron micrograph shows migratory neuroblasts that have migrated through the brain during an early stage of neuron development. Neurons don't begin to branch out with axons and dendrites until they fix themselves in place after migration.

The entire structure of the adult human brain lies hidden in the genetic code that begins to find expression at conception. When sperm slams into egg, uniting a father's and mother's DNA, the reaction causes the fertilized egg to begin dividing. At four weeks, the first brain structures begin to appear. A spoon-shaped neural plate takes shape at the head end of the developing body. A groove later appears in the center of the plate, and hemispheres begin to form on either side shortly after that. The spoon's bowl becomes the brain itself, and the handle transforms into the spinal cord. Major brain regions start to develop, with the cerebral cortex witnessing the most explosive growth.

About a quarter million neurons form *every minute* in the early months of fetal development and migrate to particular regions of the brain to take up specialized tasks. For some, the journey is long—the equivalent of hiking from Seattle to New York City. Axons and dendrites sprout when the neuron arrives at its destination. Neuroscientists once believed neurons chose their favored sites because each new neuron already had a predetermined function and sought the site associated with that function. Now, scientists believe that the journey and the destination shape

BOOM AND BUST
(Right) An ultrasound depicts a fetus at 13 weeks. Neurons explode into being in the early months of the baby's life inside the womb, but about half die before birth.

RESPOND AND GROW
(Below) A newborn's brain is primed to learn virtually anything. It develops neural circuitry in response to its unique stimulation. Cuddling a baby builds social bonding; talking aloud stimulates language circuits even before the baby speaks.

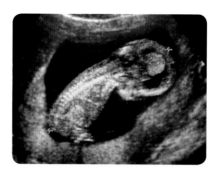

the neuron to perform one task or another.

Although the brain reacts to its environment at all times, the period of so-called "neuron migration" in the womb marks a high state of sensitivity. Toxins or anything else interfering with neurons as they move through the prenatal brain, causing them to fall short of or overshoot their destination, can have serious consequences. Dyslexia and autism, for example, have been linked, in part, to less than optimal neural migration. The brain's in utero sensitivity underscores the need for pregnant women to eat well, get exercise, and avoid alcohol, tobacco, and other substances that could hinder the neural development of their children.

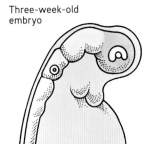

Three-week-old
embryo

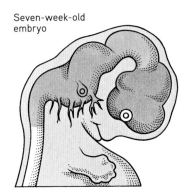

Seven-week-old
embryo

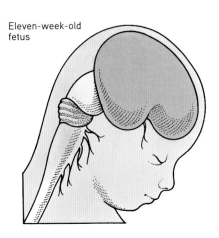

Eleven-week-old
fetus

NEURAL DARWINISM

At eight months after conception, the fetal brain contains twice as many neurons as an adult's, even though the younger brain weighs only about one-third of the adult brain. The brain cannot sustain that many neurons and neural connections, so it begins to cut back. About half of the brain's neurons die in the final weeks of fetal development. In addition, many of the neural connections grow weak and dissolve, a process known as pruning. The result, at birth, is that the brain contains virtually all of the neurons it will have for life. Brains get bigger as the child ages into an adult for two reasons. First, the brain's neurons grow physically larger by sending out more dendrites. And second, supporting cells around the neurons, particularly the glial cells, multiply to increase the brain's total volume.

After birth, the newborn's brain undergoes a kind of neural Darwinism. Neural networks compete to have the strongest links, while weak links receiving little or no stimulation undergo rigorous pruning. A widely repeated adage about the brain says, "Use it or lose it." That appears to be literally true, especially when a child's brain, primed to react to virtually ay stimulation, receives some kinds but not others.

NEURONS SPREADING
Brain development lies encoded in a child's DNA. Initial brain structures, appearing at four weeks, look a bit like a spoon. As neural count doubles and redoubles, the familiar shape of the brain emerges.

[FACT: Gray matter is thickest in girls at age 11, in boys at 12 years of age. It then thins while white matter grows. **]**

USE IT OR LOSE IT
Chinese schoolchildren tackle their lessons
for the day. The phenomenon of phonemic
contraction makes a young brain open to
mastering all sounds of human speech.
But if these girls don't hear English at a
very young age, they will not be able to
completely master English sounds later.

The Subtle Sounds of Language

The phenomenon of phonemic contraction serves as an excellent
example. Babies make all kinds of spoken sounds, or phonemes,
when they are six to nine months old. But late in their first year of
life, they start to restrict, or contract, the kinds of sounds they make
in response to the sounds they hear. If young children grow up in a
household hearing both Mandarin and English, they will be able to
hear and reproduce the full range of sounds contained in both languages. But if the children hear only Mandarin, they will have trouble later in life hearing the difference between the sounds made by
the letters "l" and "r," a distinction lacking in Mandarin phonemes.
Likewise, they will struggle to articulate the difference without an
accent. The same process interferes with native English speakers as
they try to speak Mandarin like a native of northern China.

YOUNG LEARNING

The younger the brain, the more plasticity it has. Not just language but virtually any skill is learned most easily when taught to a young brain. Thanks to his father's instruction, Tiger Woods, perhaps the greatest golfer in the history of the game, already had learned the fundamentals of the game at age two. Plasticity also makes its virtues evident when a child suffers a brain injury. Young brains have a greater capacity to rewire themselves to minimize or even eliminate the impact of a serious injury. The reason, according to University of Wisconsin neuroscientist Ronald E. Kalil, may be that the youthful brain is bathed in growth-enhancing chemicals that assist the brain in reconstruction and reorganization. Kalil found these factors in young cats, whose brains repaired themselves efficiently, but found far less of them in less-responsive adult cat brains.

TEACH 'EM YOUNG
Young brains have maximum plasticity. Tiger Woods, playing golf at age three, became such an excellent professional in part because his father taught him the game while his brain was still malleable.

BRAIN INSIGHT

EARLY ENRICHMENT
Loving interactions are a key to healthy young brains

"Doc Cortex" knows: Having a healthy brain starts Day One.

Memorial BrainWorks, an education program run by Memorial Hospital and Health System of South Bend, Indiana, aims to enrich life from cradle to grave. According to Doc Cortex, a video spokesman, life's first four-year period is crucial: "It's the starting gate for all the potential capabilities that the child has for the rest of their life!"

Memorial BrainWorks draws its programs from research that shows the brain is most active at a time when children learn to control their bodies, interact with others, and explore the world. Being a good parent is the best

LOVE FEEDS THE BRAIN.

way to help. A child needs to be touched, spoken to, and loved from birth. Using a big vocabulary may seem silly if a newborn cannot answer, but a new brain soaks up language concepts and benefits from trying to mimic words. Creative, energetic play not only helps stimulate neural pathways and motor skills but also supplies extra oxygen to the brain.

When the world seems a big, buzzing confusion, the child may cry, but a parent's comfort shows all is well, and the child is safe and loved. That sets the stage for emotional development.

The Adolescent Brain

The brain goes through a rocky phase in adolescence. It directs a physical body that resembles an adult's, but it has yet to complete its development. In particular, the foremost parts of an adolescent brain—the portion that controls behavior—usually have yet to complete myelination. That can lead to moody behavior (surprise!) as well as imperfect impulse control and other negative actions. A fully developed teenage cerebellum and motor cortex can direct the teen to smack a tennis serve into the opponent's court at 90 miles an hour. The impartially myelinated prefrontal cortex can also contribute to a temper tantrum if the teen double-faults on match point.

NOT QUITE ADULT
The adolescent brain directs a body that is like an adult's. Yet the brain lacks complete myelination, the neural insulation that maximizes electrical conductivity. As a result, teenagers, such as these running boys, sometimes act impulsively and with unbridled emotion.

In the years from adolescence to old age, the brain continues to make new connections and prune underused ones. Mature and elderly adults retain full plasticity to learn new tasks. Late in the 19th century, for example, people of all ages learned to ride bicycles when they made their appearance in the United States. Today, grandfathers of 70 and their granddaughters aged 2 can both learn how to use a tablet computer or smartphone.

AGING BRAINS

Aging brains shrink a bit as they lose some neurons and neural connections. A 90-year-old's brain typically weighs about 10 percent less than it did at its peak. The aging brain also begins to show changes in at least four important areas: speed of information processing, memory, neurons' inhibitory function, and sensation. Much of the decline occurs in the prefrontal cortex, as if the last

FACT: The hippocampus loses about 5 percent of its neurons in normal aging. But new neurons also sprout there.

THE AGE OF REASON

Your brain is not physically mature until you are in your 20s

Turning 18 is more or less the magic moment when people are expected to take full responsibility for their actions. In the United States, this includes receiving the right to vote, use tobacco products, and, generally, be emancipated from parents and handle finances. Welcome to adulthood.

But 18 isn't the age of perfect reason.

The brain's maturation includes the gradual spread of a pale, waxlike substance called myelin around axon fibers. Myelin acts like electrical insulation, increasing the speed and efficiency of information sharing among neurons. If your brain were a digital connection, myelin would boost your bandwidth.

Myelination begins shortly before birth and isn't complete until early adulthood. It begins in the motor and sensory regions toward the back of the brain and

works its way forward. Last to become fully myelinated, sometime in the third decade, is the prefrontal cortex, center of reason and control of behavior. Men complete myelination later than women.

Impulsive behavior of teens and young adults, especially among males, can be explained in part by the less-than-complete myelination of their forebrains. Nowhere is the immaturity of a young adult's brain seen more clearly than in automotive statistics. In England, men aged 17 to 20 account for one-third of all convictions for dangerous driving, despite being only 3 percent of drivers. Small wonder insuring a driver under age 25 is so expensive.

---

part of the brain to be complete were the first to decline—a case of last in, first out. Variation in the species means that the brain can show signs of cognitive decline, affecting thinking and memory, at virtually any age. However, for many people, the first signs of slowing appear around age 50. The aging brain takes more time to learn new things and store them in memory. Meanwhile, the prefrontal cortex loses a measure of its ability to hold information in working memory, a sort of computer desktop where the brain keeps information at hand for immediate use. With the decline in long-term and working memory, the brain requires more time to store memories, retrieve them, and then make decisions based on them.

The brain's inhibitory function includes filtering out distractions. Too much information can make it difficult for the brains of typical people in their late 60s to figure out what's important and what's not. That can make driving difficult, as it requires discriminating

ELDERLY ATROPHY
A magnetic resonance image of an elderly brain reveals atrophy of the cerebral cortex, indicative of dementia. Dementia is not confined to the old, nor is it inevitable for those who live long lives.

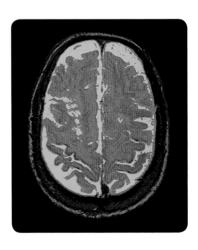

between important traffic signs and unimportant ones. Or, elderly brains may experience sensory overload on busy metropolitan streets, but be OK on rural dirt roads.

A key to **SUCCESSFUL AGING** is to understand how the brain works.

The Mystery of Aging

All of these previously mentioned issues are normal, regular responses to aging. Why that is so remains open to debate. Leonard Hayflick, a leading scientific expert on aging, describes two schools of thought on why humans—and nearly all other animals—change with age. One camp says aging results from a preexisting genetic plan for the human body, which supposes either a divine plan giving each person an allotment of so many years and no more, or an evolutionary benefit to the species arising from normal aging.

BRAIN INSIGHT

LIFELONG NEUROPLASTICITY

As bodies compensate for failing senses, brains continue to be creative all life long.

Neuroplasticity continues all life long—even in lives facing challenges in old age.

French painter Claude Monet worked to improve his craft well into his ninth decade. When cataracts began to steal his sight, he changed the way he painted—and created masterpieces of light and color at his Giverny home. Similarly, when artists James Thurber and Georgia O'Keeffe found their vision failing late in life, they developed new ways to practice their craft—Thurber by sweeping a fat crayon to create huge-scale cartoons, and O'Keeffe by switching from oil paint to charcoal and pencil.

And when German composer Ludwig van Beethoven lost all hearing at age 50, he compensated by taking the legs off his piano and setting it on the floor so he could better interpret its vibrations when he played. He also "heard" his music by clenching a stick in his teeth and touching it to his piano.

"Scientists have discovered that the brain, even an aging brain, can grow new connections and pathways when challenged and stimulated," said Nancy Merz Nordstrom, author of *Learning Later, Living Greater*. Every day that creative senior citizens used their talents to produce great works, "they were learning," Nordstrom said.

CLAUDE MONET.

As the brain ages, it typically loses a measure of its ability to quickly categorize information into what's important and what's not. That function is crucial to driving, which becomes a problem for some elderly drivers.

The other camp attributes aging to the accumulation of random events. Genetic changes in the body as a whole have their analogs in individual cells, which also age and die. This theory points to the buildup of so-called free radicals in the cells of the body, weakening the body's ability to repair itself, as a key source of aging.

Free radicals are unstable molecules with at least one unpaired electron. They seek to achieve balance by stealing an electron from a neighboring molecule. The theory suggests that free radicals, common throughout the environment, alter cell mechanics and speed aging. Diets high in chemicals called antioxidants soak up free radicals. That's one of the reasons antioxidant-rich carrots, apples, and berries are good for you. So, too, are the antioxidants found in red wine and dark chocolate, which can be beneficial to health if not overindulged.

A key to successful aging is to understand how the brain works, and to keep it active and plastic. That includes giving it the right nutrition, exercise, and mental stimulation. Another key is to be aware of changes as they occur, and to recognize the difference between normal aging and signs of something more serious. Both are explored in Part 2.

Pathways to

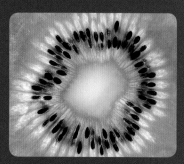

Brain Health

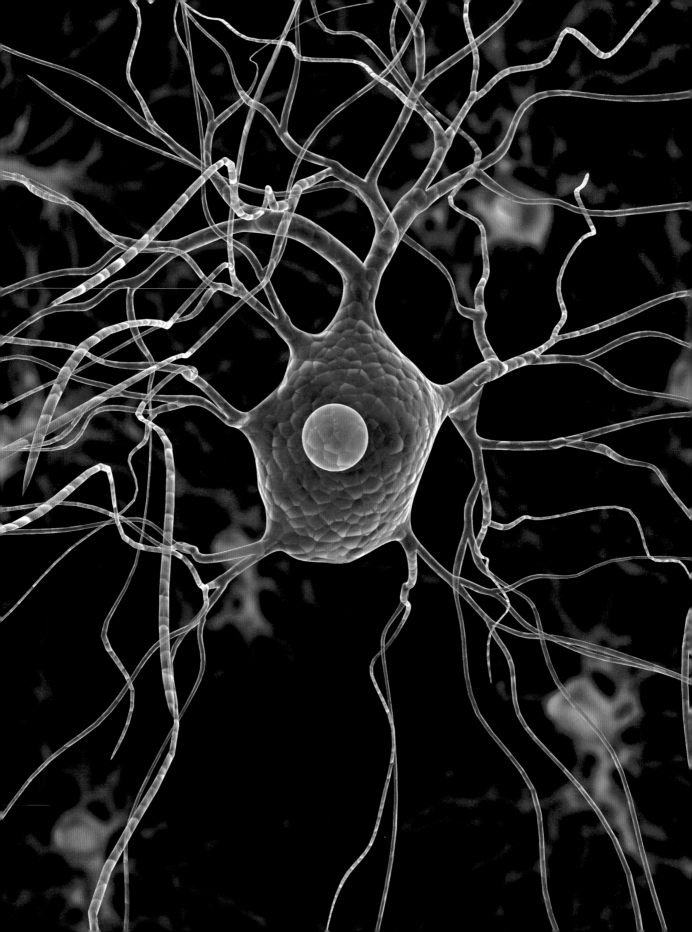

"We are an intelligent species and the use of our intelligence quite properly gives us pleasure. In this respect the brain is like a muscle. When it is in use we feel very good."
CARL SAGAN

HOW TO STAY STRONG
It's surprisingly easy to boost your brain

As you age, you have two basic strategies to improve brain health. One is to maintain or even enhance the many brain functions that make you the person you are. This strategy includes learning how to regulate mood and preserve memory, how to stay socially engaged and enjoy physical activities, and in general how to keep exposing your brain to novelty. The other is to strengthen your brain as best you can to delay or ward off the onset of disorders. These strategies are not mutually exclusive. Making your brain more complex, which occurs naturally as you challenge it with new experiences, appears to offer some protection against illness. Surprisingly, some of the most effective things you can do to promote brain health are simple, everyday acts. Do a crossword puzzle. Learn a dance. Eat berries. Test your eyes and ears. Paint. Or just take a walk outdoors.

CHAPTER 6

Defining Brain Health

REACHING OUT
(Preceding pages) A single nerve cell branches out in a network of connections.

MANY VARIABLES
(Opposite) A high school teacher puts formulae on glass. Neurons follow mathematical rules in which tiny changes in variables sometimes radically affect outcomes.

CHAOS
(Below) A Hénon map, below, expresses chaos theory as a dynamic system. Instead of a simple mathematical function, chaos is unpredictably complex.

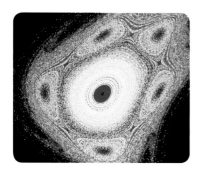

M eteorologist and mathematician Edward Lorenz wanted to know how to model weather patterns. Instead, he discovered two great truths: First, even the tiniest of events can generate enormous consequences; and second, it's impossible to forecast weather very far into the future.

At the Massachusetts Institute of Technology in 1961, Lorenz created a rudimentary computer program that simulated basic weather. The computer ran 12 equations to crunch weather data, such as air pressure, temperature, wind, and so on, that ran to six digits after the decimal point. One day, Lorenz wanted to run a longer-than-usual test, so he restarted a previous weather computation from the middle instead of the beginning. To make a compact printout, he decided to enter only the first three digits after the decimal point—representing his measurements to the thousandth part instead of the millionth. He figured that because he had made only the most minuscule changes to his input, the weather patterns would look the same.

Surprise. The new weather pattern veered dramatically away from the original. That fourth decimal place mattered. A lot.

Lorenz had discovered the roots of chaos theory. Science cannot measure everything, in infinite detail, that might affect a complex physical system. This means it is impossible to perfectly predict

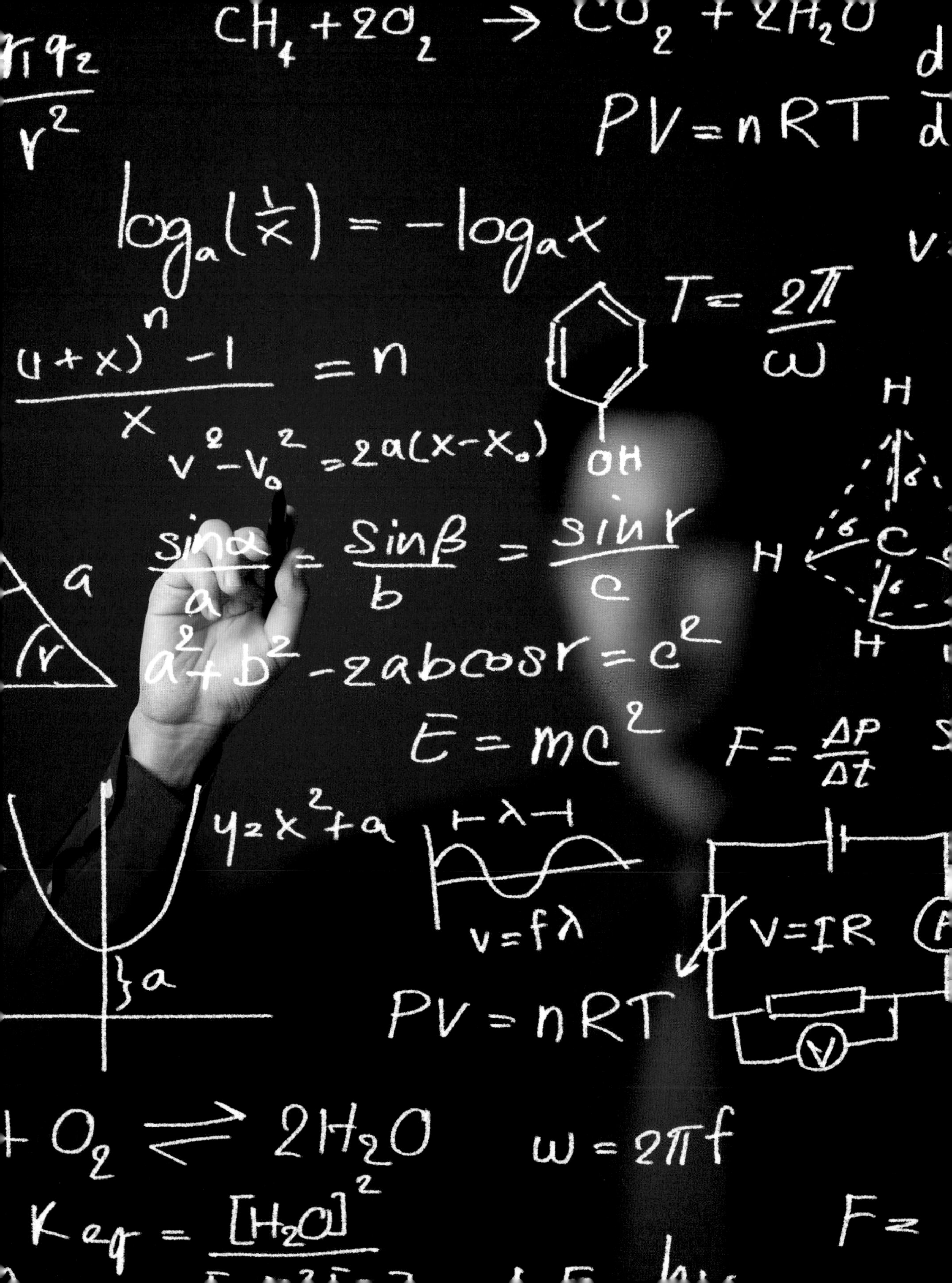

$$\frac{r_1 q_2}{r^2}$$

$$CH_4 + 2O_2 \rightarrow CO_2 + 2H_2O$$

$$PV = nRT \quad \frac{d}{d}$$

$$\log_a\left(\frac{1}{x}\right) = -\log_a x$$

$$T = \frac{2\pi}{\omega}$$

$$\frac{(1+x)^n - 1}{x} = n$$

$$v^2 - v_0^2 = 2a(x - x_0)$$

OH

$$\frac{\sin\alpha}{a} = \frac{\sin\beta}{b} = \frac{\sin r}{c}$$

a

r

$$a^2 + b^2 - 2ab\cos r = c^2$$

$$E = mc^2$$

$$F = \frac{\Delta P}{\Delta t}$$

$$y = x^2 + a$$

$$\vdash \lambda \dashv$$

$$v = f\lambda$$

$$V = IR$$

}a

$$PV = nRT$$

$$+ O_2 \rightleftharpoons 2H_2O$$

$$\omega = 2\pi f$$

$$K_{eq} = \frac{[H_2O]^2}{}$$

F =

H

H C

H

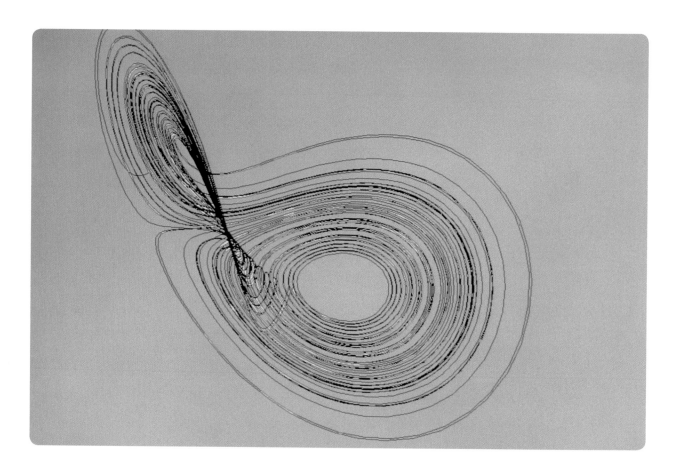

THE SHAPE OF INFORMATION
Chaos theory dictates that information flows in unknowable ways but tends to form patterns—just as neural networks act within limits.

the system's performance in the future. Long-term meteorological forecasts fail because humans can never measure every variable, such as air temperature, down to the individual molecules of atmospheric gases. Nor can they predict when a particular unmeasured quality plays a crucial role in the system's performance.

THE BUTTERFLY EFFECT

Lorenz's discovery has become known as the butterfly effect, after the title of his famous 1972 paper ("Does the Flap of a Butterfly's Wings in Brazil Set Off a Tornado in Texas?"). Most of the

FACT: Stress does not cause schizophrenia but is believed to contribute to the severity of the disorder.

time, a butterfly flapping its wings doesn't alter weather patterns. But it can! Under the right conditions, the chain of events sparked by a butterfly fluttering or *not* fluttering its wings can lead to a storm.

Although weather is extremely complex, the human brain is ever so much more so. As a complex physical system, it too is subject to chaos theory. The tiniest thing can become its tipping point, leading to a significant, concrete change.

Tipping Points

It could tip for bad or good. Missing the bus to work by ten seconds might aggravate preexisting emotions enough for something truly bad to happen, such as causing you to get fired. Or, finding an Indian head penny in the dirt could lead to coin collecting as a new hobby, or pop the cork of a dark mood and lead to a significant stretch of happiness. The decision to go for a walk around the block tomorrow morning before work, eat fresh fruit for breakfast, or do a crossword puzzle while waiting to see the dentist could

BRAIN BOOSTER

YOUR TOTAL BRAIN WORKOUT

Look for the "Brain Booster" boxes to find tested methods for boosting brainpower

Although the research on brain health is still young, current science suggests that practicing good health habits across different aspects of well-being may be our best ticket to staying sharp and lowering our risk for dementia.

Throughout this section, you will find a series of tips and exercises

based on the Total Brain Health® program, a unique approach to improving brain fitness that I have developed and taught to audiences and private clients. These exercises and tips give you scientifically grounded advice and activities that you can really use to practice better brain fitness in ways that engage your body, mind, and spirit.

Use the Brain Booster to take the information you are learning here to the next level. It's a great way to make the growing science of brain wellness something that you can really bring into your life on a daily basis.

—CYNTHIA R. GREEN, PH.D.

ROMAN LEGACY
Ancient Roman philosophers equated a sound mind with a sound body.

signal the start of a new lifestyle that strengthens both body and brain.

The difference between the brain's bad and good tipping points is largely a matter of choice. Humans don't have the ability to stop bad things from happening. They can, however, use free will—the power to choose, embedded in the uniquely human prefrontal cortex—to opt to take steps to improve brain health. Chaos theory says the smallest step can lead to enormous alterations. You might do a brain exercise or two in this book and find yourself liking how you feel afterward. That may lead you to check out other mental or physical routines, within these pages or without. Before you know it, you've made a noticeable change in your mental circuitry. Your brain's plasticity ensures it will change as it makes new connections among your billions of neurons and even grows new brain cells in the hippocampus. Your free will makes you the engineer of those changes in your brain.

HEALTHY BODY, HEALTHY MIND

Your brain and body are connected by nerve bundles that move muscles and keep organs functioning. Nerves also provide sensory stimuli from your body for your brain to process. It should be no surprise, then, that a healthy brain begins with a healthy body. Recognition of the mental–physical relationship dates at least to ancient Rome, which gave us the Latin phrase *Mens sana in corpore sano* ("A sound mind in a healthy body").

The Heart–Brain Connection

Many brain health programs begin by focusing on the body's physical health. The brain's around-the-clock work schedule consumes a quarter of all the blood the heart circulates. The stronger

BRAIN BOOSTER

SMALL STEPS TO BETTER BRAIN HEALTH

You need only a few minutes a day to build new brain connections

Sometimes making the change to better health can seem overwhelming. Where do you start? How can you fit it all in?

➲ STEP 1: Small steps
When it comes to your brain, even small steps can help you get on the road to better brain fitness. Look for small ways in which you can do something just a bit differently, such as taking a different route to work, learning a short meditation practice, or taking five minutes each day to study a poem. Such challenges offer us all the chance to wrap our minds around something in a slightly different way, forcing us to set new neural connections and pathways.

➲ STEP 2: Think differently
The Total Brain Workout activities included here offer you many simple yet fun ways to change your brain game. They are designed to make it easier for you to bring better brain health into your daily routine.

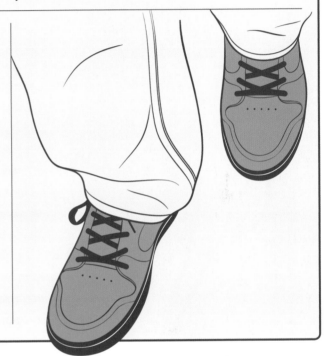

the pumping heart, the more efficient the functioning of the brain. Having a healthy heart requires a proper diet, low in fat and high in fiber and antioxidants, as well as a regimen of regular exercise and abstention from dangerous toxins such as those in tobacco and illegal drugs.

Any kind of exercise is better than none. Walking, swimming, dancing, biking . . . whatever elevates your pulse and gets you sweating improves the function of your heart and lungs, sending life-giving oxygen to your neurons. Exercise has been found to reduce the risk of heart attack, diabetes, and colon cancer, and also beneficially affects blood pressure and mood. But exercise also physically changes the brain. Aside from boosting the amount of oxygen red

SWIMMING TO HEALTH
Exercise increases blood flow to the brain and physically alters the network of blood vessels servicing neurons. Movement improves the brain's ability to control movement.

blood cells carry to the neurons, exercise increases the density and number of blood vessels in the motor cortex and cerebellum, which control conscious and unconscious movement. True exercise is the key—you can't boost the amount of oxygen to your brain simply by speeding your breathing patterns. Deliberately trying to hyperventilate, by taking fast and shallow breaths, actually decreases oxygen levels in the brain. Cerebral hypoxia, or low levels of brain oxygen, can cause fainting.

The stronger the pumping heart, the more **EFFICIENT** the functioning of the brain.

Risk Factors

In addition to heart and artery disease and lack of exercise, factors that limit the flow of blood to the brain include:

▶ **Nicotine.** Smoking cuts the flow of blood to every organ, and the brain is no exception.
▶ **Dehydration.** No surprise here: The brain is 80 percent water. When starved for water, it staggers to perform physical functions and struggles to focus attention.
▶ **Caffeine.** Not only does it directly reduce blood flow, but it also can disrupt sleep and cause dehydration. On the other hand, some evidence suggests benefits to the brain from the daily stimulus of a

measured amount of caffeine in coffee or tea. For example, caffeine improves attention, which is essential to learning and memory.

▶ **Lack of sleep.** Studies have shown that people who sleep less than six hours per night have decreased blood flow to the brain. As anyone would know when getting out of bed after a fitful night of tossing and turning, a poor night's sleep also impairs memory, mood, and overall cognitive function.

▶ **Drug and alcohol abuse.** Drugs and alcohol have a toxic effect on vessels that carry blood and other bodily fluids. Like caffeine, however, red wine may have some benefits for the brain—not because of its alcohol content, but rather because of an ingredient called resveratrol that protects blood vessels.

JAVA JOLT
Coffee, anyone? In small amounts, caffeine in coffee appears beneficial as a stimulant. Too much ruins rejuvenating sleep and reduces blood flow.

BRAIN INSIGHT

A WALK IN THE PARK

Sometimes, helping your brain may be as simple as a walk in the park

Marc Berman, a postdoctoral fellow at Toronto's Rotman Research Institute, found that walking for an hour improved cognitive function and mood among adults diagnosed with clinical depression.

Berman recruited 20 clinically depressed subjects in and around Ann Arbor, Michigan, and assigned them to two groups. The first walked for an hour in a peaceful woodland setting and the second for an hour in a noisy urban setting. A week later, the two groups switched venues and repeated the experiment.

Berman was skeptical: People with depression often seize on dark thoughts, and a solitary walk might give them time to focus on painful times in their lives.

Surprisingly, the 2012 study found that walkers in both settings experienced a boosted mood. Furthermore, those in the natural setting improved attention and working memory by 16 percent compared with those in the urban setting.

The study built upon a 2008 experiment that demonstrated that people without any diagnosis of illness enjoyed increased memory and attention after a woodsy walk.

Berman believes a peaceful, natural setting eliminates distractions that bombard the brain's memory and attention circuits, allowing the brain to relax and restore itself.

WALKING IN AUTUMN

BRAIN BOOSTER

BRAIN-HEALTHY LIVING IN TEN STEPS

What's good for your body and your social life is good for your brain, too

Here's all you need to know in just ten steps:

STEP 1
Get regular exercise.

STEP 2
Eat a healthy, well-balanced diet and maintain a healthy weight.

STEP 3
Stay on top of your health and use medications wisely.

STEP 4
Get a good night's sleep, avoid risky behaviors, and don't stress!

STEP 5
Play games against the clock to stay sharp and focused.

STEP 6
Use simple memory strategies to enhance your daily recall.

STEP 7
Keep your mind engaged through new challenges. Find little ways to "change up" your brain's routine.

STEP 8
Be social—it offers great challenge for everyday thinking skills.

STEP 9
Work or volunteer to stay intellectually challenged and socially engaged. Both activities may offer protection from memory loss over time.

STEP 10
Think positively! Self-perception can affect our performance. Practice the power of positive thinking and believe in your memory.

▶ **Other toxins.** Many environmental poisons damage blood vessels.

▶ **Diabetes.** The disease causes blood vessels to grow brittle and interferes with proper healing of damaged tissue. It also increases risk of stroke.

▶ **Stress.** When the body reacts to potential danger, whether real or imagined, the endocrine glands prepare it for "fight or flight"—to supercharge it for combat against an enemy or predator, or to prepare it to run away. The flood of the stress hormone adrenaline shunts blood to the muscles at the expense of other regions.

[FACT: Walking for just ten minutes a day can boost your energy levels for an hour. **]**

A small amount of stress can spark the brain to higher achievement, but stress that's too intense or chronic can damage the brain through changes in blood flow and pressure. Spikes in pressure caused by adrenaline can leave blood vessels vulnerable to breaking, which can be catastrophic in the brain. In addition to adrenaline, the stress hormone cortisol appears to impair memory. Studies of elderly adults demonstrated that those with high cortisol levels from long-term exposure to stress did worse on memory tests than similar adults with low levels of cortisol. The high-cortisol group also had smaller hippocampi, the brain region most closely associated with integration of memories. Children who experience prolonged exposure to high-stress environments also have trouble concentrating and learning.

POSITIVE REINFORCEMENT
Embracing positive moods, such as joy, affects brain chemistry in ways that reinforce such moods. The same is true for negative moods.

VITALITY

Besides improving physical health, exercise boosts self-esteem. That's a part of vitality, another major component of brain health. Vitality includes feeling that your life has meaning, and that you enjoy living it. It means handling the storms and sunshine of life, mentally holding both positives and negatives in balance. A healthy social life is crucial to vitality, whether found in a circle of friends, co-workers, relatives, a church, or community group.

Moods arise from chemical reactions in the brain. They also cause the brain to release chemicals that affect mood. It can be a vicious cycle. Negative mental states such as depression cause the brain to alter its balance of neurotransmitters in a way that supports negative mood and interferes with brain functions. The mood-altered brain then mechanically releases even more chemicals linked to depression. Unchecked, this cycle can lead to isolation from a social circle (which usually enhances depression), and correlates with higher risk of dementia. On the other hand, happiness releases brain chemicals that benefit both brain and body even after the moment of joy passes. Laughter truly is a form of medicine.

Brain Food

Introspective techniques such as meditation can improve vitality and increase brain health. But you don't have to be a yogi to boost your inner peace. Because brain and body are so closely connected, you are, in part, what you eat, reinforcing the body's mental–physical relationship. Take fish, for example. A diet rich in fish and shellfish has been shown in multiple studies to keep the mind sharp and lower the risk of certain brain disorders. Residents of Iceland, who eat about five times as much seafood as Americans and Canadians, rarely have depression. Fish oil and, in particular, omega-3 fatty acids

INNER PEACE
(Opposite) Meditation, practiced by a devotee of Ananda yoga, is one way to raise consciousness and boost vitality.

BRAIN FOOD
(Above) The right foods strengthen the brain. Eating a variety of fruits and vegetables is good; some studies suggest the oils in fish fight depression.

have been linked not only to brighter mood but also more efficient transmission of electrochemical signals between the synapses. Eating more fish may even raise the brain's shields to fight the onset of dementia.

BRAIN FITNESS

Along with physical health and vitality, a healthy brain requires something known as cognitive fitness. It's a measurement of the brain's functioning in four arenas: perception, attention, thinking, and language. All respond to the stimuli of new, complex activities by sprouting tangled thickets of axon-dendrite connections. The greater the complexity and novelty, the more the brain responds by making its internal connections even more complex.

NEURAL NETWORKS
Computer artwork of a brain in side view depicts the brain's networks in lines and flashes.

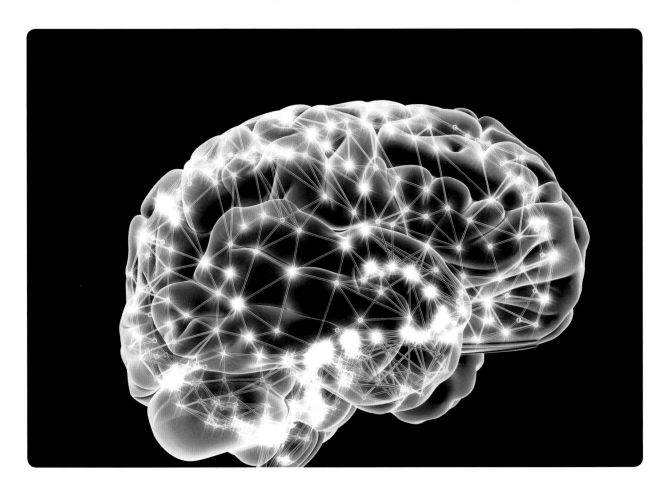

PUZZLE POWER
Doing a crossword puzzle challenges the brain. The more complexly wired the brain, the better it appears to maintain health with age.

Enhanced brain fitness has value in its own right. It feels satisfying at any age when you demonstrate mental agility and speed, as when you answer the questions while watching a game show on television or solve clever puzzles in the Sunday newspaper. But there's another, long-term benefit to engaging in brain-challenging games and activities: They raise your chances of maintaining your cognitive skills into old age. It appears that having a "brain reserve" of extra neural connections may provide a buffer against mental and physical decline with age.

Some loss is inevitable. The average human brain weighs about 1,400 grams, or roughly three pounds, at age 30. By age 90, the brain has lost 90 to 100 grams. The drop could be the result of neural death, loss of axon–dendrite connections that shrink neurons' weight, or both. Still, a popular theory posits that complexly wired brains have greater ability to hold on to their cognitive skills with advancing age. If something affects a number or percentage of neurons, it will have more impact on brains that are less fit and that have fewer neural connections. Richly wired brains still suffer neural losses, but they'll cope by shifting cognitive tasks to the web of neurons that remains.

FACT: Nicotine tops the list of the most addictive chemicals. High on the list: caffeine, heroin, and alcohol.

BRAIN BOOSTER

STICK TO IT! STAYING WITH YOUR PLAN

Be realistic when you think through your brain health program

Changing our health habits can be hard. As any dieter can tell you, we start out committed, but easily find ourselves off track. Here are some tips for increasing the "stickiness" of your brain health plan:

➔ **SET A REALISTIC GOAL**

Make sure your goal is reachable. Remembering everything is unrealistic. Learning how to remember names is just the right size goal.

➔ **SET YOUR STRATEGY**

Figure out what steps you need to reach your goal. If improving name recall is your goal, decide whether you will take a course, read a book, or use some other technique. Break down your strategy into doable steps that are clear and easily accomplished.

➔ **SET UP FOR SUCCESS—AND FOR FAILURE**

Plan the ways you can reward yourself as you move toward your goal. Everyone likes a pat on the back! At the same time, expect to hit some roadblocks. Figure out how you will get yourself back on track if you stray.

Cognitive Reserve

A cognitive reserve acts like a savings account tapped on a rainy day to pay unexpected bills, which would break the bank of someone without the extra money. To use a computer example, imagine two brains as two internal hard drives. One brain, which has undergone fitness training, has added the equivalent of a supplementary memory, such as a flash drive or CD-ROM reader and stack of computer disks. When the enhanced computer loses its supplementary memory, its hard drive still functions. The loss may not even be noticeable. Such appeared to be the case in the Mankato Nun Study described in the introduction. The nuns who had developed neurally enhanced brains through a lifetime of challenges appeared to keep their cognitive skills longer than those whose brains had less cognitive fitness. Sometimes, an autopsied nun's brain revealed the physical signs of Alzheimer's disease, even though the nun showed no evidence of Alzheimer's while alive.

Just as the body grows stronger when its muscles are challenged, the brain grows more fit when taxed by new kinds of learning. Adding a new language, musical instrument, or cooking skill are examples of creative categories of brain challenges. Smaller versions of those challenges work, too, thanks to chaos theory and neural plasticity. You don't have to learn Italian to enhance your brain fitness, for example, but if you're an opera buff, you might try learning the words—and meaning—of the soaring *"Nessun dorma"* ("None shall sleep!") from Giacomo Puccini's *Turandot*. Not an opera fan? If you've played the same six chords on the guitar since you were 15, you don't have to take up the clarinet. Instead, try mastering the melody of George Harrison's "Here Comes the Sun" on your six-string, or any other song that stretches your skills beyond your old limits. Always enjoyed basic Mexican cooking? Try making a *mole* sauce next time.

Quick Brain Fitness

The glory of a good brain workout is that you don't have to pay for a gym membership or set aside a regular part of your daily schedule to take part. Many of the brain fitness activities explained in these pages can be done in just a few minutes, virtually anywhere and at any time.

If you want to go beyond the suggestions in this book, many games are available online, and software packages designed specifically to build skills, such as short-term memory, or build a reserve through intellectual engagement, such as learning a new instrument or traveling, are offered for purchase by a variety of manufacturers. Dr. Cynthia Green provides her observations about such offerings later in this book.

The **BRAIN GROWS** more fit when taxed by new kinds of learning.

"UNA VOCE POCO FA"
Challenging the brain can be as easy as learning new things about favorite pastimes, such as the words to a beloved Rossini opera.

CHAPTER 7

Sensing the World

SIGHT AND VISION
(Opposite) An eye exam targets the brain's processing of light. Without healthy neural networks, there can be no vision.

SEEING IS BEING
(Below) Irish philosopher George Berkeley (1685–1753) summed up his ideas by the phrase "Esse est percipi" ("To be is to be perceived").

T he relationship between the world "out there" and the brain's construction of it "in here" has fed centuries of highfalutin debate. In the 17th century, British philosopher John Locke argued that the brain passively processed information it collected about the world through the five senses. The German Immanuel Kant responded a few decades later by proposing that the brain played a more active role, constructing the reality that humans navigate every day. Although the world has an underlying reality, he said, humans can never know it directly. Instead, all they have is the brain's constructed stage set of the world, with sights and sounds independent of the things they represented. A third philosopher, a contrary Irish theologian named George Berkeley, took things even further. He said there is no "real" world. To Berkeley, nothing existed without its being perceived by the brain through the senses. That idea seemed a bit much, not only to wags who wondered where the world went when it wasn't being perceived, but also to the British lexicographer and essayist Samuel Johnson, who kicked a rock and proclaimed, "I refute it thus!"

THE BRAIN-SENSES SYSTEM

T heir debate sheds light on the importance of a healthy brain and healthy senses. The nerves that sense light, sound, smell, taste, and touch are nothing but extensions of the brain. Without

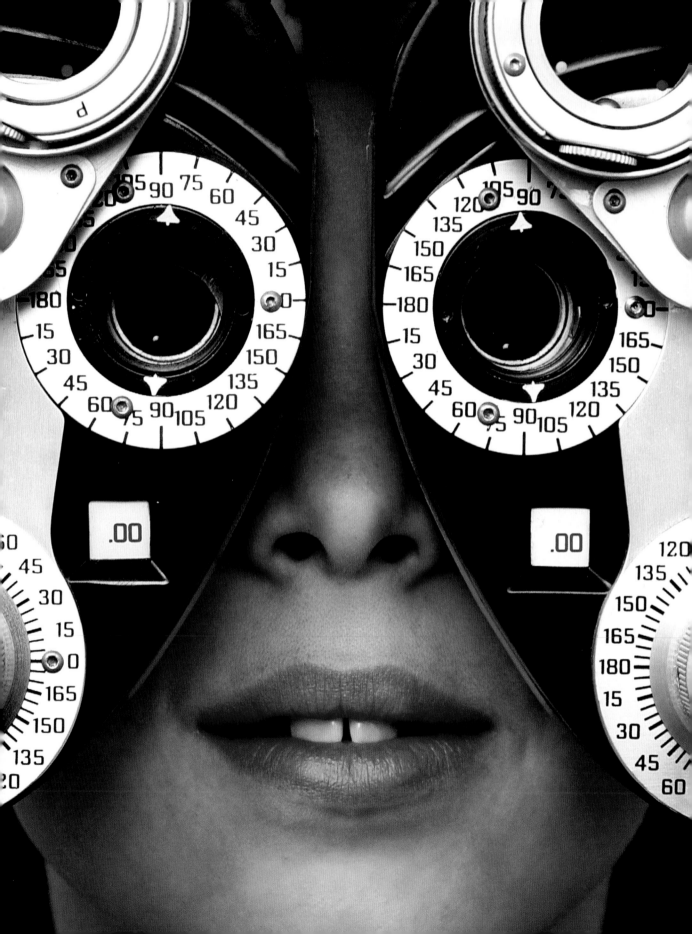

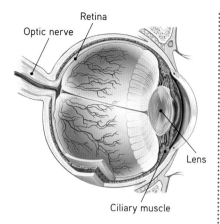

Optic nerve
Retina
Lens
Ciliary muscle

LIGHT COLLECTORS
(Above) A lateral cross-section of the human eye reveals structures to collect and focus light (at right) in image, and process it (at left).

A VIEW FROM WITHIN
(Right) The retina and optic nerve inside the human eye are extensions of the brain—neurons firing in response to stimuli.

the optic nerve and light-sensitive retina, as well as the nerves that stretch and contract the muscles that cause the eye to blink, change focus, and shift its gaze, the brain would have no information to process in the visual cortex. So, questions about whether problems such as declining vision or hearing are matters of the eye or ear, or rather of the brain, are moot. The senses and the brain act as an integrated system, mixing perception and reality beyond the ability to separate them.

Changes With Age

The aging process changes the way sensory nerves send information to the brain. All senses become less acute at some point, causing the brain to have greater difficulty distinguishing details. This occurs for a variety of reasons, but two are paramount. First, the minimum amount of information required to register on the senses, called a threshold, increases with age. It takes more sound or more light, for example, to cause sensory nerves to fire, sending

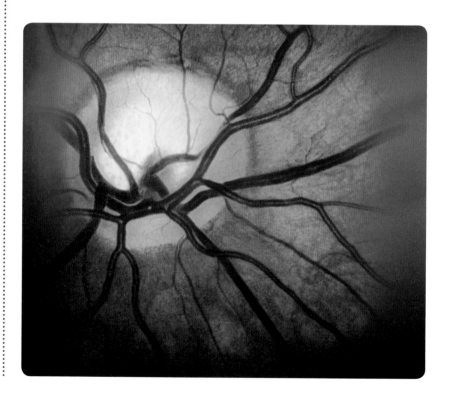

SHARPER FOCUS
A New York City street sign pops into focus thanks to corrective lenses. Aging reduces the sharpness of senses, but many other factors can alter perception.

electrical signals to the brain. Second, changes in the sense organs themselves effect changes in perception. Alterations in organs and nerves associated with vision and hearing typically have the greatest impact, as sight and sound bear the greatest burden of constructing a mental map of the world that's useful for walking, driving, working, and other important activities. But changes in smell, taste, and touch shouldn't be dismissed. A world without pleasant scents and delicious food would lose much of the flavor of life; a world without appreciation of a soft breeze or a lover's caress also would feel diminished.

[**FACT:** Aging eyes have trouble distinguishing shades of blue and are especially sensitive to glare.]

A COLOR BY ANY OTHER NAME

This famous exercise is a real test of your ability to stay focused

This attention exercise is a real classic—in fact, it comes from the dissertation of a famous early psychologist, Dr. Hans Stroop. This task is a great way to get a sense of your ability to stay focused in the face of distraction.

➡ COLORS, NOT WORDS
In the graphic below you will find the names of different colors printed in different colors of ink. Go through the list as quickly as you can, only saying out loud the color the word is printed in, not the word itself. Do it a few times to give your attention a real workout.

YELLOW	**BLUE**	ORANGE
ORANGE	PURPLE	GREEN
GREEN	RED	YELLOW
PURPLE	YELLOW	**PURPLE**
RED	**ORANGE**	BLUE
BLUE	GREEN	**GREEN**

YOUNG EYES

Many vision problems have nothing to do with aging. Myopia, or difficulty in seeing things at a distance, has become increasingly prevalent in the last few decades. It typically starts in childhood. In the United States, myopia rates have increased by two-thirds since the 1970s, a period that correlates to the introduction and diffusion of computers in the home and workplace. Theories that blamed computer monitors and other screens for the apparent epidemic emerged and gained popularity. A study of Alaskan Inuits seemed particularly compelling: They had few cases of myopia until television came to their homelands in the extreme north, when the number of cases zoomed.

However, a 1996 myopia study found no smoking gun. It said computers were no more likely than other forms of long-term, close-in work, such as reading, to be associated with myopia. The strongest indicator of a person's likelihood to develop nearsightedness, according to a 2007 study of California third graders, is heredity. Rates doubled if a child had one myopic parent and quintupled if he or she had two.

> In the United States, **MYOPIA** rates have increased by two-thirds since the 1970s.

In the Dark

A more recent study, conducted by visual disorder expert Kathryn Rose of the University of Sydney, pointed to lack of exposure to sunlight as a possible contributing factor. Sunlight boosts dopamine levels in the brain, she found, in a way that fights the development of nearsightedness. The threshold for seeing benefits from sunlight seems to be 10 to 14 hours of exposure each week, she said. Slavish devotion to computers, television, and books may be linked to myopia merely because it tends to keep people indoors.

However, evidence remains plentiful for the connection between close work and something called "transient myopia," which is the bleary vision associated with long periods of reading. It results from the eyes' constant focus on a near plane. The condition won't cause permanent myopia, but it's an inconvenience in

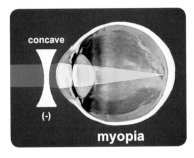

MYOPIA
(Above) A concave lens corrects for myopia, a condition that causes images to be focused in front of the retina.

VISUAL INHERITANCE
(Below) A father and child share more than a moment of reading. Their shared genes often link the quality of their vision.

SCREEN HYPNOSIS
Computers simplify lives but may come with a cost. Staring too long at a computer stresses the eyes and muscles.

SCREEN HYPNOSIS
Computers simplify lives but may come with a cost. Staring too long at a computer stresses the eyes and muscles.

PALMING
Cupping the palms of your hands over your open eyes and blinking relaxes the eyes and the mind.

a world that relies so heavily on reading. The strain of prolonged attention to a computer screen also causes stress. It can cause eyes to go dry (from lack of blinking), and result in headache and muscle pains in the neck and shoulders. Once the symptoms of eyestrain appear, sufferers can try closing their eyes and rubbing their temples to feel better, or to improve reading conditions by increasing text size on a computer screen and adjusting ambient light.

EYE EXERCISES

The eyes operate through muscle contractions. Exercise strengthens the muscles surrounding the eyes and helps keep their lenses flexible. Computer users in particular should take short breaks throughout the day to exercise their eyes. Exercises have been shown not only to help maintain a current level of vision, but also improve vision among people 65 and older.

BRAIN BOOSTER

EYE OPENER
Experience the world in a new way with just one eye

We rely on our visual perception to make sense of all that we see daily. Shouldn't we give it a good workout every once in a while?

◆ FIVE-MINUTE CHALLENGE
Try this simple exercise for at least five minutes each day (or in shorter sessions spread over the day) to challenge your visual perceptual capacity: Take a bandana, kerchief, or removable eye patch and use it to cover one eye. Keep that one eye covered and go about

your regular routine. See how well you can see with just that one eye. What changes about your perception? Next, cover the other eye and see how things change.

When you first start this exercise, try doing it while seated. If you do decide to move around, be sure to clear your path beforehand and avoid anything you might trip over. Keep in mind that your depth perception will be challenged, so move slowly and with care.

Four Activities

Eye exercises include the following, all of which should be accompanied by regular breathing to supply oxygen to the eyes, and blinking to keep the eyeball surface moist:

▶ **Palming.** This exercise, done without glasses or contact lenses, reduces stress. Sit at a table, lean forward, and put your left hand over your left eye so the heel rests on the cheekbone, the fingers lie flat on the forehead, and the cup of palm covers but does not touch the eye. Then place your right hand over your right eye in the same manner, with your right-hand fingers on top of your left-hand ones. Keep your eyes open, and blink often. This technique relaxes both mind and eyes.

▶ **Tracking figure eights.** Visually trace a reclining figure eight,

FACT: Only a tiny region in the center of the eye, the fovea centralis, can see sharply enough to support reading.

ZOOMING
Exercising the eyes, such as focusing on your thumb as you zoom it in and out, helps maintain visual acuity.

FIND THE TARGET
Elderly subjects improved vision with a brain challenge depicting a cross (below left), then a stimulus array containing a central target and peripheral target (vertically oriented diagonal line pattern, below center), and then a masking pattern (below right).

in the shape of the infinity symbol, about ten feet in front of you. Reverse the pattern once in a while.

▶ **Switching focal length.** Put your finger a few inches in front of your eyes. Focus on the finger, then focus on something in the distance beyond it. Switch back and forth.

▶ **Zooming.** Hold your thumb at arm's length. Focus your eyes on it as you bring your thumb close to your face, and move it back again.

Vision relies on neural networks in the brain. Like other neurons, they require stimulation to remain strong. "Use it or lose it" applies to seeing as much as it does to other brain activities. This was demonstrated by a study in 2010, in which test subjects improved their vision with the use of brain-challenging exercises.

Letters and Lines

A research team at the University of California, Riverside, and Boston University found that a specific set of eye exercises could clarify vision for a test group aged 65 and older. Subjects were shown a series of visual stimuli consisting of a letter embedded amid a field of horizontally oriented lines. The stimulus also included an array of peripherally located lines, in a diagonal orientation, that formed a vertical or horizontal object, and that always appeared in the same quadrant. Immediately after flashing an image, the researchers put up a masking pattern. The test subjects had to identify

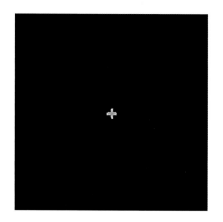

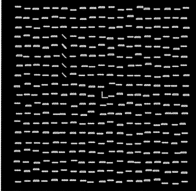

the central letter and peripheral object. Thus, their task was to perceive and process a confusing image in an instant. Two days of training in one-hour sessions with difficult stimuli prompted older subjects to substantially improve their vision, said chief researcher G. John Anderson. The improvement, related to physical changes in the visual cortex, lasted up to three months.

THE AGING EYE

Around age 40, most adults start to experience an age-related decline in their ability to see things clearly at short distances, a condition known as presbyopia. It manifests itself gradually, but eventually causes difficulty in reading print. Those with the condition may find themselves "playing trombone," zooming a handheld

---

BRAIN BOOSTER

MIRROR, MIRROR
Challenge your mind with reverse perceptions

Here's a great way to reflect on the power of your perception.

➲ **LIFE IN REVERSE**
Place a small- to medium-size mirror in front of your keyboard or workspace. Then work a few minutes every hour or so while looking in the mirror, so that your actions are reversed. You can also try this when doing the dishes (make sure it's OK if the mirror gets splashed), writing, or doing other tasks where you can study your reflection.

Have young ones around? Mirror, Mirror is a great exercise to do with kids as well. Try it with them as they tie their shoes, do homework, or even color. It will bring about giggles but also some keen observations about what can happen when our visual perception is flipped.

This shift in your visual perception will definitely challenge how your brain usually sees the world.

page in and out until the eyes can bring it into focus. People who are already nearsighted sometimes find they have better close-in vision when they remove their eyeglasses. Some get two pairs of glasses, for near and distance vision, whereas others choose a single pair of bifocals or multifocals.

Presbyopia occurs as the lens—a transparent, flexible structure behind the iris—grows more rigid. The condition cannot be prevented or cured. It typically gets gradually worse, requiring changes in eyeglass prescriptions every two years or so, until about age 60, when it grows more stable.

Other conditions associated with aging of the visual system include the need for more light—to compensate for nerves' rising threshold—to read and perform other tasks; blurred vision and changes in the perception of color, especially blues and greens, as the lens becomes cloudy and the cornea grows flatter; reduced production of tears, especially in postmenopausal women; greater incidence of glare, caused by the less-flexible lens scattering light on the retina instead of focusing it sharply; and pupils dilating less in low light.

> Older people may use a **RED LIGHT** to reduce glare and make a room more **VISIBLE.**

BRAIN BOOSTER

STAY FOCUSED!
Strengthen those eyes with a little exercise

Try this simple exercise designed to give your visual coordination a workout. All you need is a pencil:

➡ 1. Staring straight ahead, with your head level, hold a pencil with the eraser side up in your hand.

➡ 2. Next, bring the pencil's end to eye level, and move the pencil from side to side, toward and away from your face, up and down, all while tracking the eraser with your eyes. Remember to keep your head still!

➡ 3. Do this for a minute at first, building to about five minutes total each day (broken into several sessions if you prefer).

THE PROPER GLASSES, ALWAYS READY

Ben Franklin's resourceful answer to presbyopia

Benjamin Franklin wore glasses for much of his life. As he aged, he had trouble not only with a general loss of visual acuity, but also a more pronounced blurriness when he looked at nearby objects.

The latter condition, called presbyopia, begins to affect many people around age 40. Unlike astigmatism, nearsightedness, and farsightedness, which arise from environmental and genetic factors reshaping the eyeball, presbyopia stems from the slow thickening and stiffness of the eyes' lenses with the passing of the years.

The 18th-century solution to Franklin's problem was to switch between two pair of glasses: one for reading, and one for general vision.

Franklin tried that for a while but thought better of it. "Finding this change troublesome, and not always sufficiently ready, I had the glasses cut and half of each kind associated in the same circle," he wrote. "By this means, as I wear my spectacles constantly, I have only to move my eyes up or down, as I want to see distinctly far or near, the proper glasses being always ready."

Although he may not have invented bifocals (historians argue the point), he was among the first to wear them, and he popularized them in the United States.

BEN FRANKLIN

Strategies for Older Eyes

Compensation strategies allow many people to cope. Some may find it too difficult to drive at night, but will be perfectly comfortable behind the wheel in daytime. Older people may use a red light in a darkened room, instead of a frosted-white or clear-bulb night-light, to reduce glare and may make a room more visible at night. Or they may adjust for the brain's lowered ability to distinguish blues and greens by decorating with more discernible reds, oranges, and yellows. Bright, warm colors make good accents not only on walls and furniture but also in pillows and afghans, which stimulate vision and sense of touch. These substitutions may help avoid bumps and bruises.

[FACT: When the brain detects a loud sound, it signals the eardrum to become less flexible, reducing potential damage. **]**

HEARING

Ears transform the vibrations of sound to electrical impulses that the brain can interpret in meaningful ways. The process begins when sounds collected by the outer ear travel to the eardrum, a thin flap of tissue that separates the outer ear from the middle ear, and set it to vibrating. High-pitched sounds make it vibrate more quickly than low ones, while loud sounds move the surface greater distances in and out. Each sound's distinct vibrations are passed through a succession of three tiny bones—the hammer, anvil, and stirrup—and wind their way to the inner ear. There, they strike tiny hairs growing in the cochlea, a snail-shaped organ that plays perhaps the most crucial role in hearing. The hairs transform the vibrations into electrical impulses, the only form of communication that can be read by the brain, and forward them along the auditory nerve.

To maintain optimal hearing, it's best to **AVOID** exposure to **LOUD SOUNDS.**

The eardrum automatically grows more rigid in the presence of loud, low sound, which offers some protection against neural damage. But it remains vulnerable to sounds that blast too loud or last

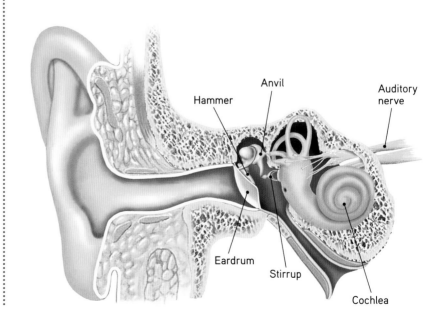

INSIDE THE EAR
A diagram of the interior of the ear indicates primary structures that turn vibrations in the air into electrical signals that can be read by the brain. Hair cells in the cochlea, at right, are crucial; damage to these cannot be repaired.

Anvil

Hammer

Auditory nerve

Eardrum

Stirrup

Cochlea

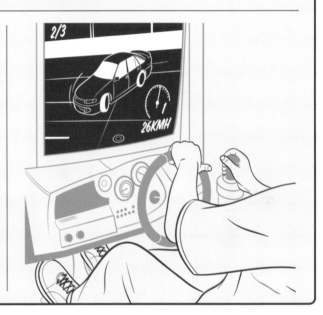

BRAIN BOOSTER

REFRESH YOUR DRIVING SKILLS
Software can keep your mind and hands nimble

Keeping your eyes and your mind on the road are critical to staying safe while driving. Keeping our brain's focus, reaction time, and nimbleness up to speed as we grow older can be part of maintaining good driving habits and, for many older adults, our ability to stay independent and care for ourselves.

➜ GO FOR A VIDEO DRIVE
Take your brain for a test drive using a software program that reinforces the brain skills underlying good driving. There are several on the market: You might even find discounts or free versions through your auto insurance company. Find one that gives your attention, visual processing, reaction time, and flexibility a real workout. When you've found the one that suits you, make it a habit to spend some time each week tuning up your brain. It's a habit worth getting revved up about!

too long. Such sounds can weaken and even kill the sensitive hair cells in the cochlea. Once those cells are damaged or dead, they cannot be repaired or replaced. Cochlear implants bypass the hair cells by converting sounds into electrical impulses that directly stimulate the auditory nerve, but the implant-induced sensations lack the richness of natural sound. To maintain optimal hearing, it's best to avoid exposure to loud sounds, or to use protective ear wear if such exposure cannot be helped.

How much noise is too much? It depends on the loudness of the sound as well as duration of exposure. A single, powerful impulse, such as an explosion next to the head of a soldier in combat, can be enough to cause a condition called noise-induced hearing loss. On the other hand, long hours of moderately loud music can have a similar effect. In general, the louder the sound the less time it takes for the sound to cause serious damage.

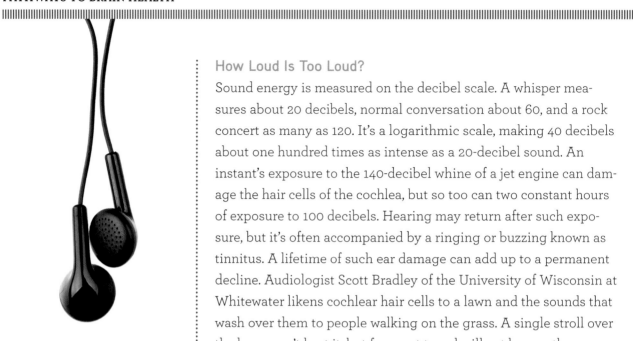

How Loud Is Too Loud?

Sound energy is measured on the decibel scale. A whisper measures about 20 decibels, normal conversation about 60, and a rock concert as many as 120. It's a logarithmic scale, making 40 decibels about one hundred times as intense as a 20-decibel sound. An instant's exposure to the 140-decibel whine of a jet engine can damage the hair cells of the cochlea, but so too can two constant hours of exposure to 100 decibels. Hearing may return after such exposure, but it's often accompanied by a ringing or buzzing known as tinnitus. A lifetime of such ear damage can add up to a permanent decline. Audiologist Scott Bradley of the University of Wisconsin at Whitewater likens cochlear hair cells to a lawn and the sounds that wash over them to people walking on the grass. A single stroll over the lawn won't hurt it, but frequent travel will cut bare pathways.

Music lovers may not be aware of the potential for damage, despite warnings since the 1980s about portable music players equipped with headphones. More recent technology, which

---

BRAIN INSIGHT

TURNING IT UP TO ELEVEN
The unwanted legacy of rock and roll

"Tommy, can you hear me?" Pete Townshend of the Who wrote those lyrics for his 1969 rock opera, *Tommy*, about a boy unable to see, hear, or speak.

It's also a question that hits home for Townshend, who lost much of his hearing after a lifetime of performing and recording loud rock music. Now in his late 60s, Townshend relies on two hearing aids, and according to a bandmate must stand next to the speakers to hear any of the music.

For a while, the Who held the world record for the loudest concert, a 1976

PETE
TOWNSHEND

affair in London where the music topped 120 decibels. Other bands have broken that mark, and many other rockers have suffered hearing loss.

But Townshend puts primary blame on wearing earphones for studio work, and not concerts, for his decline. Prolonged exposure to loud music in earphones and their modern iPod cousin, earbuds, can damage hearing. One study at Wichita State University found students experiencing 110 to 120 decibels during normal earbud use. Constant exposure to 100 decibels can cause damage in two hours.

fits earbuds into the exterior opening of the ear canal, has only increased the risk.

"We're seeing the kind of hearing loss in younger people typically found in aging adults," said Dean Garstecki, a Northwestern University audiologist. He partly blames in-ear earphones, which can boost sound intensity by six to nine decibels. Garstecki's advice: To protect your ears, turn down the music.

Diet for Better Hearing

Diets rich in antioxidants appear to strengthen neurons in the brain's auditory system against noise-induced hearing loss. Antioxidants neutralize free radicals, which damage neurons, including those that sense and process sound. Studies conducted in 2004 on Marines undergoing rifle training in California suggested that boosting the

OW!
Exposure to loud noises is physically painful and can permanently damage hearing.

THE VIRTUES OF BERRIES
(Right) Blueberries, blackberries, and raspberries are rich in antioxidants that help protect neurons from damage, including noise-related injury.

DIMMING OF THE DAY
(Opposite) As senses lose their edge with age, they may contribute to feeling cut off from others. Simply being alone might not be bad, but feeling lonely or depressed isn't healthy.

amount of antioxidants in their diet could lessen the effects of later exposure to loud battlefield noises—and possibly even help protect their cochlear hair cells if the antioxidants were ingested immediately after hearing extreme sounds. About 10 percent of Marines typically suffer some hearing loss as a result of rifle training. Now, daily doses of a drink that tastes like herbal tea and contains the supplement N-acetylcysteine, or NAC, may help them maintain their hearing.

AGE-RELATED HEARING LOSS

Other forms of hearing loss occur naturally with age. The eardrum thickens and becomes more rigid, making it less sensitive to soft and high-frequency sounds. The ability to hear high-frequency sounds weakens more and more with age, with men older than age 70 experiencing hearing loss the most at the highest frequencies. Speech encodes vowel sounds in the lower range and consonant sounds in the higher range. As consonants carry more of the information of speech than vowels, high-frequency sound

FACT: "Haptic touch" refers to handling objects to sense their tactile qualities. Skin sensors connect body and world.

impairment can interfere with speech comprehension. That, in turn, can lead to social isolation and the mental health issues associated with it, such as loneliness and depression.

Most people experience some degree of presbycusis, or age-related hearing loss, and significant impairment strikes about a third of people older than 65. Loss of sharpness in the sense of hearing begins to be noticeable around age 50. Two common causes are changes in the auditory nerves and the buildup of wax in the ear canal. The latter can easily be remedied by a doctor's cleaning.

Age-related hearing loss can be slowed by practicing healthy habits. Any exercise that increases blood flow raises the level of life-giving oxygen available to the tissues surrounding the hair cells of the cochlea, likely extending their lives.

FIND THAT CRICKET
(Above) Closing your eyes and pinpointing a moving sound, such as the pop of a metal clicker, exercises the brain's auditory circuits.

CLOSE OUT DISTRACTIONS
(Below) Shutting out distracting noises, below, to concentrate on a particular conversation also sharpens the brain's ability to process sound.

BRAIN BOOSTER

THE SCENT OF SOMETHING NEW

Build your olfactory memory with unfamiliar smells

This week, try "learning" new scents.

➲ Find new or unusual spices, herbs, or oils that are unfamiliar to you. Teach yourself to identify them by smell alone (no peeking!). Exercising your sense of smell will build your olfactory memory, and perhaps even boost the volume

of your olfactory bulb, where scent memory resides.

Want to take this tip a bit further? Certain aromas have been associated with health benefits. Try rosemary to enhance learning, lavender for calming and sleep, or citrus scents such as tangerine or orange for increased attention or energy.

Exercise Your Ears

As with vision, exercises can help maintain or even increase the ability to detect sounds. One such exercise involves closing the eyes and pinpointing a sound merely by analyzing the slight differences in wave patterns hitting your left and right ears. Stand in an open area, shut your eyes, and have a friend stand at least several yards away from you. Have your friend make a gentle sound, such as clicking a metal cricket. Point to the origin of the sound. Keep pointing as your friend moves around and repeats the sound. In another exercise, try carrying on a conversation as you add distracting noises in the background one at a time—a radio, computer, television, and so on. Although it may be confusing, your brain should sort out the screening noises and let you concentrate on the sounds you want to follow. In addition to exercising the ears themselves, regular workouts of the body's muscles, heart, and lungs also help keep hearing sharp. Regularly working up a sweat increases blood flow to the ears' cells and removes damaging waste products.

Age-related **HEARING LOSS** can be slowed by practicing healthy habits.

OTHER SENSES

The perceptions of taste, smell, and touch also change with time. The brain senses flavor through nerves embedded in taste buds that cover the tongue, as well as through specialized receptors in the nose. The senses of taste and smell grow weaker with age, as thresholds change. After age 60 or so, the ability to taste begins to wane for most, but not all, people, and the sense of smell declines as well. Salty and sweet tastes usually go first, followed by bitter and sour. The loss is gradual. In general, it takes a greater concentration of sweetness to taste something sweet, and a less intense sourness to taste something sour. Why this happens remains a bit of a mystery, but speculation centers on the fact that the mouth grows drier as saliva production decreases with age; environmental factors, too, add up over a lifetime. The number of taste buds also decreases with age, starting at about age 40 in women and age 50 in men. The remaining taste buds lose some of their mass, further reducing the surface area of the mouth sensitive to flavor. Other causes of diminished taste include tooth decay, mouth sores, certain medicines, and poor nutrition.

HOT AND COLD
Sensitivity to taste and temperature, such as the qualities of a hot drink on a cold day, changes with age—more stimuli are needed to register sensation.

The Sense of Touch

The sense of touch also dulls a bit with age, typically lifting the threshold of sensation for pain, heat, cold, pressure, and vibration. Lowered sensitivity to heat and cold can be life-threatening, so it is recommended that the elderly cap their water heaters' maximum temperature at a safe level, and be careful to dress appropriately when they leave the house during periods of high heat and cold.

The origin of changes in skin receptors may be a reduction in blood flow, typically resulting from a more sedentary lifestyle and greater use of medications. Or it could be the aging process itself or health disorders that elderly people more commonly experience. One compensation occurs around age 70: As the skin grows thinner, it often becomes more sensitive to a light touch, such as the caress of a hand.

NEW SENSATIONS

Challenging the senses in novel ways helps the brain keep existing neural pathways open and create new ones, allowing the brain to maintain and even expand its processing of information from the five senses. Leonard Katz, a neurobiologist, promotes the concept of exercising the brain by making multisensory associations. He says this can be done in two ways: by combining two or more

TASTE MAKERS
A color-enhanced scanning electron micrograph shows taste buds on the surface of the human tongue.

BRAIN BOOSTER

PLAY ONLINE
Now you have a good reason to spend time on online games

How would you like the chance to boost your brain power by taking ten minutes a day to play? What could be more fun than that?

➲ Research has shown that we can better maintain intellectual skills, such as attention, speed, executive control, and memory (all of which can change as we age) by giving them a good workout. One of the best ways to keep these skills challenged is by playing games against the clock, since timed activities force us to focus, think fast, and be nimble in our approach.

➲ Games we play online tend to be timed and can give our brains a terrific skills challenge. Look at free games on sites such as Miniclip.com (Sushi Go Round is still one of my favorites), or check out some of the enjoyable brain fitness software products on the market.

BRAIN BOOSTER

WHAT'S IN THE BOX?

Your sense of touch needs exercise, too

Have you ever groped around your night table in the dark searching for your glasses or bottle of water? I bet you never considered while doing it that you were giving your tactile perception a workout.

Although we use our sense of touch constantly, rarely do we isolate the experience so that we focus solely on it. Even less likely are we to deliberately exercise that sense. Yet our tactile ability, like other aspects of our brain health, certainly can benefit from a workout.

Try this fun exercise to hone your sense of touch:

1. Take several small household objects (utensils, coins, paper clips, keys, small game pieces, and so on).

2. Place the objects together in a shoebox or similar size container.

3. Cover the box with a dish towel or other cloth.

4. Place your hand in the box under the cloth and try picking up the different objects and naming them using your sense of touch alone. How many can you identify correctly?

Want to take it up a notch? Try doing this exercise with your nondominant hand.

senses in unexpected ways, or by using one of the five senses in a new context. The former might be appreciating a particular bit of music while smelling a pleasant aroma. Vivaldi's *Four Seasons*, seasoned with vanilla, for example. The latter technique might involve reliance on sound, touch, or sight to carry out a task that normally relies on the use of one sense. So, for example, your family might prepare and eat dinner in silence, using only visual cues to get everything set up, and then pass and use things on the table as needed.

FACT: The sparsest concentration of touch receptors is in your back. Densest concentrations are in lips and fingers.

Turn Off Your Vision

You might also pretend to have lost your sense of sight for a short time. After you park the car in the garage, close your eyes, open the car door, and try to get into the house and hang up your coat. This might involve paying extra attention to the contours of your keys in order to pick out the right one for the door from the garage to the living room. Once you've found it and turned the lock, you would rely on touch and sound—the softness of the carpet under your feet after the tile of the entryway, the ticking of the mantle clock as an aural anchor to orient you as you make your way across the living room—to complete your task. If you try this, go slowly, and try to re-create your house visually in your mind's eye. You'll find landmarks by touch and sound. Just don't storm ahead and bark a shin on the coffee table, or you'll get an unwanted sensory stimulation: pain.

Katz also recommends giving your senses a break from their routines. This can be as simple as taking a new route to work or rearranging the furniture in your living room.

EXPLORING THE SENSES
Want to challenge your senses? Try wearing a blindfold for a while and experiencing the world without vision.

COMBINE SENSES
Awakening new neural circuits in the brain can be as easy as combining multiple senses—hearing, taste, touch—to build new connections.

CHAPTER 8

Balance and Coordination

A DELICATE BALANCE
(Opposite) The brain of a modern dancer acts like a symphony conductor, coordinating conscious and unconscious movement to achieve balance.

INTIMATE CONNECTIONS
(Below) A colored scanning electron micrograph reveals the junctions between a nerve cell in green and a muscle fiber in red. Nerve stimulation makes such muscle fibers contract.

For most people, grasping a pen from an out-stretched hand, walking up a flight of stairs, or riding a bicycle seems a simple task. At one point, though, these skills required tremendous mental effort. It takes a baby months to learn to coordinate muscles, joints, and the sense of balance first to crawl, and then to master the antigravity circus of walking upright. During those early months, figuring out how to keep the body balanced, both at rest and in motion, requires fierce attention. Even so, the child toddles and falls a lot before learning the basics of walking.

Time passes, but still, the most basic of body movements arise from the brain directing an amazing, complicated symphony of three basic functions: movement of individual muscle fibers, coordination of muscle groups, and balance.

HOW MUSCLES MOVE

Muscles move in response to the brain's conscious and unconscious orders, executed along nerve fibers. Electrochemical signals cause muscle fibers to contract. Even when you extend an arm or a leg, the process works only when the fibers contract—nerve signals never cause a muscle to stretch itself. These contractions act like binary digits: Muscle fibers either contract completely, 100 percent, or not at all. When your body needs extra strength, for lifting something heavy or twisting a stubborn

SMOOTH MOVES
Balance provides the foundation for coordinated movement in sport, such as a basketball player's smooth shooting motion.

jar lid, the brain recruits more and more muscle fibers to add their contractions to the existing total and increase the force your body applies.

Muscular Teamwork

Muscles work in groups. Shooting a basketball, for example, calls upon the brain to orchestrate the muscles of the fingers, hands, wrists, arms, shoulders, legs, thighs (bend your knees on those free throws!), and so on. The result, at least for a professional basketball player, is a smooth, well-coordinated movement that flows in properly

[FACT: Young children can communicate with gestures before they are able to use words. **]**

executed order through muscles and joints to direct the basketball through the hoop. Without the brain's coordination of the sequence of neural firing, the ball might miss the rim, or even the backboard.

The brain could not pull off this amazing feat without a well-developed sense of balance. It's the body's response to gravity that keeps it upright. Without stable posture, muscle fiber contractions to reposition the body would have no foundation, no reference point. A dizzy or wobbly basketball player would never lead the league in scoring.

MOTION CIRCUITS

Just how the brain coordinates movement became better understood in the late 19th century when British neurologist John Hughlings Jackson examined patients with epilepsy. He noticed that,

---

BRAIN BOOSTER

TAP A TUNE
Let your fingers do the dancing while you're stuck at your desk

This better Brain Booster is sure to get you moving to a different beat. Go ahead and make up a little tune by tapping your fingers on your table or desktop (the actual desktop, not the computer, though I guess you could make up a tune bopping on your computer if you are so inclined). You can use two hands or a nearby pen, if you like.

➲ CHOOSE YOUR OWN RHYTHM
Your tune can be short or long, simple or complex, though I would suggest going for more than just one "note." Tapping a tune will challenge your brain to think about the world in a slightly different way, and get you to coordinate your movement, auditory, and memory skills. Imagine—all that in just a few minutes today.

Who knows, you could even come up with your own personal theme song!

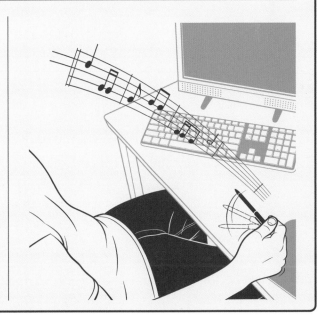

A FIRE IN THE BRAIN
The study of epilepsy, revealed here in a magnetic resonance imaging scan, led to the discovery of brain regions' associations with particular body parts.

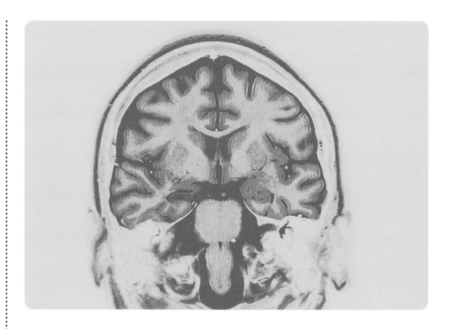

in some patients, the convulsive movements associated with epilepsy seemed to flow in sequence from one body part to another. He concluded that muscular tics and jerks arose from the disorder affecting first one brain region and then another. The obvious conclusion was that discrete brain regions control movements in particular body parts.

Today, we know that most of the brain's circuitry is involved in both voluntary and involuntary movements. Key components include huge portions of the cerebrum, which houses the motor (movement) cortex; cerebellum; basal ganglia; brain stem; and the spinal cord, which not only carries signals to and from the brain but also organizes and responds to a variety of signals from the body's periphery. Most, if not all, of these parts of the nervous system work together to create movement. Movement is seldom the result of a single muscle's activation. Touching your nose with your forefinger activates muscles in fingers, hand, arm, and shoulder, as well as your eyes. Executing the same motion while dizzy may call on other muscles to compensate.

> Most of the brain's **CIRCUITRY** is involved in both voluntary and involuntary movements.

Staying Upright

The spinal cord contains about 20 million axons. These nerve fibers, as well as those in the brain stem, neck, and legs, respond to gravity to keep the body stable and upright. Neurons in the brain stem and cerebellum react to slight changes in body position to automatically contract the right muscles in the right amount at the right time to maintain an upright posture. Damage to neurons in the cerebellum often announces itself by affecting the ability to stand upright for any length of time. Long-term abuse of alcohol can manifest itself in the cerebellum, resulting in an unsteady gait—or worse. Likewise, damage to crucial neurons from Parkinson's or stroke may impede movement in a variety of ways, from muscle rigidity to lack of balance. Certain health conditions, medications, and inner ear problems also affect the body's ability to maintain balance.

MANY PIECES TO THE PUZZLE
Rigidity and loss of flexibility arise from many sources, including arthritis, although age itself doesn't appear to be at fault.

CITRUS BOOST
(Above) Vitamin C in oranges and other citrus fruits helps keep joints healthy and protects against free radicals.

PREP WORK
(Below) It's important to warm up, such as with time on an exercise bike, to prepare muscles for exercises that benefit both body and brain.

FLEXIBILITY

Motor skills tend to degrade with age. With advancing years, it takes more time to get moving. Once under way, movements take longer to execute, and they lose some of the fluidity of youth. Older joints tend to lose flexibility, growing more rigid.

Science has discovered that age itself is not to blame. Rigidity and loss of flexibility, or range of motion, in joints stem from lowered levels of physical activity associated with age, as well as health conditions such as arthritis. Inflexibility can take hold at virtually any age. However, diet and exercise can help maintain range of motion, and even restore some that has been lost.

A balanced diet, rich in antioxidants, is crucial to maintaining maximum joint movement. Growing evidence points to vitamin C playing a singularly important role. Not only is this vitamin,

BRAIN BOOSTER

STRETCH AT YOUR DESK

Get rid of those deskbound doldrums

Spending all day at your desk or on the phone can really take a toll on your body and your mind. Taking small breaks to move, even in little ways, can help break the routine and give you a mental change of scenery.

➔ WIDE ARMS

Find a few minutes several times over the course of the day to get up from your desk and stretch. Try standing up and spreading your feet comfortably, to give yourself a firm base. Next, stretch your arms wide at shoulder's height. Then imagine a sense of pulling out toward your hands and feet to give yourself a nice stretch.

➔ BACKBEND

You can also try countering that hunched-over position we can find ourselves in at our desks by doing a gentle, slight backbend from your waist, or bending forward from the waist while seated in your chair and letting your arms and head dangle for a few moments (just be careful to protect your neck as you sit back up).

plentiful in citrus fruits, an excellent counterweight to destructive free radicals, but it also helps the body construct proteins found in joint cartilage.

Exercises for Flexibility

Good exercises to maintain flexibility include stretches, which can be incorporated into a regular workout routine or performed by themselves. Stretching also has the added benefits of helping prevent injuries caused by muscle tightness and also of reducing stress.

Tai chi, yoga, and Pilates classes can increase flexibility as well as balance. If you don't want to commit to a regimen of classes with

[FACT: "Muscle memory" is the common name for how the neuromuscular system learns skills. **]**

STRETCH AND FLEX
A young woman stretches before an outdoor run on a cold day. Stretching improves flexibility.

a group, you can do some simple stretching exercises at home.

Try these:

▶ **Warm-ups.** Cold stretches can cause muscle injuries. The best time to stretch is when muscles have already done some basic work and begun to heat up with energy and blood. So start with five to ten minutes of walking, pedaling on a stationary bike, or doing some other simple exercise.

▶ **Spine stretches.** Lie on your back on the floor with your arms and hands at your sides. With your legs straight, bring your feet up in the air. Try to raise them far enough to angle your feet back over your head. Count to five, lower your legs to the floor, and repeat ten times. This stretches your spine, an excellent way to minimize the risk of back injury.

▶ **Seated stretches.** Sit on the floor with your legs crossed and your back straight. Lean forward until your back is arched and your head and neck are parallel with the floor. Count to ten, then revert to your starting position. Repeat five times. When you're done, stand and get loose.

▶ **Trunk twists.** Stand with your hands on hips and arms akimbo. Your feet should be a short distance apart and not move during the exercise. Twist your trunk slowly to one side and look behind you. Hold that position for five seconds. Then twist the other way and repeat. Do this a few times to stretch your trunk.

[FACT: Learned motor skills fall into two categories: fine and gross. A baby's gross motor skills develop first. **]**

▶ **Leg lifts.** Stand next to a desk or table, positioned to one side of you. Grasp the edge with one hand. Slowly raise one leg until it is parallel to the floor. Lower the leg and repeat with the other leg. Do this ten times with each leg to boost flexibility in the hips.

If those exercises are too strenuous, you might try the following easier ones. Try repeating these three to six times at first, and then add more repetitions or go on to some of the previous exercises:

▶ **Reach for the sky.** Sit or stand so your back is straight. Raise your arms above your head and stretch for the ceiling. Return your arms to your sides to relax for a moment.

BRAIN BOOSTER

TAKE A YOGA BREAK

How about bringing a little "om" into your life?

In many ways, yoga is the perfect brain health exercise. As a physical activity, yoga supports your more vigorous aerobic workouts by building strength and stamina (not to dismiss the fact that yoga itself can be aerobic, depending on your practice). In addition, yoga helps build sustained focus, which we all need to learn and remember on a daily basis. Finally, yoga is a terrific resource for maintaining emotional balance, and can be used to reduce stress, anxiety, and relieve depressed moods, all of which may lower our everyday mental performance.

➲ ACTIVITIES

Try taking a five-minute yoga break each day. Kripalu, a center for yoga in Massachusetts, offers a series of such breaks you can download to your computer or other media player (*www.kripalu.org*). If you have time and are feeling even more ambitious, try an online yoga class from Yoga Today (*www.yogatoday.com*) or another online source. Consider looking for yoga classes in your area and making yoga part of your path to better brain health.

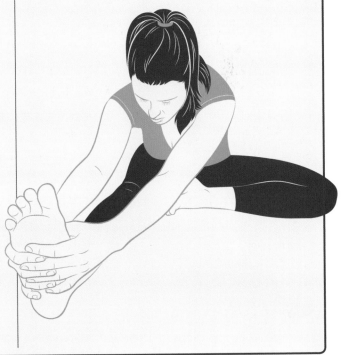

BRAIN BOOSTER

STRIKE A BALANCE

Bring your "weaker" side up to par

A key component of coordination and balance can be the degree to which we have evenness, or symmetry, of ability across both sides of our body. Most of us have dominance on either the left or right side. We favor that side, hand, or foot when we do things such as write, play sports, or perform other tasks that require fine motor dexterity and coordination. Yet what about your other half? Doesn't it need to stay in the game?

➔ **ACTIVITIES**

A great way to challenge our nondominant side and encourage better balance is through activities that ask us to coordinate and engage both sides of our brain at the same time. Hobbies like knitting, playing instruments such as the piano or violin, or juggling do just that.

Challenge yourself with exercises that get both sides of your body on par. You may find your nondominant side slower and less agile at first, but keep up the work!

- ▶ **Side to side.** Stand tall with your feet apart and your arms at your sides. Bend to one side, letting your hand drag along your thigh toward your knee. Then straighten up. Bend to the other side, and repeat equally on both sides.
- ▶ **Toe loops.** While sitting in a chair, keep one leg bent while straightening the other before you. Stretch your toes toward your head and then downward. Then slowly circle the foot at the ankle. Repeat with the other foot.
- ▶ **Leg extensions.** Sit in a chair with your knees bent a bit. Straighten and stretch one leg before you, then let it drop. Repeat with the other leg.
- ▶ **Elbow loops.** Sit or stand with your elbows bent and your fingertips on your shoulders. Slowly rotate one of your elbows in a big,

backward circle. Repeat with the other elbow. Or try simply bending and straightening the elbow again and again, which helps build arm flexibility.

▶ **Waist watchers.** Lean slightly forward while sitting in a chair with your knees bent and your feet on the floor. Bend forward slowly from the waist and stretch your hands toward your feet. Then slowly straighten and relax. After you've tried this exercise for a while, switch to a trunk twist. Put your right elbow on your left knee by twisting at the waist. Then straighten up, pause, and shift your left elbow to your right knee.

Be sure to breathe regularly, without holding your breath at any point. Don't bounce as you stretch, as bouncing tightens muscles and can cause minute scarring in muscle tissue. If you find any unpleasant level of discomfort from any of the exercises, stop immediately and try again another day. Persistent pain caused by simple exercises can be a sign you should see your doctor.

ON A ROLL
(Above) Tennis star Martina Navratilova, playing in Queens, New York, in 2006, advocates stretching to improve blood flow.

PLAY IT AGAIN
(Below) Being open to the challenges of the playground at any age keeps the motor cortex from falling into too-familiar patterns.

Stretch and Play

In addition to the previous exercises, you can invent your own or make use of your surroundings to promote strong balance and agility.

Tennis star Martina Navratilova, now in her mid-50s, likes to stretch with a foam roller, the kind sold in a sporting goods store. The roller stretches the fascia, connective tissues that surround the muscles, and improves blood flow, she told AARP.

Stephen Jepson, in his early 70s, has converted his yard into a playground to keep his body and brain sharp. Jepson, featured in a video in the Growing Bolder Media Group's series celebrating active senior citizens, believes the key to staying mentally fit is to return to the playgrounds of childhood. Jepson challenges the

BALANCING ACT
Balance, crucial to Chun Hing Chan of Hong Kong as he makes a turn in the 2010 Asian Games, depends upon complex feedback in the brain.

CLUMSY NEANDERTHALS?
Studies of Neanderthal skulls, such as the one in the foreground, suggest they had less agility and balance than *Homo sapiens,* at rear.

movement-coordinating circuits of his brain by riding an elliptical bicycle, walking slack ropes strung between trees, hopping barefoot from rock to rock, and otherwise providing new and unusual stimulation to his motor cortex. The practice not only has maintained his balance and agility, he said, but has also sharpened his memory.

BALANCE

The human ear carries out two important jobs. One, of course, is to translate vibrations into sensations the brain constructs as sounds. The other is to coordinate the body's position to keep it in balance.

The latter function relies on the vestibular system, which along with the cochlea occupies the inner ear. The vestibular system comprises a series of fluid-filled tubes called the semicircular canals, plus the vestibule, a space that connects the canals with the cochlea. Special sensory cells that detect motion occupy the

[**FACT:** When you stretch out, always do equal amounts on each side of your body: You don't want to get out of balance.]

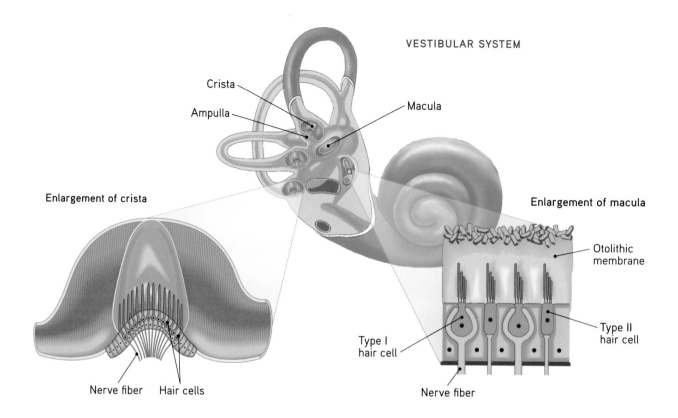

VESTIBULAR SYSTEM

Crista

Ampulla

Macula

Enlargement of crista

Nerve fiber   Hair cells

Enlargement of macula

Otolithic membrane

Type I hair cell

Type II hair cell

Nerve fiber

THE EAR'S OTHER JOB
Inside the human ear, the membranous labyrinth of the vestibular system contains the organs of balance, including the cristae and maculae.

vestibule and semicircular canals and send signals via nerve fibers to the pons and medulla oblongata.

The Body in Space

The neural circuitry of balance ties together sensations in the ear with vision and other sensory systems. The brain uses the eyes and specialized sensory cells in the feet to gather information about the position of the body in space. The vestibular system's fluid-filled tubes detect motion of the head, both in a straight line and in a curve. Fluid movement bends sensory neurons in the tubes, initiating electrical signals in the connecting nerve fibers. The brain swiftly integrates this incoming information and sends signals to the arms, legs, trunk, and other body parts to shift in reaction to changes in body orientation to the ground. The brain also directs the movement of the eyes to redirect their gaze, when necessary, to provide feedback as the body moves. So, for example, when you stumble, your eyes flash to the ground before you.

Proprioception is the brain's unconscious sense of the body's motion and spatial orientation. The system is amazingly complex and interconnected, yet you probably never give your balance a second thought—until you start to fall.

An Evolutionary Advantage?

Anthropologists have noted an interesting fact about the vestibular system. Humans evolved over millions of years to walk upright on ground. This development freed the hands for carrying tools, such as axes, clubs, and spears that could aid in the hunt for food. Differences in the ability to coordinate upright movement may account in part for the extinction of humanity's evolutionary cousins, the Neanderthals. *Homo neanderthalensis* shared space with *Homo sapiens* until the former disappeared about 30,000 years ago. Recent

> You probably never give your **BALANCE** a second thought—until you start to fall.

BRAIN BOOSTER

GET JUGGLING
Keep those balls in the air and build some brainpower

Have you ever tried juggling? And not just your schedule?

➔ WHY JUGGLE?
Complex motor integration activities such as juggling have been shown to increase brain volume and improve everyday memory performance. Researchers in Germany found that juggling increased volume in the white matter of their subjects' brains. Such activities boost brain health by getting us to move and forcing us to focus and think about what we are doing. Best of all, they rate very high on the fun factor.

Chances are you may have tried juggling at one time in your life, only to give it up as too difficult. This is your chance to give juggling another shot. Start with one or two balls or scarves (scarves may be a bit easier at first) then slowly work your way up to three.

Want more direction? You can easily find instructional help on the Internet.

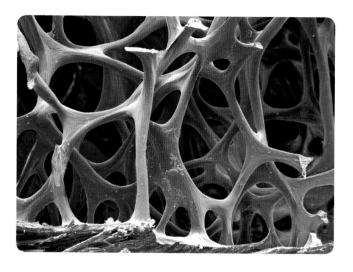

SUPPORT STRUCTURE
(Above) Interior, spongy tissue, revealed by a colored scanning electron micrograph, provides support and strength to bones. Brittleness in aging bones makes falls dangerous.

DYNAMIC BALANCE
(Opposite) Dynamic balance, active during motion such as walking along a branch, begins to decline in young adulthood but can be bolstered by balance-enhancing exercises.

examinations of Neanderthal skulls revealed that, compared with modern humans, Neanderthals had smaller vestibular systems. They would likely have had a less developed sense of balance and less agility. That could have made Neanderthal second best at hunting game, an evolutionary disadvantage in the long term.

As previously noted, aging causes the structure of the ear to change. Most notably, the eardrum thickens, which not only may affect hearing, but also impacts balance.

Balance and Age

Maintaining balance into old age is a key component of enjoying life. Journalist Scott McCredie, who wrote a book about the human sense of balance, said it's vital to challenge the sense of balance to keep it sharp. "[As] we move into our 60s . . . we can't afford not to think about it," he wrote. "Not just to prevent a potentially lethal fall, but to be able to continue moving gracefully through the world, to stay glued to the tightwire of life."

Two body systems linked to balance—vision, and the sensitivity of cells in the feet that inform the brain about the body's position—also typically decline with age. In addition, loss of muscle mass and less flexibility in the limbs mean that when an aging body begins to totter, the brain must rely on weakened tools to avoid a fall. Each year, one in three Americans older than age 65 loses balance and suffers a fall. Brittleness in elderly bones often causes them to break in such falls, sometimes with catastrophic results.

The sense of balance has two forms: static and dynamic. The former keeps the body upright when still. The latter maintains

[**FACT:** About two million Americans seek treatment each year for vestibular balance disorders.]

THE WATER CURE
The brain is mostly water, and it needs to stay wet. Dehydration can bring on a host of problems, including fainting.

Chronic
DIZZINESS
increases the odds
of falling by two
to three times

balance while the body changes its relationship with the surface of the Earth, as when climbing a hill or stairs, or turning a street corner on a bicycle. Both begin to gradually erode beginning in the body's third decade. Unless the deterioration is checked by deliberate steps, the result often is dizziness or loss of balance later in life. Compromised balance may not seem like much of an impediment, but it can interfere with driving, walking, and even sitting upright. People with continuing troubles with balance often have trouble holding a job.

DIZZINESS

Chronic dizziness increases the odds of falling by two to three times. Dizziness is classified in four types, all of which become more common with advancing age:

► **Loss of balance; unsteadiness; a feeling of being about to fall despite normal muscle strength.** Disorders in the inner ear and the cerebellum, such as damage caused by alcoholism or stroke, can bring on this condition. So too can the use of too much sedative or anticonvulsant medication, as well as nerve disorders that affect the sensation of the position of the legs.

► **Faintness.** This feeling of impending blackout can stem from dehydration, nervous system disorders, abnormal heartbeat, and adverse reactions to blood pressure medication.

► **Vertigo.** This feels like movement in the body or the body's surroundings, despite both being at rest. Causes can include middle-ear infections, migraines, decreased blood flow to the brain, motion sickness, or something as simple and transitory as a sudden movement of the head.

► **Lightheadedness.** This vague feeling may arise from a panic attack, hyperventilation, depression, or other mental disorders.

Exercises can maintain and even improve balance. Such exercises work the hips, knees, ankles, and feet. They also challenge the

WALK ON BACK

Put it in reverse and learn to walk all over again

Looking for a simple way to mix things up and challenge your coordination? Try walking backward.

→ **A NEW DIRECTION**

Walking is something we do every day. In fact, it is one of our most overlearned motor activities (and one that gets parents most excited when their children first master it). So why not get your brain to focus differently by changing up this very simple, everyday activity?

Before you begin your backward walking, make sure that the area in which you are practicing is free of obstacles and has an even surface. Start slowly and walk carefully.

As you practice your "walk on back," notice how your sense of balance and coordination shifts. Chances are that the exercise will feel odd and awkward at first. But, like a child learning her first steps, you should find it gets easier the more you practice.

neurons of the vestibular system to keep it firing and wiring. These exercises require no special training: They're as easy as balancing on one foot for as long as you can, or walking by placing one heel directly in front of the toe of the other foot and continuing to walk in a straight line.

Test Your Balance

Physical therapists Marilyn Moffat and Carole B. Lewis, authors of *Age-Defying Fitness*, suggest that before beginning a regimen to improve balance, you should assess your current state. They suggest the following exercises, to be performed near a table or some other sturdy piece of furniture you can lean on or grab as needed: Begin by putting on a pair of flat, closed shoes. Stand straight with your arms folded across your chest. Lift one leg until the knee is bent at about a 45-degree angle. Close your eyes and begin to time yourself; use a stopwatch if you have one. Stay balanced on one leg. Stop timing the exercise as soon as you uncross your arms, bend to one side

BRAIN INSIGHT

THE BIRD AND THE SNAKE

The peaceful benefits of a martial art

Legend says tai chi began when a 12th-century Taoist monk fled the cities to find peace in the mountains and wondered how to protect himself. The monk, Zhang Sanfeng (or Chang San-Feng), studied martial arts at his monastery, but an epiphany allowed him to move beyond his teachers. Zhang saw a bird and snake fighting. Instead of charging one another, the antagonists adjusted their movements to penetrate the adversary's defenses. Zhang saw that moving with an opponent's force, instead of opposing it, could be the foundation of a new martial art based

on mimicking animals. Thus was born *tai chi chuan,* or "supreme ultimate fist."

Despite the martial name, tai chi today is practiced most often by those seeking inner peace instead of victory in combat. The dancelike, deliberate movements aim to bring mind, spirit, and body into alignment and operate them under a universal source of energy, called ch'i.

The discipline has a mystic, Eastern aura, but you don't have to understand how tai chi works to benefit from it. Its gentle, stress-free movements can be done at any age, but it has particular benefits for the elderly: Regular workouts improve balance, flexibility, and mobility, reducing the risk of falls. They may even combat depression.

more than 45 degrees, touch your bent leg to the floor, or move your foundation leg. When you're done, switch legs and start again.

Take your times and compare them to your age group. The norm for people 20 to 49 years old is 24 to 28 seconds. It drops to 21 seconds for people in their 50s, 10 seconds for those in their 60s, and 4 seconds for those in their 70s. Most people age 80 or older cannot count off even one second.

File away your numbers for comparison after dedicating yourself to the following exercise: Once again while wearing flat, closed shoes, stand near something you can grab. Plant your feet shoulder-width apart with arms stretched straight in front of you and parallel to the floor. Keep your eyes open. Lift one foot behind

[**FACT:** Dancers learn that balance involves constantly making small muscle adjustments.]

you by bending your knee about 45 degrees. Freeze for at least five seconds, if you can. Do this exercise five times, and then do exactly the same with the other leg. When you feel you have begun to make improvements, continue, but with your eyes closed.

You can practice this skill at any time during the day, such as when you're getting ready for work or bed. Incorporate a one-leg stand into brushing your teeth or combing your hair. (Best not to mix this exercise with a shaving razor, however.)

Sit and Stand

Another useful exercise boosts the strength of ankles, legs, and hips to help the body better deal with the potential dizziness of suddenly standing after sitting a long time. To get the most out of this exercise, sit up straight on something firm without having your back touch anything. Rise until you stand straight, and then sit again as quickly as you can without using your arms. Repeat three times at first. Over time, try to extend the exercise until you can do it ten times.

You also might specifically target the strength of your ankles by walking for a while on your toes, then switching to using only your heels.

Tai Chi

Tai chi, an ancient Chinese muscle-training discipline, appears to be one of the most effective systems of improving balance. Studies have shown practitioners of its slow, deliberate movements decrease their likelihood of falling. Tai chi is not only a discipline of exercise, it's also a form of meditation; Chinese practitioners call it "mindful exercise." Studies at the University of Massachusetts Medical School at Worcester reveal that the combination of physical and mental exercises in tai chi can lower anger, depression, and tension.

MINDFUL EXERCISE
A tai chi festival in Dalian, China, brings out many practitioners of the ancient discipline.

CHAPTER 9

Words and Language

FINDING THE RIGHT WORD
(Opposite) As the brain ages, it builds vocabulary and creates complex links among concepts, but may have greater difficulty finding the words to express ideas.

MYSTIC MESSAGES
(Below) Myth says the Delphic oracle, seen here in an engraving, knew truth but struggled to communicate it.

At the ancient Greek town of Delphi, an oracle—a woman chosen for her purity—sat atop a tripod next to a hole in the ground. According to legend, the god Apollo had earlier tossed the body of the monstrous serpent Python into that very opening. Gases from the decomposing body rose to the surface and met the nose of the Delphic oracle. She inhaled and fell into a trance in which Apollo spoke to her. The oracle shared her revelations, prophesying to the people. But she did so in an unintelligible tongue. Thus, the oracle at Delphi knew great truths, but could not communicate them in plain language. Priests of the temple came to her rescue, translating the oracle's gibberish for the people.

A modern-day, medical parallel to the oracle's problem can be found in a rare disease called Wernicke's aphasia. German neurologist Carl Wernicke described the disorder in the 19th century. It strikes the nerve fibers in a particular part of the posterior temporal lobe. People with this disorder lose their ability to understand language and speak intelligibly. Their words often come out with apparently good syntax, but they make no sense. Their speech patterns and intonation seem normal, but they insert wrong words and randomly jumble words together. A so-called "word salad" of a patient with Wernicke's aphasia might sound like this: "Fly to the oven and get the government mystery. Repeat the library, fourteen alphabet monster."

WHAT'S THAT WORD AGAIN?

The conditions of the oracle and a patient with Wernicke's aphasia lie at the extreme end of a scale of language-processing difficulties. At the lower end lies the occasional problem of searching for, but not finding, the right word to say. Somewhere between the two is the paradox of the aging brain's skill with language. If a brain stays active and builds vocabulary, it may have a far richer treasure trove of words from which to choose than a much younger brain. But an aging brain struggles more to find the words it wants. Wise elders sometimes wrestle with the maddening problem of knowing what they want to say, but being unable to retrieve the correct words from memory—and the problem typically increases with age.

TIP OF THE TONGUE
"Tip-of-the-tongue" experiences are things you know, and know you know, but cannot find words to express.

BRAIN BOOSTER

SENTENCE SCRAMBLE
Make your own sentence out of randomly selected words

Word games can be addictive. Many of us love these puzzles, and they are without doubt the most popular kind of brain game among adults.

How are word games good for our brains? Such activities grab our attention, get us to make new connections, and give us the chance to "stretch" our minds and think outside of our mental box.

Here's a word game you may not have played before—Sentence Scramble. It's a quick diversion that gives your creativity a boost as well. To play:

➔ STEP 1
Find a newspaper, magazine, or book and turn to a random page.

➔ STEP 2
Select a paragraph (any one will do) and go through it. Write down every fifth word, until you have a list of eight to ten words.

➔ STEP 3
Now you are ready to play! Take that list and make up a sentence, using only those words—the quirkier and sillier your sentence, the better.

SAUCER	FENCE	RADIO
POSTER	ROCK	GIRAFFE
CALENDAR	JUMP ROPE	BUMPER

Scientists call this problem the "tip of the tongue" experience, which occurs when a word exists in a person's lexicon but temporarily remains inaccessible to the brain. It's a normal part of aging—tip-of-the-tongue problems typically begin around age 40—and is reported as one of the most frequent and troubling problems of older adults. As brains mature into middle age and beyond, they think more deliberately, and for a longer time, before making decisions. They may know the answer to a question, but fail to come up with it quickly.

Research associate Meredith Shafto of Britain's University of Cambridge studies normal cognitive aging. She told the *Washington Post* that tip-of-the-tongue experiences are "part of what we call normal or healthy aging ... With normal aging there are changes that are noticeable and distressing and irritating, but they are not pathological."

[FACT: Reading and writing use different neural networks. And speaking and listening to speech use still others. **]**

THE INSULA AND LANGUAGE

A research team led by the Pomona College Project on Cognition and Aging, and headed by Deborah Burke, discovered that tip-of-the-tongue experiences increase as the density of neurons in a brain region called the left insula decreases. The insula, deep between the frontal and temporal lobes, recently has drawn neurologists' attention for a variety of reasons. It has been linked to neural processing of sound. It lights up in brain scans when the body feels or anticipates pain, empathizes with others, desires a drug, or responds to jokes or music.

The **INSULA** may be a key performer in the reconstruction of words.

STORING THE PAST
(Opposite) Memories are not stored as entire experiences in particular sites, like items in drawers, but are distributed as data throughout the brain.

THE INSULA
(Below) Decreased density of neurons in the insula, shown in a cutaway view deep inside the brain, has been linked to the struggle to find words.

Use Them or Lose Them

Burke's team relates the insula's age-related decline in gray matter to a theory equating atrophy with disuse: Neural connections that encode words grow weak and decline if those words aren't often spoken aloud. Those neural connections are scattered around the brain, but the insula may be a key performer in the networks' reconstruction of words.

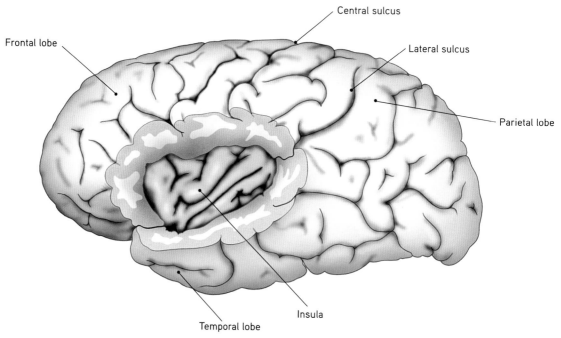

Central sulcus

Frontal lobe

Lateral sulcus

Parietal lobe

Insula

Temporal lobe

SORRY, BRAD
(Right) Despite popular misconceptions, there is no single brain site for "Brad Pitt" or any other concept. Images, sounds, and context lie scattered among sensory circuits.

HELLO, MY NAME IS . . .
(Below) Wearing a tag helps the brain connect names and faces. Names are particularly hard to remember because few have an obvious link to appearance.

"We like to think of words as being stored in a unit in our head, and that we have a little place in our minds where we have [for example] Brad Pitt, and we know what he looks like and what movies he's been in and his name and all that," she told the *Post*. But word-related information isn't stored in such an integrated way. Various neural circuits encode how a word sounds, what it means, how it fits into the syntax of language, how it's associated with images, and so on. The brain can lose access to one part of the related circuits and not the others.

Sound and Meaning

The circuits for word sounds and objects appear to be particularly vulnerable to decay because there seldom is a logical connection, except for onomatopoeia words such as *bang* and *splat,* which take their names from their sounds. Why is a rose called a rose?

As a result of this disconnect between a word and the thing it represents, you might recognize Brad Pitt in a magazine photograph but not recall his name. Your brain's connection to the network containing his name deteriorates. This happens when the circuits lie dormant for too long, and leads to so-called "transmission deficits." If you don't hear the name Brad Pitt while looking at his face, the connection can wither.

Sounds are more vulnerable to decay than other kinds of experiences, Burke said. That would explain why you can know a word, and know you know it, but struggle with the tip-of-the-tongue experience to retrieve it. However, there are also ways to combat this common problem, ranging from memory techniques to methods that allow you to follow a mental trail of clues to the missing name.

> **SOUNDS** are more vulnerable to decay than other kinds of experiences.

BRAIN BOOSTER

DO A WORD SEARCH
A familiar word game is great verbal exercise

This word search game gives your brain a boost by pressing you to be more nimble in your thinking and to shift your usual way of seeing things. Take the following words and see how many other words you can come up with, using only the letters of the original word.

➲ Working the word is a simple activity, yet a great way to get a quick mental workout and intellectual challenge.

Want to up the ante? Give yourself one minute a word.

Happy searching!

RESOLUTION

SUFFICIENT

BENEFICENCE

SYNAPSE

PROPAGATION

WORD SEARCH
Actively searching through a broad swath of your vocabulary, as when playing a word game, can improve ability to recall elusive words.

PRIMING THE PUMP

Burke and other researchers discovered that the recall of tip-of-the-tongue words increased with "phonological priming." That's a fancy way of saying that when a person struggling to come up with a word on the tip of the tongue experiences other words containing similar sound—especially the initial sound, number of syllables, and stress patterns of the hidden word—the desired word often comes to mind. For example, aiming at the target word *Velcro,* Burke's team supplied to test subjects the words *venerable, pellet, decreed, overthrow,* and *mistletoe.* For the target word

[FACT: Musical memory often outlasts verbal memory in patients with Alzheimer's. **]**

Columbus, Burke's team supplied the words *cologne, conniver, alumnus, omnibus,* and *amoebas*. Reading and saying aloud those words brought success. "It has been suggested that a [tip-of-the-tongue] target word pops into mind 'spontaneously' when phonological components of the word occur inadvertently during conversation," Burke's team wrote. Perhaps trying to think of words similar to the missing one will help, especially if the word's initial sound can be recalled. If you're stuck in a tip-of-the-tongue moment, Burke recommends focusing on words that spring into your mind as you search for the missing target. Their related sounds may prime the pump and restore connection to the lost word or phrase.

The Pomona College Project on Cognition and Aging's research on the insula and tip-of-the-tongue problems predicts that keeping neural connections strong for a broad vocabulary will reduce failures to find a particular word. "Using language in ordinary activities like socializing or in games like Scrabble may help keep words accessible and off the tip of the tongue," the project's team wrote. Reading aloud and talking to your companions at dinner may help maintain the neural circuits associated with words and their sounds.

There isn't much you can do for retrieving names from your past, but you can increase the strength of encoding for current acquaintances. That's a memory-enhancing skill discussed in Chapter 11.

Focus on
WORDS
that spring into
your mind as
you search for
the missing
target.

CONVERSATION SKILLS
Conversation at meals doesn't just fill silence. It helps stimulate the brain's language circuits.

BRAIN BOOSTER

NAME THAT CATEGORY

Reinforce your verbal recall with a name game

Here's a fun, short exercise that will build on your ability to think of words quickly (always a challenge as we grow older) and test your recall.

➡ ANIMALS, ANIMALS
Get a piece of paper and pen or pencil. Set a timer for two minutes (or just keep track on your watch or phone). Ready? Go ahead and write down as many animals as you can in those two minutes.

They can be from the land or the sea, the jungle or the desert—just see how many you can come up with in that time frame.

➡ CHANGE CATEGORIES
You can keep this exercise going by simply changing categories each time. Try using foods, plants, colors, countries—anything you can categorize will work well. See if your lists become longer as you become more practiced at this exercise.

VERBAL FLUENCY

Tip-of-the-tongue problems form a subset of verbal fluency studies. Verbal fluency is the ability to quickly and smoothly access vocabulary when writing or speaking. It typically declines with age, and also can be affected by developmental disabilities, brain injuries, cancer, and some neurological disorders. It is not a strong measure of intelligence, as some smart people do poorly on verbal fluency tests.

Tests of verbal fluency sometimes are used as indicators of possible cognitive impairment, as they may reflect changes in the brain's word-processing centers. In a typical test, doctors might give a patient 60 seconds and prompt a patient to list as many words as possible that start with the letter "P." The test taker counts and analyzes the words, as some might not fit the criteria.

FACT: Tonal languages, such as Chinese, are processed in the left hemisphere, not in the regions associated with music.

The 1996 movie *Phenomenon* depicts a verbal fluency test. In one scene, a doctor asks an ordinary man whose cognitive functions have been enhanced to name as many mammals as he can in 60 seconds. The test subject responds by instantly reeling off 26 mammals in alphabetical order from aardvark to zebra.

Health and Fluency

The subject of *Phenomenon* achieved greater verbal fluency via a terminal brain tumor that created new neural pathways. Not a pleasant option for cognitive enhancement, to say the least. More practical

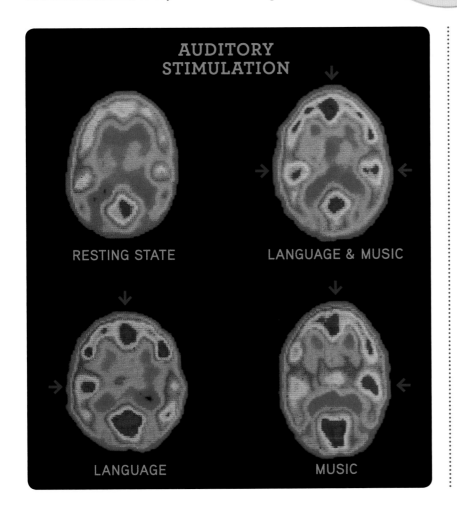

AUDITORY STIMULATION

RESTING STATE

LANGUAGE & MUSIC

LANGUAGE

MUSIC

SOUNDS IN THE BRAIN
In four positron emission tomography scans, active brain regions appear red or other warm colors in response to different kinds of sounds.

methods of improving verbal fluency, and cognitive strength in general, focus on general health. Sleep deprivation can decrease verbal fluency, as can a poor diet. Studies have shown that skipping breakfast, for example, can hurt verbal fluency, apparently by depriving the brain of its optimal nutritional needs. On the other hand, obesity has been linked to lowered verbal fluency and other cognitive functions. In particular, a 2010 study of more than 8,000 postmenopausal women using data from the Women's Health Initiative, a major national U.S. health study, found that as a person's body mass index rose, cognitive functions tended to decline. The group performing the worst on tests of verbal fluency and other cognitive tasks had a high ratio of hip circumference to waist size, meaning they carried excess weight on their hips.

READING THE NEWS
Verbal fluency increases through exposure to new words and topics—easily accomplished via digital platforms that quickly access text and, if necessary, definitions.

BRAIN BOOSTER

GET VERBAL

A word a day keeps the doctor away

Resources readily at hand on your shelf or via your computer can help get your mind engaged by expanding your vocabulary. Building your word skills can really make you think and is a great prep for word games, writing, and other intellectual challenges. Research has demonstrated that such mental activities may reduce our risk for serious memory impairment by as much as 26 percent. And this exercise is fast, free, and fun!

➔ There are some great online sources for getting more out of your vocabulary. Try Freerice.com (and donate rice to the World Food Programme at the same time), or sign up for one of several sites to receive a "Word of the Day." You can also simply pull out the dictionary—an old-fashioned approach to building your vocabulary that still works!

If you want to improve your verbal fluency, try exposing your brain to new vocabulary words as well as new ways of putting them together. With practice, words become more familiar and you are more apt to easily retrieve them. If you read only the business section of the paper, you'll know plenty of business-related words, but you'll be less fluent in other lexicons. So try reading the editorial page or the sports section. If you're reading online or on a handheld digital device, you can easily look up unfamiliar words. Many digital readers have a touch-screen function for definitions. If you go to the trouble of mastering new words by processing and understanding them in context, you'll strengthen verbal fluency.

FEEDING A VOCABULARY
Eating breakfast sharpens the tongue—figuratively speaking—by fueling the brain and increasing its verbal fluency.

MUSIC AND MEMORY
A study shows that a child who learns music might have an improved memory for spoken words as an adult.

SPEECH AND MEMORY

An individual's cognitive resources dramatically affect the ability to recall spoken and written words. As older adults usually have less working memory than their younger counterparts, it makes sense that they must make greater demands on their working memory to process language as they grow older. Studies in the 1990s demonstrated that older adults have good comprehension when they hear simple, short sentences spoken aloud because they don't tax the working memory as much as longer, more complex ones. But in controlled experiments, older adults showed more difficulty in language processing than younger adults as sentences sprouted more clauses and phrases. The difference appears both in accurate recall of the words themselves as well as comprehension of their meaning. Too much information, delivered too quickly, can overload an elderly brain.

On the other hand, the brains of older adults work with nearly youthful efficiency when processing communications such as spoken conversations and instructions that are delivered in short, simple bursts. The decline in processing of language is not as big a problem for text on a page for obvious reasons: If the reader misses something on the first pass, he or she can back up and reread the difficult passage—at a slower pace, if necessary. So, enjoying a 19th-century Russian novel need not become just a memory for the elderly bibliophile.

> Too much **INFORMATION,** delivered too quickly, can overload an elderly brain.

BRAIN INSIGHT

LEARNING TO SPEAK AGAIN

Congresswoman Gabrielle Giffords shows just how resilient the brain can be

"I pledge allegiance . . . to the flag . . ." By leading the pledge at the 2012 Democratic National Convention, former Arizona Congresswoman Gabrielle "Gabby" Giffords demonstrated how far she had come. And how far she still has to go.

Giffords was shot through the left side of her brain in January 2011. Details of her injuries have never been made public. However, the left hemisphere controls speech and right-side body movement. Giffords suffered impaired mobility and aphasia, the inability to speak.

Music therapy helped her talk again. While the left side of the brain controls language, both hemispheres process music. In an amazing feat of neuroplasticity, Giffords' singing therapy helped

GABRIELLE GIFFORDS

her brain move her speech functions to the right hemisphere. She still slurred a few words and walked stiffly at the convention, but her achievement touched many viewers.

Traumatic brain injury can strike anyone. But you can do two things to reduce your risk. One is to protect your head with a helmet when riding a bike or motorcycle, or engaging in rough sports. The other is to build up your cognitive reserve to make your brain more richly connected and to increase its plasticity, should it ever be needed.

Music and Language

Memory for spoken words has been shown to be stronger in mature adults if they had musical training before the age of 12. A 1998 study at Chinese University in Hong Kong revealed that adults who learned how to play a musical instrument as a child scored 16 percent higher on tests for word memory than those who had no such training. The sample was small—a total of 60 college students—but the results nevertheless were intriguing. Thirty students who had at least six years of musical training before they turned 12 demonstrated better recall of words read aloud from a list than a group of 30 who lacked comparable musical training. The memory enhancement did not extend to visual designs, which usually are processed in the brain's right hemisphere. The musically trained students had no advantages at remembering and drawing simple designs they saw.

Neural plasticity apparently explains the Hong Kong study's results. Brain scans of professional musicians have noted an expanded region of neurons in the left planum temporale, a roughly triangular region of the temporal lobe. The region plays a role in processing not only music but also verbal memory. The research supports other work suggesting that musical training prepares the brain for more than just music. Learning to read and play music requires the brain to rapidly recognize and process groups of symbols. Enhanced sensitivity to grouping of symbols likely transfers to the symbols of letters, standing for sounds, that join to form words.

NO GENERATION GAP
Brains of the elderly and the young perform equally well on some communication tasks, such as reading or understanding short, simple sentences.

BRAIN BOOSTER

WRITE A HAIKU

This Japanese verse, which can be easily learned, will stretch your word skills

What better way to boost your brainpower than with a mind-stretching exercise certain to be poetry to your ears? Writing haiku is a wonderful way to get out of your "boxed-in" brain and challenge yourself to think differently and creatively.

Haiku is a time-honored Japanese form of verse dating back centuries. Haiku is known for its simple form, which in its traditional English-language version requires a pattern of five syllables, seven syllables, and five syllables. Classical haiku also makes use of images that are seasonal and sensory in nature.

➲ Although I am by no means a haiku expert, here's my try at this exercise to get you going:

> She sat at her desk
>
> The snow glistened in the sun
>
> The tree shivered cold.

For more about the art of haiku, take a look online at one of the many instructional sites or find translations of some of the haiku masters, such as Basho or Buson, at your local library.

A SECOND LANGUAGE

Decades ago, some scientists believed that learning a second language caused linguistic confusion or even cognitive deficits in young children. Instead, the brains of bilinguals, as children and adults, tend to have a stronger executive function than those of people who speak only one language. The executive function, centered in the prefrontal cortex, keeps the brain focused on what's important. It supports the ability to hold two things in the mind and switch back and forth as needed, such as conversing while following a game on television. Or it can tune out distractions to focus concentration. Children who learn a second language generally are better able than their one-language counterparts to maintain attention while being bombarded with irrelevant stimulation.

BRAIN BOOSTER

LEARN A NEW LANGUAGE
It's never too late to learn a foreign tongue

Learning a new language seems to be one of the most popular ways in which folks keep their brains sharp. Although mastering a new language can become more difficult as we grow older, the task itself is one that many of us seem to find compelling and engaging. Often, it is something we have wanted to do for many years, or it gives us a chance to perhaps recapture the language of our grandparents or great-grandparents. Without doubt, the process of learning a new language is a terrific challenge that can build new connections in the brain.

➡ Figure out which language you'd like to study. Next, look at the many resources for learning that new language and figure out which path you'd like to take. You can attend a class or take one online, find a tutor, or use a language program. Even better, why not plan a trip to the country that is home to your newly mastered tongue?

"If you have two languages and you use them regularly," cognitive neuroscientist Ellen Bialystok of York University in Toronto told the *New York Times,* "the way the brain's networks work is that every time you speak, both languages pop up and the executive control system has to sort through everything and attend to what's relevant in the moment. Therefore, the bilinguals use that system more, and it's that regular use that makes that system more efficient." Differences occur at a sensory level. Studies at Northwestern University in 2012 found that brains of bilinguals react differently to sounds than brains of people who speak only one language.

[FACT: Some stroke victims can read normally except for certain kinds of words, such as adjectives. **]**

Bilingual Advantages

That's important for success as teens and adults. Barbara Lust, a developmental psychology and linguistics expert at the Cornell Language Acquisition Lab, says a strong executive function is "responsible for selective and conscious cognitive processes to achieve goals in the face of distraction." Those goals include academic readiness and success, both as children and later as adults.

Enhanced cognition for bilinguals extends into old age. Bialystok found that bilingual elderly adults outperform monolinguals on tasks that test executive function. Furthermore, after studying the records of 400 patients with Alzheimer's, she found that bilingual people exhibited symptoms of the disease an average of five to six years later than monolingual people. These findings appear to support the nuns of Mankato study that suggested correlations

TUNE OUT DISTRACTIONS
Executive function grows stronger in brains of bilinguals. That's useful for many things, including ignoring distractions, as evidenced by a student reading amid a Beijing crowd.

EARLY EXPOSURE
(Opposite) A boy in San Francisco learns to write Chinese in a language-immersion program that begins in kindergarten. Young brains soak up new languages.

between higher levels of education early in life, as well as expanded cognitive reserves of an enriched brain, with maintenance of cognitive functions, sometimes despite physical evidence of the initial stages of Alzheimer's.

EASY LEARNING

Although humans can add a second language at any time, the best and easiest time to learn is early childhood. Young children who learn two languages at the same time don't have the adult disadvantage of their primary language interfering with their acquisition of new sounds, grammar, and meaning. "When you're a kid, all you're working at is acquiring a language, and you don't have anything to get in the way of that," Lisa Davidson, an associate professor of linguistics at New York University, told *Forbes*.

BRAIN INSIGHT

POLYGLOTS

Verbal fluency reaches a peak in people who speak dozens of languages

Bilingual people speak two languages. Trilingual people speak three. Those fluent in four or more are *polyglots*, Greek for "many tongues."

The most famous polyglot in the United States was probably Thomas Jefferson. He fluently spoke and read English, Greek, Latin, French, Italian, and Spanish. Jefferson also attempted German and dabbled in Arabic, Gaelic, and Welsh.

Other notable polyglots included Heinrich Schliemann, excavator of the ancient city of Troy, who spoke German and at least 12 other languages, and Jean-François Champollion, who spoke more than a dozen languages by age 20, and went on to crack the puzzling hieroglyphs of the fabled Rosetta stone.

One of the most amazing polyglots was German diplomat Emil Krebs. By the time he entered Berlin's Foreign Office school for interpreters, he already spoke a dozen languages. He insisted on learning the toughest ones, which led him to Mandarin. In a few years, he was sent to China as Germany's chief interpreter. The empress dowager took tea with him to enjoy hearing him speak. By his death in 1930, Krebs had learned at least 65 languages, including Armenian, which he grasped in nine weeks. Postmortem examinations of his brain revealed unusual cellular organization in Broca's area, a region associated with speech.

ROSETTA STONE

WHAT DOES THE COW SAY?
A child in the United Kingdom reads a book in a variety of languages. Reading and telling stories in other languages stimulates a child's brain.

"When you're an adult and you already have a language, the one you already know filters sounds and you get substantial interference from it."

Immersion of a child in an environment where two languages are spoken all the time smooths the path to bilingualism. Regardless of a child's age, acquiring a second language appears to be easier if the child hears it constantly in conversation and other everyday use in a family or community setting rather than a more structured schoolroom environment. Hearing multiple speakers controls against acquiring an accent that is particular to one person. The sooner a child learns a second language, the more likely the child will master the accents and tones of a native speaker.

Steps to a Second Language

The Cornell Language Acquisition Lab recommends the following to help a child learn a second language:

- **Social exposure.** Surround the child with conversations and social settings that expose him or her to the extra language.
- **Keep a "home" language.** If the child is learning a second language outside the home, keep the heritage language of the child's family at home.
- **Find playmates.** Give the child opportunities to play with children who speak the second language.
- **Enjoy story time.** Read and tell stories in both languages.
- **Keep it fun.** Share music, film, and other fun language-learning environments in both languages.

Young people and adults have different aptitudes for learning a nonnative language, just as they have aptitudes for math or geography. Experts agree that the best way to master a second language varies with the individual. But in general, learning a second language gets harder with age.

REPEAT AFTER ME
People respond in different ways to language instruction. For some, the best method may be a software program combining images, sounds, and speech recognition.

Sticking With the Program

To find their best learning method, adults might try audio or audiovisual programs, classes, conversations with native speakers, or immersion in the second language. When they find what works, they should stick with it. The key is to work a bit every day on acquiring the new language, and then expand vocabulary and sophistication. After achieving fluency, challenging the brain further might involve going to a higher level of instruction, such as taking a history or political science class in the second language.

[**FACT:** The "choral effect" suppresses stuttering when people sing or speak in unison with others.]

CHAPTER 10

Paying Attention

A music teacher who appeared to have unusual vision problems went to his ophthalmologist, but the doctor could not help him. He referred the man to neurologist Oliver Sacks, in hopes that a brain specialist could succeed where an eye specialist could not.

Sacks saw the man and his wife during an office visit. The man, whom Sacks calls "Dr. P.," acted strangely. He cocked his head to face Sacks with his ears, not his eyes. And when Dr. P. did turn his gaze toward Sacks, it flicked from place to place in an unnatural way. Sacks sensed that Dr. P. was checking out his features one at a time. When the visit was over, Dr. P. got ready to leave. He reached for his wife's head and tried to lift it as if it were his hat. His wife reacted as if it happened all the time.

For the next visit, Sacks went to Dr. P.'s home. Sacks wore a rose in his jacket lapel, but Dr. P. could not fathom what it was. He described it as "a convoluted red form with a green attachment." Only when Dr. P. smelled the rose did he realize what it was.

Like this subject, described in Sacks's book *The Man Who Mistook His Wife for a Hat,* a man in England also developed a strange change in his brain's visual processing system late in life. In 1988, the man, named John in the story related in *The Tell-Tale Brain* by Vilayanur S. Ramachandran, went into the hospital for an operation to remove his appendix. While there, the 60-year-old suffered a stroke

STANDING OUT
(Opposite) The brain learns to recognize patterns at an early age, as well as instances when the pattern breaks, such as a red flower in a field of gold.

OLIVER SACKS
(Below) Neurologist Oliver Sacks, speaking in 2009, not only chronicles disorders of perception but also has great difficulty recognizing faces.

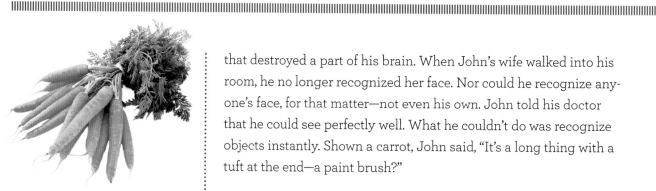

SHAPE RECOGNITION
(Above) Vegetable or paintbrush? The brain assembles bits of data to reach a conclusion; disorders may lead to wrong conclusions.

THE WHOLE PICTURE
(Below) A portrait emerges as the brain synthesizes images of makeup, below. A brain disorder known as prosopagnosia affects the ability to recognize the whole from the parts.

that destroyed a part of his brain. When John's wife walked into his room, he no longer recognized her face. Nor could he recognize anyone's face, for that matter—not even his own. John told his doctor that he could see perfectly well. What he couldn't do was recognize objects instantly. Shown a carrot, John said, "It's a long thing with a tuft at the end—a paint brush?"

Visual Agnosia

Both men had a form of visual agnosia, a disorder that keeps the brain from recognizing or understanding the visual signals it receives via the retinas. Patients with agnosia often can describe shape, color, texture, and other details of what they see but cannot put the whole picture together. Typically, the disorder arises from damage to the posterior occipital lobes, home of the visual cortex, and the

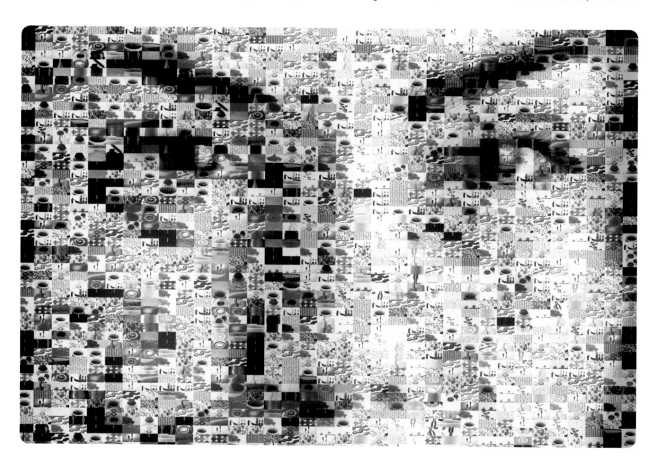

BRAIN BOOSTER

SEE SQUARED

Sharpen your perceptions by spotting shapes in your surroundings

Puzzles that challenge your perception are a great way to give your visual abilities a good workout. Even the familiar childhood challenge of finding shapes in a complex setting can help adult perceptions.

➲ Look at the picture at right, for instance. How many squares can you find?*

➲ **Want to stay squared?** Try looking for squares in your surroundings, such as in your office or family room. Challenge other family members, colleagues, or friends to find the squares with you and see who can find more.

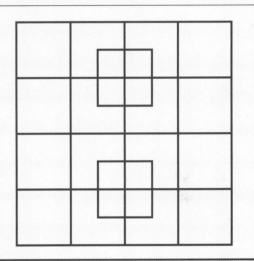

*Up to 40! Don't forget the 3x3 squares.

temporal lobes. John's particular case included prosopagnosia, the inability to recognize faces. People with the condition often develop coping strategies, such as John's technique of recognizing his wife by her voice. Interestingly, Sacks discovered in middle age that he had some degree of prosopagnosia himself. He had great difficulty with faces, especially when seeing them out of context. He realized that, beginning as a child, he recognized people by individual characteristics—a pink dress, big eyebrows, a thatch of red hair, and so on.

The Complex Mind's Eye

For the vast majority of children and adults, visual perception works easily and unconsciously. You look upon the world, and it makes sense. But that's because 30 visual areas of the cortex synchronize

[**FACT:** The part of your brain that recognizes an object is different from the part that locates it.]

their work to process individual bits of visual data, provide feedback to one another, and assemble an image. Once light bounces off an object, enters the eye, and is focused on the retinas, it is broken into electrical impulses. These impulses—like dots and dashes of Morse code—fly to the visual cortex for sophisticated processing. It no longer makes sense to speak of whole "images" in the brain. Signals for shape, color, movement, and so on go through processing before the brain's visual networks construct a comprehensible representation of the world in the "mind's eye." Failure anywhere along the line can cause trouble. You can have fully functioning eyes and still not see.

> You can have fully **FUNCTIONING** eyes and still not see.

ILLUSIONS

The brain's role in constructing meaning out of what you see is easily demonstrated by optical illusions.

Illusions can emerge from retinal processing of the visual primary colors of red, green, and blue in the eye's cone cells, or deeper in

BRAIN INSIGHT

FINDING WALDO
The search for the cartoon figure involves a coordinated mental effort

You probably know Waldo. Tall, thin. Wears jeans, a red-and-white pullover, and a matching cap. Round eyeglasses. Gets lost in crowds.

For years, neuroscientists were split on how the brain orchestrated the search for Waldo's tiny cartoon image amid huge illustrations in the popular *Where's Waldo?* children's books of Martin Handford. Some said the brain's visual system worked like a spotlight, moving from image to image, in a manner known as serial processing. Others said the visual system took in the entire

illustration and then used its focusing abilities to pull Waldo's colors and shapes out of the jumble, in a manner known as parallel processing.

WALDO IMPERSONATORS

Turns out, both sides had part of the answer, according to Robert Desimone, director of the McGovern Institute for Brain Research at MIT. He led a study tracking brain activity in macaque monkeys executing a Waldo-like search. His team found that neurons in the V4 region of the visual cortex synchronize their signals to direct attention toward colors and shapes being sought. Desimone likens it to a chorus rising above a noisy party. Individual neurons detect and fire, and then join together to force a shift in gaze toward the object sought.

the brain's neural networks. Two good examples of illusions resulting from neural processing are the Necker cube and Ames room.
The former takes its name from the Swiss crystallographer Louis
Albert Necker, who was looking at a cubic crystal through a micro-
scope in 1832, when the back and front sides of the cube seemed to
spontaneously flip. Necker repeated the illusion by devising a simple
drawing of a transparent wire-frame cube whose perspective shifted
as he gazed upon it. The viewer's brain imposes order on the cube by
selecting one face to be the one closest to the eyes. However, in short
order, the brain switches orientation, sending the previously foremost square face to the back side. The brain chooses one perspective
or the other, and cannot hold both images in mind at the same time.

The Ames room, named for inventor Adelbert Ames, Jr., is
a grossly distorted room of trapezoidal shape that, when viewed

AMES ROOM
(Above) A specially constructed room
causes confusion about its occupants.

NECKER CUBE
(Below) The brain flips between one ori-
entation and another for the Necker cube.
It cannot see both at the same time.

159

from one point directly front and center, appears to have normal right-angled walls, floor, and ceiling. One corner opposite the viewer is much farther away than the other, but clever manipulation of perspective makes the room seem rectangular with the far wall parallel to the room's front. A person in the far corner seems tiny while another person in the near corner appears gigantic; walking from one corner to the other makes a person appear to grow or shrink. The illusion works because the brain insists that the room must be a three-dimensional rectangular shape, which it has been conditioned to expect.

RELATIVE SIZE
Purdue University researcher Jessica K. Witt has found that golfers who play well perceive the hole as larger than those who don't.

BRAIN BOOSTER

WEAR YOUR WATCH UPSIDE DOWN

Small changes in familiar sights can exercise your brain

➔ TODAY'S TIP WILL MAKE TIME FLY

Give your brain a little stretch each time you check your watch by wearing your watch upside down. This subtle change won't take much effort, but will force your brain to think out of its comfort zone in making sense of time gone a bit topsy-turvy. This is a great exercise for your visual perceptual skills, as you are forced to reinterpret familiar information in an unfamiliar way. Exercises like this, sometimes called "neurobics" (a phrase coined by Dr. Lawrence Katz), may seem fun and simple, yet are a terrific way to challenge our brain's flexibility and routine.

Like this exercise? Keep it going for a few more days.

Have a good time!

Seeing the Ball

Illusions can have a practical side, tricking the brain into improving performance.

Psychologist Jessica Witt of Purdue University, who won a gold medal at the World Games as part of an Ultimate Frisbee team, examines the phenomenon of altered perception among athletes—those moments when the basketball rim seems larger or smaller, or the tennis net seems to get higher or lower. She noted that softball and tennis players report that when they're hitting well, their brains perceive the ball as larger than normal. Witt performed a study, published in 2012, to make a golf cup seem larger. She and co-authors Dennis R. Proffitt of the University of Virginia and Sally A. Linkenauger of the Max Planck Institute-Tübingen set up a golf hole on a ramp. A projector shone 11 small circles around the cup, creating the illusion of the cup appearing larger than its normal diameter of four and one-quarter inches. College students using the optically enhanced cup sank 10 percent more putts than those without the enhancement. Expanding on her research, Witt said visual distractions confuse the brain and make it harder for athletes to perform. Crazy fans wagging giant foam fingers under the basket may actually alter the performance of free-throw shooters.

VISION THERAPY

Eye specialists sometimes perform image-based therapy to treat the complex interactions of eyes, brain, and body. So-called vision therapy has been used for a variety of conditions, including weak or missing binocular vision (resulting from poor coordination between the nerves of the two eyes); amblyopia, or "lazy

STRABISMUS
A baby exhibits strabismus, the medical term for crossed eyes. Vision therapy treats that condition and a host of others.

eye"; strabismus, or "crossed eyes"; and other deficiencies in how patients' brains process visual sensations. Exercises may include viewing three-dimensional images to encourage the brain to process the dual eye signals that promote depth perception.

The Three-Dimensional World

Children sometimes are misdiagnosed with disorders in their prefrontal cortex when instead they have difficulty processing visual data in the occipital lobe, such as seeing in only two dimensions or failing to maintain focus. Illusions and graphics used in vision therapy challenge the brain to make sense of a three-dimensional world, by adding depth and dimension, and encourage the growth of neural pathways to process new ways of seeing.

VISUAL distractions confuse the brain and make it harder for athletes to perform.

BRAIN BOOSTER

JIGSAW GYM
Jigsaw puzzles are more than just a pleasant pastime

Jigsaw puzzles are a simple yet terrific way to give your visual skills a true workout. These visual brainteasers force us to flex our visual perception and problem solving. In addition, they are a great way to get a good dose of mental challenge.

➲ SET UP YOUR PUZZLE
Go ahead and get yourself a good-quality jigsaw puzzle. Look for a puzzle of at least 500 pieces (1,000 is an even greater challenge). Set up the puzzle in a space where you can leave it and work on it over time. Spend some time each day working on solving the puzzle. You can also invite family and friends to help you put the puzzle back together—the more the merrier!

BRAIN INSIGHT

MIRROR BOX

Your eyes can fool your brain

Derek Steen had his left arm amputated after shredding it in a motorcycle accident. Trouble was, he continued to feel the arm—a phenomenon called "phantom limb." And the arm was in pain.

Steen's condition occurred because his brain redrafted its body map after losing contact with arm nerve impulses. It misinterpreted signals from other body parts as originating in the missing limb, making it feel real.

In the mid-1990s, neuroscientist Vilayanur S. Ramachandran tricked Steen's brain into taking away his pain

MIRROR BOX
EXPERIMENT

by reacting as if the missing arm had been restored. Ramachandran constructed a simple mirror box, open at the top with a hole on the side for

inserting Steen's right arm. The box's central mirror made it appear as if Steen had two healthy arms. Seeing his "left arm" let Steen access and fire the neurons for its movement. After three weeks of mirror box therapy, his pain went away. Mirror boxes have since been used to treat a variety of conditions.

The box underlines how the brain constructs reality out of feedback loops combining vision, other senses, body movements, and motor commands. The brain reacts to what it sees, even if what it sees is a lie.

A 3D WORLD
(Opposite) Seeing depth, such as the effect you get with 3D glasses, helps the brain map its surroundings. Without therapy, the world looks as flat as a 2D movie to some people.

Versions of 3D imaging systems have existed since the 19th century, when stereographs transported viewers to the pyramids, European capitals, and distant battlefields. A wood-and-glass stereograph viewer held a card, bearing two pictures side by side, that the viewer could examine through two lenses that resembled binoculars. The two pictures were taken at the same time by a special camera with lenses a few inches apart, approximating the distance between human eyes. This parallax view created the 3D effect. Modern versions of the stereograph include polarized images, 3D movies and glasses, and Magic Eye stereograms—those pictures that look like random collections of colored dots until, when stared at long enough, a 3D picture emerges.

FACT: Subliminal advertising—flashing microsecond messages to an audience during a movie—does not work.

BRAIN BOOSTER

MAP IT
Remember good old paper maps? They built our visual skills

Are you a good map reader? Those of us with visual strengths may find it an easy task. Others find map reading doesn't come easily at all, and that deciphering directions and symbols is a skill that needs practice. Also, in this GPS age, our map-reading skills can get a bit rusty.

➲ For this exercise, take out some good old road maps. Pick a spot you'd like to navigate to, and go ahead and plot your course. Use the legend (the key to the symbols—remember what that is?) to help you figure out how long your trip will take, any places of interest along the way, and so forth. You can even try plotting a few alternate routes.

KINDS OF ATTENTION

Attention allows the brain to consciously pick out salient sensory information and ignore the rest. At a cocktail party, selective attention lets you understand the conversation of someone sitting next to you by focusing on the sound of a voice and the motion of lips and face. Laboratory experiments have examined visual selective attention by having test subjects pick out words, letters, or pictures from similar images acting as background noise. The greater the similarity between the targeted image and the distractors, as between the letters O and Q, the greater difficulty the brain has in finding its prey. Research has also shown that the brain has greater difficulty as it ages in executing so-called conjunctive searches, which involve seeking two unrelated but linked visual characteristics. A simple search would target a chocolate-iced doughnut in a room full of vanilla-iced doughnuts. A conjunctive

> **ATTENTION** allows the brain to pick out salient sensory information and ignore the rest.

search would make the target a chocolate-iced doughnut in a room containing vanilla-iced doughnuts and chocolate-iced eclairs. That particular search requires comprehension of shape (round versus rectangular) and color (brown versus white).

Experience Counts

One study found that young brains outperformed old brains in the conjunctive search for a red X in a field of green Xs and red Os. However, this age-related deficit decreases if the older brain has experience with the targeted object and distractors. For example, middle-age medical technicians performed as well as younger medical technicians when evaluating x-rays, a task that requires

A VOICE IN THE CROWD
When immersed in noisy chaos, such as in this theater lobby, the brain uses selective attention to follow a single conversation.

seeking particular information amid a host of distractors. Broader applications suggest themselves. You'll improve your handling of loose change, including distinguishing one coin from another, if you practice. So too will you improve your sorting of buttons, stamps, or shoes. What you practice with your visual and prefrontal cortices, you improve.

When your brain "pays attention," you choose where to pinpoint your focus. A related phenomenon called visual attention occurs below the level of consciousness. It happens as you drive, read, or interact with other people. When you're behind the wheel of a car heading down the highway, for example, your brain automatically scans the environment looking for anything requiring a reaction. It could be anything from a dog running onto the pavement to a car entering the highway via an on-ramp and inching sideways toward you.

BUTTON, BUTTON
(Opposite) The more you practice using your senses, such as sorting buttons by color, size, and tactile qualities, the better your discrimination becomes.

> When your brain "pays attention," you **CHOOSE** where to pinpoint your focus.

Attentional Blink

One measure of visual attention is the so-called attentional blink. It's the time required for the brain to shift from one

---

BRAIN BOOSTER

X MARKS THE SPOT
Strengthen your ability to focus in on the things that matter

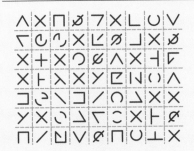

Visual scanning is a mental skill we use all the time but rarely think about. We use visual scanning to check out our world and pick out the things that matter to us in a busy scene—for example, when looking for our keys on a cluttered desk, or for our kids in a crowded playground.

Use the following exercise to challenge your scanning skills:

➜ Set a timer for one minute.

➜ Then search and see how many Xs you can find in the picture at left.*

*14.

BRAIN BOOSTER

BEAT THE CLOCK

Games that ask you to race against time build your mental muscle

Want to stay sharp no matter what your age?
Try playing games against the clock.

➲ THINK FAST!
Research shows that training in these skills can help stay more effective at them, no matter what our age. Timed activities force us to pay attention, work fast, and think nimbly—you can't beat the clock without doing so!

There are so many great brain games we can play, from board games to electronic games to computer-based, brain fitness specific training games (which have no unique scientific benefit, but can boost your stick-to-it-iveness by acting as a personal trainer for your brain). In addition, games that we play on our phones or other mobile devices meet all my criteria for getting in a bit of brain skills training.

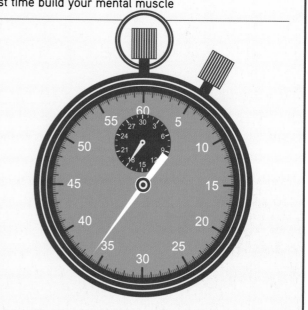

stimulus to another one. Research on attentional blinks has focused on video games and challenges as ways to improve visual attention for young and old.

A team at Rochester University has found that skilled players of action video games, the kind where the player typically has to react instantly to shoot a monster or enemy soldier, have a shorter attentional blink than people who don't play video games or players who prefer slower simulation games. Some action-game players, including Shawn Green, one of the researchers, shift attention so rapidly that they lack a measurable attentional blink entirely.

[FACT: Consciousness, though hard to define, includes a component of understanding the passage of time. **]**

Green found that action-game players can easily keep track of five objects at the same time on the video screen. Non-gamers handle only three. Further investigation revealed that these differences are neither inborn nor a matter of people with various attentional blink levels self-selecting their preferred games. When nonplayers took up video gaming and practiced the high-action kind, they shortened their attentional blink.

Similar studies of people performing Internet searches—the manipulation of words in search engines to maximize

MULTITASKING
(Left) Some video gamers have enhanced ability to mentally manage multiple tasks at once, such as handling a tablet, a phone, a coffee, and whatever else comes their way.

QUICK REACTIONS
(Below) Players of action video games, such as a product at the Tokyo Game Show, can shift attention so quickly that the delay cannot be measured.

THE DRIVING GAME

THE DRIVING GAME
Lights from traffic converge on a building in Shanghai. Driving calls upon multiple mental functions, now being targeted by brain-boosting software.

returns—revealed that practicing search techniques increased activity in the frontal lobes, particularly in working and short-term memory, complex reasoning, and decision making.

Driving and Attention

Software and online companies have developed programs to increase visual attention as well as cognitive processing speed, memory, and executive function. Those are exactly the skills that make a good driver, so it makes sense that computer-based programs have sprung up to improve driving skills. These include DriveSharp by Posit Science of San Francisco, a visual memory system that aims to train a driver's brain to think and react faster. The manufacturer claims that people who use the system three times a week reduce their crash risk and improve their reaction time. One of the Posit Science games, US 66 Road Tour, aims to improve the useful field of view to get drivers to hit their brakes in time to avoid an accident. Players must match cars on the screen with those that appeared previously. Then, they must continue that challenge while adding a new one: pinpointing a road sign when it appears. Cars and signs eventually appear for only a moment, making more demands on visual attention.

Insurance companies have shown interest in Posit Science and other companies' brain-training software for drivers. One company, for example, invited 100,000 of its Pennsylvania customers to try Posit Science's software. Only 8,000 accepted. The *San Francisco Chronicle,* which reported on the insurance company's offer, raised a concern: Insurance companies might hold bad scores on a driver-improvement game against the players.

> Computer-based programs have sprung up to **IMPROVE** driving skills.

BRAIN BOOSTER

ARTFUL ORIGAMI
Create original origami and stretch your visual imagination

The ancient Asian art of origami is a wonderful way to exercise your visual problem-solving skills and your imagination. Here, we are going to try a twist on the classic form of origami—instead of providing you with directions to fold and shape something specific, you are going to set out and use your mind and your creativity to see what you can come up with on your very own.

➲ FOLD IT FREESTYLE
Take a blank, square piece of paper of any size. Next, try folding it in many different ways (there is no right or wrong option in this exercise). Have fun as you fold, and see which shapes you can create along the way.

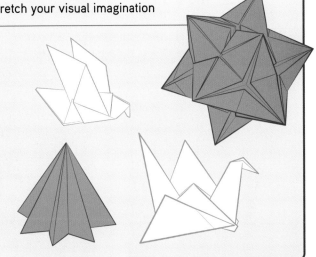

CHAPTER 11

The Art of Remembering

MEMORY AND IDENTITY
(Opposite) What you remember, such as family events captured in photographs, sets a course for what you are and will become.

EMOTIONAL LINKS
(Below) Memories affect your moods and reactions. How you feel about something may be your brain's link to memories of similar things.

When you picture yourself, you're drawing upon memory.

Just as your body and brain construct themselves out of the food you eat, your concept of self emerges from your memories. Your likes and dislikes, your feelings about family, friends, politics, school, religion, and so on arise from your brain's processing of experiences. What you remember equals who you are.

Memory was once conceptualized as a mechanical process. Scientists formerly thought that memories were filed in networks of neurons like papers in a cabinet or videos in a DVD library. When you wanted to recall something, the brain opened the file or library, found the memory it sought, and played it on the viewing screen or read it on the table of your mind. Memories that faded were like lost files or locked library rooms to which the brain lost the key.

These ideas have received widespread acceptance among the public. A nationwide survey in 2011 found that two-thirds of Americans bought into the video camera metaphor of memory, and half believed that once a memory had been encoded, it would never change. Nearly 40 percent said the testimony of a single confident eyewitness should be sufficient for criminal conviction. Yet the first two statements are demonstrably false: A host of

ADDING TO THE PICTURE
What you remember about your childhood is colored by what has happened, and been remembered, since then.

variables affects the encoding of memories, often causing distortions, and memories change over time. As for the third statement, confident witnesses are wrong about 30 percent of the time.

THE COMPLEX WEB OF MEMORY

Scientists now know that memory is much more complex and fluid than previously believed. For even the simplest memories, the brain scatters bits of information throughout its nooks and crannies. Sensory information is stored in the brain regions associated with processing the original sensations. Visual memories are maintained in the visual cortex at the back of the brain, while sounds (including words), smells, and other data are kept elsewhere. When you conjure the image of a teapot in your mind, you call from memory separate packets for its shape, color, size, hardness, hotness, and so on. The color and taste and smell of the tea, not to mention the tea bag, may be called up from storage, as memories tend to stick to things your brain associates with them. You might recall a pleasant tea party as a child, or that green tea is on sale at the corner store.

Once you're finished remembering something, you don't just return the memory to storage unchanged, like a library book you've kept clean and neat. Associated memories called to mind may adhere to the original memory as it returns to the neural circuits of your brain. In other words, the act of remembering changes memories. To use the library book metaphor, you almost always add margin notes or edit the text before you return it.

MEMORY is much more complex and fluid than previously believed.

BRAIN BOOSTER

MAKE THE CONNECTION

Forgetting a name or a number? Connect it to something familiar

Here's one of my favorite memory strategies: When you need to remember something new, make a mental connection between the new information and something that you already know. Meeting Florence? Connect to your great-aunt Florence, Florence Henderson, or Florence, Italy.

➜ MAKE IT MEANINGFUL
Using the "connection technique" forces you to pay better attention to the information and makes it more meaningful to you. These critical steps will definitely boost your memory for any information you want to keep in mind, be it a phone number or a name. Try the connection technique and see how this habit can rev up your recall.

LIMBIC SYSTEM

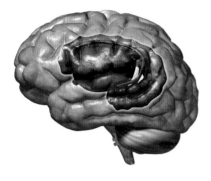

MEMORY STRUCTURES
(Above) The limbic system includes the hippocampus, key to long-term memory, and amygdala, which can boost memory intensity.

MENTAL CATALOG
(Below) An old-fashioned library card catalog listed each book's location. If each card were a neuron, memories would put bits on many cards.

KINDS OF MEMORY

Memory is generally categorized as short term and long term. Short-term memory, believed to reside in the prefrontal cortex, allows you to keep information in mind for a short time. It lets you know immediately where you have been, where you are, and where you're going. When you speak aloud, short-term memory keeps the first words of your sentence in your prefrontal cortex long enough for you to formulate the end of the sentence with proper grammar and syntax—delivering a witty remark, saying a solemn prayer, or reciting a limerick.

Long-Term Memory

Long-term memory comes in two kinds: implicit and explicit, also known as nondeclarative and declarative. Implicit includes actions that are nonverbal, outside consciousness, procedural, and emotional. Explicit memories are verbal, conscious, and contextual, and are typically categorized further as semantic and episodic. Your implicit memories include the instructions your brain sends to your fingers as you type; once you've mastered the skill, you no longer think about what your fingers should do. Semantic, explicit memories include facts, the kind we think of as book learning. Episodic memories, as the name implies, provide pictures of personal events. Knowing the 50 states is semantic memory. Remembering your visits to 47 of them is episodic.

Although remembering is a whole-brain activity, two regions play enhanced roles in remembering: the hippocampus and the amygdala, both of which are part of the limbic system. The hippocampus orchestrates the transfer of information from short-term

FLASHBULB MEMORY
Pop! An exploding flashbulb captures details. So-called flashbulb memories of extremely emotional moments similarly freeze events.

to long-term memory. Anyone without a hippocampus, such as the patient HM mentioned in Part 1, forever lives in the present moment, unable to encode new memories in long-term storage. The amygdala plays a key role in encoding implicit memories, particularly those with emotional content. The most powerful, which combine encoding by the hippocampus and amygdala, are called "flashbulb" memories. They seem to capture every vivid detail, as when a flashbulb illuminates the darkness for a stop-action photograph. A personal memory encoded with great joy, sorrow, or fear gets an extra boost

[FACT: Mozart was able to play a 12-minute choral composition from memory after hearing it twice. **]**

of encoding from the amygdala. Thus, most people remember many details of where they were and what they were doing when President Kennedy was shot, when the space shuttle *Challenger* exploded, or when they heard a close relative died.

Memory Is Plastic

Not many decades ago, science thought of memory as a fixed process in adults. However, again and again, studies have demonstrated the brain's plasticity, or ability to rewire itself as it learns new information, at any age. We now know that older brains may take longer to process and learn new information, but once it is learned, it is just as accessible as similar information in a youthful brain.

WHERE WERE YOU?
Thanks to the amygdala, the explosion of *Challenger* or death of Princess Diana plant themselves firmly in memory.

BRAIN INSIGHT

MARK TWAIN'S MEMORY GAME

The famous author invented more than colorful characters

A riverboat pilot needs an excellent memory to navigate. Yet Mark Twain, a pilot in youth, notoriously forgot the "shape of a river." His absent-mindedness became a joke.

Twain wanted his children to strengthen their memories. He hit upon a way to combine facts and images by driving pegs into his driveway. Each represented a British king, with the intervening spaces the lengths of their reigns. Henry II ruled 35 years, so 35 feet separated his peg from that of his heir, Richard the Lionhearted.

Richard's peg was ten feet from King John's, and so on.

In 1885, Twain's idea morphed into "Mark Twain's Memory-Builder" game. Players stuck colored pins into a board as they announced a fact and date. For example, "You stick a pin in 64 (in the *third* row of holes in that compartment—'Minor Event'), and say 'Shakespeare born, 1564.' " Players memorized new dates and facts from adversaries' plays, and might eventually use them in the game.

Twain considered his game so important he put *Huckleberry Finn* on hold to develop it. But the public found the game too complicated. One critic dubbed Twain's board "a cross between an income tax form and a table of logarithms."

MARK TWAIN

The act of memory is plastic. It can be trained to expand and break through your previous limits.

MAGIC NUMBER SEVEN

A half century ago, Harvard psychologist George Miller found himself haunted by a particular number—"persecuted by an integer," as he famously wrote in an academic paper in 1956. That number was seven, and he titled his paper, "The Magical Number Seven, Plus or Minus Two: Some Limits on Our Capacity for Processing Information." He found that the brain can hold only about seven chunks of information in short-term memory at a time. Chances are, you can hold a seven-digit phone number in your prefrontal cortex for a few seconds after hearing it—long enough to dial accurately. But if given a ten-digit number, or an even longer one for an

> Memory can be trained to expand and break through your previous LIMITS.

PHONOLOGICAL LOOP
Holding a number in your head probably requires you to repeat it over and over silently.

international call, your memory likely would fail to capture it. Unless, Miller learned, you broke it into small chunks and put each chunk in short-term memory.

The Phonological Loop

When you try to hold a small group of numbers in working memory, you likely repeat them silently in your head, perhaps over and over. Scientists have dubbed this internal voice the "phonological loop." It holds sounds for a few seconds in working memory, and then drops them unless you are trying actively to memorize them. So, for example, without returning to the

BRAIN BOOSTER

MAKE A MATCH
Find that card and its counterpart in this traditional game

Maybe you played this card game for fun as a kid. As an adult, you can still build your visual focus and memory by playing good old-fashioned Memory Match:

HOW TO PLAY

➜ Divide a deck of playing cards in half, taking two of each kind of card for each half.

➜ Lay out all the cards facing downward.

➜ Now, turning over one card in one half and one card in the other half, one pair at a time, try to find the matching pairs.

➜ Miss the match? Turn the cards back over and try again. Keep going until you have found all the matching pairs.

Want a more modern approach? Look for computer-based versions of the game online. A version of Memory Match was recently used in a German study that found subjects who became proficient at the game boosted not only their visual memory but also their overall IQ. **So go ahead and make the match!**

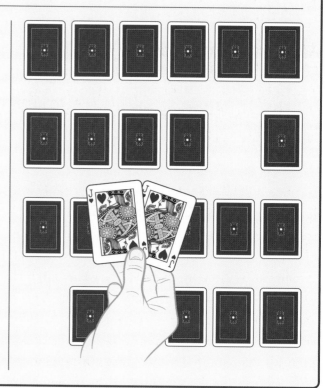

STICKING TO SEVEN
As far as the brain is concerned, there's some magic in the number. Short-term memory can hold about seven things.

beginning of this sentence, you probably can recall the sentence's first three words: *So, for example.* The beginning of the sentence before that one likely escapes you—unless you peek.

Some strings of numbers make their way to extremely long-term memory through you repeatedly hearing them in the phonological loop as well as repeatedly retrieving them, which causes them to be re-encoded for storage after use. Chances are, you remember the phone number of your childhood home. And you probably committed it to memory as three chunks: a three-digit area code, a three-digit group, and a four-digit group.

BRAIN INSIGHT

HOW TO STUDY FOR A TEST
Improve your grades by learning how to learn

If you're facing an important test, you should begin preparing days, if not weeks, in advance:

▶ Start by giving your brain the fuel it craves. Meals with plenty of fruits, grains, and vegetables enhance your ability to pay attention and think quickly. High-fat, low-fiber diets, such as those heavy with red meat, do the opposite. On the morning of the test, eat a slow-digesting, carbohydrate-rich food such as oatmeal.

▶ Study the test material without distractions. Although many college students swear they study better with music in the background, research by Professor Nicole Dudukovic at Trinity College in Connecticut demonstrates that students learn more thoroughly in silence.

▶ Test your memory again and again during review, forcing your brain to recall information upon demand. Learning things in a logical sequence—such as a chronological or geographical narrative—is more effective than rote memorization.

▶ Don't pull an all-nighter. A good night's sleep before a test helps the brain cement memories in place. Don't get up too early, either, because it might interfere with the crucial stage of sleep known as rapid eye movement, or REM.

▶ Finally, be at peace. Meditation and self-confidence can reduce anxieties, which hurt clear thinking.

ACT SHARP TO GET SMART.

CHUNKING

Very long numbers can be memorized by breaking them into chunks. But how far could an ordinary brain extend the process? How much could someone, using chunks no larger than Miller's magic number, commit to memory? In the early 1980s, researchers at Carnegie Mellon University set out to find the answer. They took an undergraduate, known in academic circles as SF to protect his privacy, and paid him to try to learn strings of numbers. SF sat and heard digits read aloud at the rate of one a second. When he started, he could only remember seven digits.

[FACT: Memories are more likely to stick if they combine information and emotion. **]**

But nearly two years later, after hearing those digits read aloud for 230 hours, SF could hear a string of 79 random digits and repeat it back without error. He had found a way to place the digits into long-term memory with only a modicum of mental effort. He could even recall sequences he had heard days earlier, demonstrating that his long-term memory had grown much stronger.

Mnemonics

SF received no instructions or clues from the researchers. Instead, he found his own way to make the strings of digits meaningful, and therefore more memorable, using memory cues known as "mnemonics" (pronounced ne-MON-iks). As an avid runner, he knew many recorded race times. When he heard the number 3492, he converted it into 3 minutes, 49.2 seconds, close to the world

RUNNING THE NUMBERS
A Carnegie Mellon University study found that even an untrained undergraduate could break his memory limits. The student linked long numbers to track times.

record for the mile. When the researchers gave SF numbers chosen because of the difficulty of converting them to running times, SF's performance declined. Later, SF added a new encoding method by changing some numbers to ages, such as turning 893 to 89.3, the age of a very old man.

Researchers K. Anders Ericsson, William G. Chase, and Steve Faloon concluded that the better a person could associate new number strings with things pulled from long-term memory, the more the person's memory would increase. With the right system, they said, "there is seemingly no limit to improvement in memory skills with practice."

SF was just an ordinary guy, and not a memory expert. Journalist Joshua Foer, who also had no prior memory training, set out to

OLD MEMORIES
A competitive memory technique involved linking numbers to ages, such as those of a very old man.

BRAIN BOOSTER

CHUNK IT

Remember a long list by breaking it into shorter, easier-to-remember sets

Did you know that it is naturally easier for us to learn several shorter lists than one long one? This is one of the reasons that long number patterns, such as phone numbers, are broken into shorter groupings, making it easier to learn and recall them.

➡ **SHORT AND SWEET**
Next time you have a long list to memorize, try this simple strategy that takes advantage of our innate learning patterns: Break that long list into several shorter lists, and memorize those shorter sections. Chunking is a great technique for numbers, as well as any list that can be broken into several shorter segments, such as a grocery or packing list.

FOREST	CARPET	GUITAR
CUSHION	TOWEL	STOOL
GARAGE	PACKAGE	BOTTLE
HARE	LEMON	WHEEL

6	1	3	66	88	0	12	34	6	78
87	4	1	9	23	45	8	12	43	
2	6	2	14	3	0	45	88	10	
12	34	56	78	65	3	1	55	7	

learn the tools of memory experts for his 2011 book *Moonwalking With Einstein*. He began by visiting Ericsson, who had been on the team that conducted the experiments on SF. Ericsson, Foer learned, has shifted his focus to study what distinguishes experts from other people. The answer, Ericsson said, is that experts see the world in much more complex and sophisticated ways. Their expertise is not innate. It is the result of acquiring complex skills and the proper mental state to best use them. Experts improve by powerfully focusing their attention on analyzing, practicing, and critiquing their craft. To use memory experts as an example, they have broken the lock imposed on the brain by the number seven. Their method is to drink in a wealth of sensory information and relate it to vivid memories. Memory experts create rich, detailed mental images to connect to the data they wish to memorize.

Memory experts create rich, detailed MENTAL images.

MEMORY PALACE
(Opposite) An ancient technique associates things to be remembered with specific places in a familiar building.

MEMORY COMPETITION
(Below) Elaborate memory contests, such as the United Kingdom open championship of 2009, often include random word lists.

THE METHOD OF LOCI

This may seem like a modern idea, but it is actually very old. Many people who train their memories today use a variation of a method first described more than 2,000 years ago by the Roman philosopher Marcus Tullius Cicero. Writing in the first century B.C., Cicero described the legend of Simonides of Ceos, a Greek poet who lived four centuries earlier. Simonides had gone to a banquet in Thessaly so he could regale his host with a lyric poem praising him. Something caused Simonides to step outside the banquet hall for a moment. While he was gone, the building's roof fell, crushing and mangling the bodies of the host and his guests beyond recognition. Grieving families wanted to know, who was who? Simonides found that he could identify each body by consulting his memory. He pictured the interior of the banquet hall and visualized each guest, one by one, according to the spaces they occupied. Cicero wrote that Simonides concluded that many things could be committed to memory by forming mental pictures of specific locations and storing desired facts as images placed in the image in a specific order. The order of the places "will preserve the order of the things, and the images of the things will denote the things themselves, and we shall employ the places and images respectively as a wax writing-tablet and the letters written on it," Cicero said.

[FACT: Visuospatial memory prompts the remembrance of the placement of objects in space. **]**

The technique has the academic name "method of loci," from the word *locus,* Latin for "place." Because many who practice it use images of large buildings, the method is sometimes referred to as a "memory palace."

Memorably Odd Images

The method of loci has two components: images representing the data you want to remember, and specific, familiar places where you store those images for recall. Here's a simple example. Imagine a building you know very well, such as your childhood home. Make a shopping list of two dozen or so items, which, for reasons unimportant except for this exercise, you wish to memorize in order.

PENNIES

The "method of loci" technique links words and concrete images, such as "percent" with the cents tossed in a wishing well.

One at a time, convert each item on the list to a vivid mental picture related to the item itself. Strange and even erotic images are best because they are so weirdly memorable.

A Memorable House Tour

Put the first item at the place you associate with entering the house—at the mailbox, driveway, or front door, for example. Suppose the first item was "2 percent milk." You'd need an image that suggests the number two, the word *percent,* and milk. An image that would meet all three criteria is two bathtubs full of milk, each containing a mountain of pennies—representing the "cent" of "percent"—placed on the patio outside your front door. The image would be strange enough that it would strike you as odd, and its unusualness in a familiar place would fix it in memory.

Next, you would turn to the second item on your list into a word-picture. Let's say it's a pound of Bing cherries. You might create an image of singer Bing Crosby (or, for those under age 40-something, the home page for the search engine Bing). Have him sit on a giant pound sign—that crosshatched symbol on your phone that looks like a tic-tac-toe board—and eat a cherry pie. In your mind's eye, pass beyond the bathtubs of milk on the patio of your home, go through the front door, and place that image on the floor or furniture just to the right or left.

Next on your list is spinach. What better image could you have than the spinach-loving cartoon character, Popeye the Sailor Man,

CHERRY REMINDER
Memory techniques, once learned, can make a shopping list obsolete. Can you associate cherries with a particular person?

FACT: Got a song stuck in your head? Your "sequence recall," crucial to doing learned tasks, is repeating.

I YAM WHAT I YAM
Want to remember to buy fresh spinach on the way home? Think of an overly amorous Popeye.

on your sofa? If you want to be sure to get fresh spinach instead of frozen, you could imagine Popeye's girlfriend, Olive Oyl, slapping his face. (He was "fresh"—get it?) Make a similarly bizarre image for each item on your list, and place them in a logical sequence throughout your house. When you want to remember the entire list, bring the first image to mind. Then tour your house in the order in which you laid out the images.

It sounds odd, but it works.

PERFECT MEMORY

Some extremely exceptional people attain nearly perfect memory without trying. Soviet neurologist A. R. Luria tested just such a subject in the 1920s. The man, known as "S" in the academic literature, walked into Luria's laboratory and asked to have his memory tested. Although S found nothing unusual in his own memory, others had declared him exceptional and referred him to the specialist.

Luria found that S remembered *everything*. After hearing the first four lines of Dante's *Divine Comedy* in Italian, a language he did not speak, S recalled every word. He repeated the lines perfectly 15 years later. Given long strings of random words, syllables, and numbers, S remembered them all, immediately and again after many years. When Luria probed into how S remembered things, he found his subject experienced synesthesia, a mixing of sensations including sounds, colors, textures, and tastes. For example, S described a voice he heard as "crumbly" and "yellow." His mind automatically supplied concrete images as he remembered things. Hearing the name of a color, for example, his mind provided a sharp image focused on that color, such as a man in a red shirt when he heard the word *red*. The complex sensations associated with each word made them memorable. When S applied himself to memorize a long list, he created his own memory palace without thinking. He created an image for each item to be memorized and placed them along the paths he walked in Moscow or at his home in Torzhok. S automatically imagined starting at Mayakovsky Square on Gorky Street in Moscow, for example, and distributed the items to be recalled at houses, gates, and storefronts.

REMEMBERING RED
An amazing memory master in the 1920s, known as "S," saw words in sharp detail, such as a man in a red shirt when hearing "red."

S described a
VOICE
he heard as
"crumbly" and
"yellow."

TALES OF THE LAND
A Crow storyteller reconstructs a tale from memory for a boy. Native Americans associated story details with landscape.

The Hazards of Photographic Memory

S's amazing memory floored Luria, but the scientist found it had its drawbacks. Photographic memory meant Luria never forgot anything, but some things are so painful or bad that they are best forgotten. Vivid memories of mistakes and painful setbacks can be paralyzing. Furthermore, S's mental images were so powerful that they competed in his mind with the reality of the moment, and he had trouble sifting important memories from those that were trivial. Past threatened to overwhelm present. S had trouble holding down any job other than stage performer showing off his incredible ability. Today, he might be considered a candidate for a diagnosis of autism spectrum disorder, a class of brain phenomena linked to difficulties in social interactions and interpersonal communication as well as repetitive behaviors.

Like S, memory champions have entire subdivisions of buildings or other geographical features fixed vividly in their minds to store their memories. Each may be designated for a particular set of memories. One memory champ in Malaysia used his body parts as the topography that allowed him to memorize 56,000 words in a Chinese-English dictionary. Native Americans taught themselves long stories by associating bits of the narrative string with familiar mountains, streams, hills, and other geological features surrounding their homes.

Memories of the Hunt

Evolution may explain the method of loci's effectiveness. Over millions of years, evolution of the human brain has selected in favor of genes that enhance the encoding of memories of specific physical places. Remembering the places where meaty animals have been plentiful in the past, as well as how to return home

LURIA
Alexander Luria of Moscow University laid much of the foundation for modern memory research.

A PREDATORY ADVANTAGE
Remembering places where prey, such as this rhino, could be found, would have promoted survival for our ancestors and given them an evolutionary advantage.

after the hunt, provides a distinct advantage for survival. Those well equipped to remember topography are more likely to survive than those who struggle with such images. The former then pass their genes along to their offspring, planting the skill in successive generations.

DIFFICULTY WITH NAMES

Evolution may also explain why some things are hard to remember. The best example is a person's name. Unless, for example, someone with red hair is named Rose, there is no logic linking a person's name to his or her appearance. Forgetting a name, although embarrassing, seldom sparks the kind of serious consequences that could prevent an individual from reproducing, and thus influence the descent of the species. Hundreds of years ago—an eyeblink on the evolutionary timescale—a

> There is no **LOGIC** linking a person's name to his or her **APPEARANCE.**

BRAIN BOOSTER

MAKE A MOVIE
Put that new piece of information into mental motion

One great way to boost our attention and remember a name or any new piece of information is to put it into action: to "see" a short movie for it in your mind's eye. Just imagine you are making a brief YouTube video for whatever you are learning.

➡ MOVING PICTURES
Keep in mind that the "make a movie" technique requires you to both visualize the information and keep it in motion. For example, let's say you met someone named Sam Waterford: You can make his name more memorable by picturing your new acquaintance fording a wide river with actor Sam Shepard or the biblical prophet Samuel.

This technique is a lively strategy for making sure that new information sticks in your mind.

name had some logic behind it. A stonecutter might be named Mason. An artisan with wood might be a Carpenter. Draper made cloth, Wainwright made wagons, and Baker made bread. Upon learning a new name and face, a learned medieval person might see the appropriateness of the name while watching a Cartwright making carts. Today, however, most names have nothing to do with a person's profession, background, or other family details. Obvious logical threads have been cut.

Memorizing names to go with faces is a part of the five-event USA Memory Championship. The other four events in 2005—when Foer observed the championship to write about it for an online magazine—were memorizing random words, a 50-line poem, random digits, and the order of a shuffled deck of cards. (The championship events were essentially the same in 2011: qualifying rounds of names and faces; speed numbers, speed cards, and poetry; and championship rounds of memorizing words, cards from a double deck, and biographical information provided aloud by five strangers at a "tea party.")

MEMORY CHAMPION
Joshua Foer, a 2006 USA Memory Championship winner, celebrated his victory—but later forgot about his car.

Names and Faces

Foer discovered that names can be made memorable using the technique he already knew of linking things to vivid images. He trained to compete in the memory championships himself and applied the method to a stack of 99 faces and names. To memorize the name Edward Bedford, linked to a photograph of a black man with a goatee and receding hairline, Foer pictured the man fording a river on a bed. The movie character Edward

[**FACT:** At least 117 kinds of molecules play a role when neurons construct a memory.]

WORDS ON PAPER
An illustration portrays the workshop of Johannes Gutenberg (1400–1468). His printing press dealt a body blow to the need for strong memory.

Scissorhands—his image called up to remember the man's first name—accompanied Bedford on the crossing.

The technique may seem strange, but it was known throughout society for many hundreds of years. Literate people learned the tricks by reading Cicero's *De Oratore* and an anonymously written Latin tract, *Rhetorica ad Herennium,* penned during the first century B.C. The nonliterate used mnemonic devices to learn long narrative poems by heart. Bards memorized thousands of verses of epic poems by relying on images, associations, and rhymes.

THE IMPACT OF PRINT

Until Johannes Gutenberg invented the printing press in the mid-1400s, books were rare and, because they were hand copied, expensive. Few people were literate. Important knowledge for everyday life had to be committed to memory. But the advent of writing, followed by cheap and plentiful printed books, eroded much of the need for an excellent memory. The ancient Greek philosopher Plato lamented that the invention of writing was a thief of memory. He said writing "will produce forgetfulness in the souls of those who have learned it, through lack of practice in using their memory, as through reliance on writing they are reminded from outside by alien marks, not from inside, themselves by themselves." Learning through reading, rather than the richer experience of face-to-face discussion with a teacher, would reduce wisdom, he feared.

Record Keeping

Many people would argue that writing and plentiful books have freed the mind from the work of memory, allowing it to devote itself

DIGITAL MEMORIES
The digital information age has further eroded memory. Want to fix visual data? Snap and store.

BRAIN INSIGHT

GORDON BELL'S LIFELOG
A Microsoft researcher takes the examined life to an extreme

GORDON BELL

Gordon Bell constantly updates his book of life.

Bell, principal researcher at Microsoft Research Silicon Valley Laboratory, turns every Web page he views into a PDF. He saves every email. He records and files every phone call. He makes digital copies of receipts. He carries digital video and audio equipment, including a special fisheye camera, called a SenseCam, that automatically takes a picture every few seconds.

Everything goes into computer memory. He calls his project MyLife-Bits and his work "lifelogging."

Critics point out the potential privacy and security risks of making a searchable database of a person's entire life, but Bell says positives outweigh the negatives.

"What an e-memory does, to me, is [it] gives me a really wonderful free feeling," Bell told CNN. "It's like having a multimedia transcript of your life."

The lifelog is practical. Bell tracks his diet, exercise, and physical pains to adjust his regimen, and he annotates his files to make them searchable by keyword. His brain-only memories in effect act as Web page addresses that direct him toward stored data. Bell reasons that if he forgets where he put his keys, he can find them in his sequence of digital pictures. Fortunately, he can turn his SenseCam off for minutes at a time, allowing him to use the toilet in privacy.

to other pursuits. A common method of bolstering memory is to fix its data outside the brain. For example, keeping all daily schedules in only one appointment book, and keeping it at hand, can eliminate many hazards of faulty memory. An extreme proponent of externalizing personal memory is Microsoft's Gordon Bell, who for more than a decade has recorded everything he sees, hears, and reads with digital cameras and sound equipment. Everything gets filed to computer memory that he can search as necessary. So, for example, if he forgets where he put his glasses, a consultation with his records for the previous few hours would show him putting the glasses down.

The problem with such a system is that it does not guard against forgetting why a person wears glasses, or what the word *glasses* means. Disorders ranging from normal "tip-of-the-tongue" grasping for words to severe dementia affect the power of memory for millions of adults.

Growing awareness of Alzheimer's disease and other forms of dementia and their ability to destroy memory has caused adults to look more for signs of memory loss than for any other potential

> The ordinary effects of **AGING** may mimic dementia's early stages.

86 ACROSS
Puzzles and games test memory. As the brain ages, it loses some of its memory power, perhaps making the daily crossword more difficult.

BRAIN BOOSTER

USE CATEGORIES
Use your natural tendency to categorize as a memory aid

Take full advantage of your memory's natural learning style and use the categories technique to boost your list recall.

→ BREAK IT DOWN
The next time you have to commit a list to memory, try breaking it into several shorter lists that belong to the same meaningful category. For example, divide your packing list by type of clothing (underclothes, shirts, and so on), or by day of travel (Monday, Tuesday, and so on).

Want another great way to use this strategy? Always depend on the same categories for lists you use again and again: Your grocery list, for instance, might always be categorized by type of food or by the aisle in the store. That way, if you forget that list at home or in the car (which happens to me from time to time!), the categories will act as a prompt for those items you need.

impairments of the aging brain. One difficulty that arises when trying to detect the first signs of dementia is that the ordinary effects of aging may mimic dementia's early stages.

THE IMPACT OF AGE

Some cognitive decline apparently is inevitable with age. Some is not.

A Japanese study of subjects 40 to 79 years old found that the power of memory declines more and more with advancing age. Difficulty in recalling memories held true not only for recent events, but also for events in every decade of life, exploding the myth that older memories are more shielded from decay. And that's just for subjects in a test environment who aren't under the stress of living. Elderly brains are more vulnerable than younger ones to the interference

A VICIOUS CYCLE
Anxiety and depression affect the ability to remember things. And the inability to remember can contribute to anxiety and depression.

that stress, anxiety, and depression can inflict on the ability to recall memories. This can be a scary catch-22 for people wondering whether they're showing signs of dementia: As they search their memories for particular information, they may struggle because of the ordinary slowing of a mature brain. The struggle may cause anxiety, which only makes it more difficult to remember. Instead of dementia, they may just be worrying themselves into forgetfulness.

What Brain Scans Reveal

The aging brain also has greater difficulty memorizing new information. High-tech brain scans reveal a key reason for the change. Positron-emission tomography (PET) scans measure brain cells'

[**FACT**: Patients with dementia are often more confused at sundown. The reasons aren't clear.]

use of oxygen. The more oxygen a neuron uses, the greater its activation, a sign that the brain has called upon a neural circuit to perform work. When new memories are encoded, PET scans reveal heightened use of oxygen in the hippocampus.

In studies run by the National Institute on Aging, experimenters asked test subjects to observe and memorize faces. Subjects in their 60s and 70s turned out to have a lower level of activation in their hippocampus during this activity than those in their 20s. The lowered hippocampal activation correlated with the elderly subjects' greater difficulty in recognizing images of faces they had seen when mixed with ones they had not.

When test subjects in both groups failed to easily recall information, PET scans revealed greater activation of their frontal lobes,

BRAIN BOOSTER

BE A PLANNER
Using a planner actually helps keep your brain in order

Chances are you use a calendar or planner. But did you know that your paper or digital helper may be the most critical brain tool you employ?

Planners and other memory tools get us to pay better attention and keep better track of the things we need to do. Planners help us organize and manage all the details, freeing our focus for other things.

WANT TO PLAN FOR YOUR PLANNER?
➲ Make sure your scheduler can fit all your plans in a day's entry space but is small enough that you can always have it available.

➲ Keep in mind that no planner will work if you don't use it effectively. Get in the habit of taking five minutes every morning to check out your plans for the day. Weigh in weekly by setting aside ten minutes at the beginning of the week to review all your upcoming events and tasks.

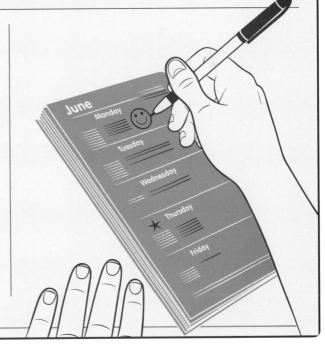

site of the brain's executive functions: The frontal lobes' neurons apparently burned more oxygen as the brains tried to force remembrance. However, the elderly brains had lowered levels of activation in the left frontal lobe. It was as if the elderly brains tried to compensate for the lowered hippocampal action but could not perform as well as they had in youth.

The study concluded that although memory impairment can affect people of any age, younger brains in general outperform older ones in storing new memories. Elderly brains often compensate by calling up greater energy and effort to perform mental exercises, including the recall of information. Fortunately, once an elderly brain learns a new skill, such as playing a card game or using a computer mouse, it maintains that skill as well as a younger brain.

BRAIN BOOSTER

SCHOOL DAYS
Old memories may be easier to retrieve than you realize

Are you ever surprised by what you can retrieve from your long-term memory? Much of the early information we have learned, even if it was a long time ago, stays with us. Names of college classmates or our first phone number are examples of things we may remember, even if we aren't trying to hold onto them.

Although we may find our retrieval of well-learned information is slower than we might like at times (as you might experience when groping for a word in conversation, or the name of an actor), we have in general saved much in that long-term memory "bank."

➲ ELEMENTARY, DEAR WATSON
Try this simple exercise that taps your long-term recall: Make a list of your teachers from kindergarten through high school. You may not have given them much thought lately, but chances are those teachers are not as distant a memory as you think.

50 YEARS
Beyond that age, nearly everyone has some measure of memory impairment. But there are strategies for coping.

REACHING AGE 50

A rough dividing line seems to be age 50. Beyond that age, practically everyone has some degree of memory impairment. Scientific studies have measured this drop-off by having test subjects listen to a story told aloud. As soon as the story is over, the researcher asks the subject to respond to a list of questions about the story and its characters. Only ten minutes later—usually to the subject's amusement—the researcher asks the same list of questions and then compares the answers. The process is repeated again 2 hours later and then 48 hours after the story. Starting at age 50, the accuracy of respondents' answers shows a slow and steady decline. By way of contrast, a patient in the early stages of Alzheimer's disease loses a profound amount of information in ten minutes or less. In a similar test, early Alzheimer's subjects could only remember one or two words from a list of ten, after the lapse of ten minutes.

Beyond age 50, practically everyone has some degree of **MEMORY IMPAIRMENT.**

As noted, the longer people live, the more likely they are to experience a decline in memory. For most people, cognitive skills remain fairly constant, showing only a gradual decline in memory and in the speed with which they process information. A minority experiences dementia, a more dramatic, progressive deterioration affecting multiple cognitive abilities. Memory lapses no doubt cause frustration, no matter when they occur, but forgetting an appointment or a birthday is no cause to jump to conclusions about dementia. The slowing of memory retrieval is often confused with memory loss, but they're not the same thing. Usually, with time, the memories come when called. Furthermore, lapses of memory do not affect judgment or the wisdom gained from a lifetime of experiences.

CAUSES AND TYPES OF DEMENTIA

Age-related memory loss derives from natural chemical and physical changes. One such change is the decreased flow of oxygen-rich blood to the brain that often accompanies constriction of arteries as well as the more sedentary lifestyle of the old versus the young. Others include the aging body's decreased ability to absorb brain-boosting nutrients, the body's decline in production of certain hormones and proteins that protect and repair neurons, and deterioration of the hippocampus.

Sources of Dementia

Dementia's major symptoms include memory loss, moodiness, and difficulties in speaking, reading, or writing. The ability to perform routine daily tasks, a form of stored memory, also declines as the disease progresses. Causes of dementia include:

▶ **Alzheimer's disease.** It accounts for 60 percent to 80 percent of dementias and has struck more than 5 million Americans, but an absolute diagnosis can occur only when a physician examines the

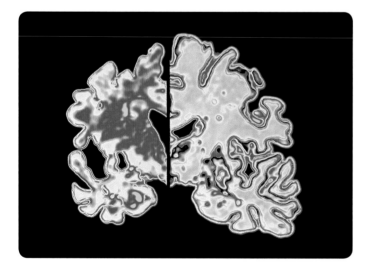

THE DAMAGE OF ALZHEIMER'S
A computer graphic of a vertical (coronal) slice through the brain of an Alzheimer's patient (left), compared with a normal brain (right), shows shrinkage due to degeneration and nerve cell death.

ALZHEIMER'S CHECKLIST

Learn the difference between normal signs of aging and those of Alzheimer's disease

The Alzheimer's Association lists ten signs that might indicate the onset of Alzheimer's disease, depending on severity and frequency of occurrence. If you think you have some of these symptoms, don't panic, but follow up with a medical evaluation:

ALOIS ALZHEIMER, THIRD FROM RIGHT, BACK ROW

1 Memory loss. It's one of the most common signs of Alzheimer's. Alzheimer's erases the memory of recently learned information or important dates or events. Increased reliance on notes, electronic devices, and family members as memory prompts also may be a sign of Alzheimer's. However, forgetting names or appointments, followed by remembering them later, can be just a typical change related to aging.

2 Challenges in planning or solving problems, such as following a familiar recipe or balancing a checkbook. Or the common task may take significantly more time. An occasional math error when totaling the month's expenses is likely unrelated to Alzheimer's.

3 Difficulty completing familiar tasks, such as forgetting the rules of a favorite card game. Less concerning is the occasional need for help operating electronic devices.

4 Confusion with time or place, particularly with things that happen outside the current moment and location. People with Alzheimer's might forget where they are. On the other hand, a typical age-related error is to forget the day of the week but remember it later.

5 Trouble understanding visual images and spatial relationships. Trouble reading or grasping the distance to an object or its color—all of which affect driving—may be signs of Alzheimer's. This is different from physical impairments such as cataracts, which cloud vision.

6 New problems with words in speaking or writing. Some people with Alzheimer's have difficulty following conversations, forget what they are saying, or struggle with the names of ordinary objects. However, trouble coming up with the right word—the tip-of-the-tongue problem—is a common result of aging.

7 Misplacing things and losing the ability to retrace steps. It's a warning sign when a person starts putting things in strange places, like toothpaste in the refrigerator.

8 Decreased or poor judgment. Giving away large sums of money on short notice might be a sign of Alzheimer's. So too might indifference to personal grooming. The occasional bad decision is a normal part of life.

9 Withdrawal from work or social activities. Alzheimer's may cause isolation, including spending less time on favorite sports and hobbies. This might happen when a person suffering from Alzheimer's notices obvious changes and chooses to avoid others to keep from embarrassment. A typical age-related change is the occasional feeling of weariness in fulfilling obligations.

10 Changes in mood and personality. People with Alzheimer's may become easily upset or fearful, or exhibit strong emotions not common beforehand. On the other hand, many people find comfort in routines as they age and become irritable when a routine is broken.

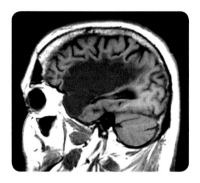

THE LOOK OF STROKE
(Above) An MRI reveals a large area of stroke damage surrounding the region of a patient's sylvian fissure.

BRAIN SCAN
(Below) A patient and technician, below, prepare for a magnetic resonance imaging scan to see inside the brain.

brain after death and notes the physical changes wrought by the disease. Alois Alzheimer, the German doctor who described the disease in 1906, made the first description of those changes when he examined the brain of a middle-aged woman whose mental faculties declined until she died, bedridden, at age 51. All brains lose some neurons as they age, but this patient with Alzheimer's had lost 25 percent of the neurons in parts of her cerebral cortex. Thick, tangled bundles of fibers appeared in many of the remaining neurons. Their presence in patients with Alzheimer's apparently interferes with normal brain functions. In addition, neurons in a brain with Alzheimer's contain clumps called *plaques,* which are composed of beta-amyloid proteins. Plaque buildup may prevent neurons from sharing information electrochemically, in effect isolating them from making or executing the kind of rich

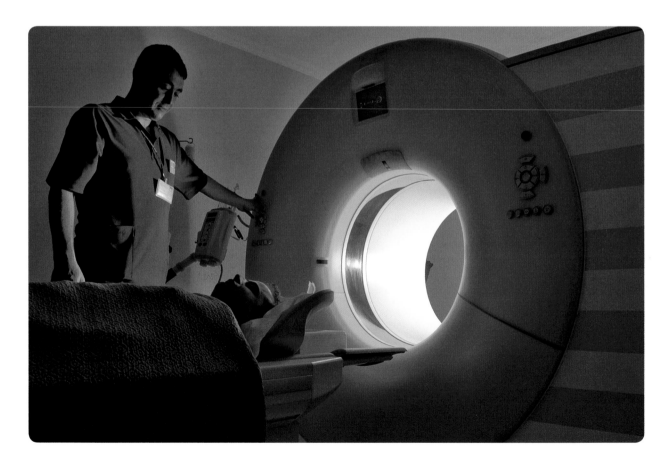

connections that promote complex behavior. Guidelines published in the last two years define three stages of Alzheimer's as "preclinical," "mild cognitive impairment," and "dementia." The first stage is mild impairment in which the brain exhibits physical changes but the typical Alzheimer's symptoms have yet to appear. The second includes obvious memory lapses that stop short of interfering with independent living. The third stage, dementia, brings hampered judgment and reasoning, the inability to speak clearly, and visual and spatial impairments.

A LOSS OF SELF
Alzheimer's disease gradually erases identity as it erases memory.

▶ **Stroke.** It cuts the flow of oxygen to neurons, causing them to die. Two major types are ischemic and hemorrhagic stroke. The former blocks the flow of blood, usually when a clot obstructs a blood vessel. The latter occurs when a blood vessel in the brain bursts, often as a result of high blood pressure. This damage can impair memory and cause dementia just as surely as neurological disease. Strokes can be verified with brain scans of living subjects. They appear as dead zones amid active regions of the brain.

▶ **Frontotemporal dementia.** This is a degeneration of the neural networks in the frontal lobe. Symptoms of the disease vary widely among patients, making a diagnosis difficult.

▶ **Dementia with Lewy bodies.** Like Alzheimer's, it can only be verified postmortem. The disease causes the growth of spherical lumps of alpha-synuclein and ubiquitin protein in neurons, damaging brain tissue. Symptoms include damage to memory, concentration, and speech.

▶ **Other causes.** A host of other diseases, including AIDS, Korsakoff's syndrome, and Creutzfeldt-Jakob disease may bring on dementia.

[FACT: Disordered REM (dreaming) sleep can be an early symptom of dementia. **]**

STRATEGIES FOR HEALTH

When considering the likely decline of the brain as it ages, it is important to distinguish between two simultaneous scientific paths of investigation. The first aims to enhance or preserve existing cognitive functions. The second seeks to stave off the onset of dementia. Although the former has shown concrete results, the latter has yet to demonstrate achievements that hold up to rigorous scientific scrutiny.

Training Works for Healthy Brain

A nationwide study known as the ACTIVE trial—short for Advanced Cognitive Training for Independent and Vital Elderly—raised hopes about maintaining or improving memory and other cognitive function when published a decade ago. The trial trained 2,802 participants aged 65 or older in three areas: memory,

BRAIN BOOSTER

REPEAT, REPEAT
Reinforce your memory with the habit of repetition

Repetition is a simple, yet incredibly powerful, strategy anyone can use to remember better. It also is one of the most popular methods I teach, because it suits just about everyone's ability and lifestyle.

➲ MAKE IT A HABIT
The repetition technique only asks that you get into the habit of always repeating something when you are learning it. Doing so focuses your attention on the new information and gives you the opportunity to practice it. Feel free to repeat the new information as much as you need to, as this only reinforces the learning process.

Practice the "repeat" technique when learning a new name, password, or phone number and see for yourself how easy it is.

reasoning, and the speed of information processing. Participants received brain-enhancing training for two and a half hours a week for five weeks. The results indicated long-lasting improvements in all three areas covered by the training, roughly counteracting the declines that normally would be expected for most elderly people who do not have dementia.

Researchers from Johns Hopkins University and the University of Massachusetts Medical School found similar results in 2012. They performed a "meta-analysis," which analyzes previous analyses. They looked at every scientific, English-language study published before January 2010 that examined the impact of memory-training techniques. Thirty-five included a control group to contrast with the experimental group, as well as measurable gains (or losses) in memory. The study found that the most common memory-improvement

ACTIVE MEMORIES
The "Laughter Yoga Club" exercises at Laguna Beach, California. Exercise can help memory by increasing blood flow to the brain.

method was some variation of the ancient visual imagery technique, although 71 percent of the programs relied on more than one memory-enhancing technique. Overall, the 35 studies showed an average increase in specific memory tasks. The math is complicated, but in layman's terms, the typical improvement was enough to move someone from average skills to slightly-above-average skills, from roughly the 50th percentile to the 62nd. Some memory-improvement programs seemed largely ineffective, the researchers noted.

Many experts now believe that unusual sensory stimuli, as compared with routine actions and thoughts, promote the growth of dendrites and help maintain cognitive skills. Neurobiologist Lawrence Katz popularized the term *neurobics* for simple exercises designed to provide unusual stimulation to the brain. Examples include dialing a phone number with the fingers of your

DIALING DIFFERENTLY
Challenging the brain can be as easy as punching the digits for a phone call using your nondominant hand.

SMOKE SCREEN
Smoking not only contains toxins, but it also restricts the flow of oxygen-rich blood to the brain.

nondominant hand, carrying out a daily routine with your eyes closed, and the brain-healthy exercises provided by Dr. Green throughout this section of the book. Memory-enhancing techniques such as simple strategies based on the ancient method of loci similarly provide unusual stimulation to the brain.

The Quest to Prevent Dementia

On the other hand, efforts to prevent cognitive decline have not led to clear results. A 2010 "State-of-the-Science" conference conducted by the National Institutes of Health on methods that might prevent cognitive decline and Alzheimer's disease concluded that scientifically rigorous studies have yet to conclusively demonstrate the value of *any* preventive measures. Studies of diet, physical activity, and medication "did not show any consistent benefit," said Martha L. Daviglus, a professor of preventive medicine and gerontology at Northwestern University, who chaired a panel for the conference. The strongest risk factor for developing dementia, and Alzheimer's in particular, remains age, she said. Smoking, depression, and the

> Unusual sensory stimuli promote the growth of **DENDRITES** and help maintain cognitive skills.

presence of a particular gene known as ApoE also have shown some evidence of association with a higher risk of cognitive decline and Alzheimer's.

Daviglus concluded that a regimen of mental and physical activity, including a good diet and regular exercise, combined with avoiding risk factors such as smoking, appeared to be the current best strategy to maintain brain health. That conclusion received endorsement in April 2012, in a study conducted by Rush University Medical Center. The study found that daily physical activity may—emphasis on *may*—reduce the risk of developing Alzheimer's disease. Test subjects whose lifestyle put them in the bottom 10 percent of the population in terms of total physical activity were more than twice as likely to develop Alzheimer's as those in the top 10 percent.

GET MOVING
Daily exercise, such as mountain biking, combined with good diet may reduce the risk of developing Alzheimer's disease.

Understand the Benefits and Limits

What should the public make of this? Dr. Green summarizes her view this way: The history of inquiry into activities that may decrease the risk of cognitive decline, including memory loss, is young, and the science is very complicated. People should make a distinction in their understanding of such activities, realizing that some may support better intellectual performance, while others may support a lowered risk of cognitive decline, such as memory impairment. In other words, some lifestyle factors boost the good while others retard the bad, and some activities, such as exercise, seem to do both. Finally, even though the science is young, most of the lifestyle behaviors linked to good brain health, such as getting regular exercise, support good overall health. The ratio of risk to reward is all to the good.

BRAIN BOOSTER

POETRY JAM

Enrich your mental library with memorized poems

Committing a poem to memory offers us a different kind of brain workout. Doing so sharpens our rote memorization skills, which we used quite a bit in school but may not practice frequently in "real life."

➡ Such skills need to stay flexed, as we rely more than we may realize on simply learning something by heart (or head). Poetry memorization is one of the contests that make up the USA Memory Championship, so it is clearly a brain challenge worth taking on!

Want to give our poetry jam a try? Find a poem and spend some time memorizing it. Try learning it in chunks of a few lines at a time (see "Chunk It," page 187). Need a great poetry resource? Try *www.poets.org*, the website of the Academy of American Poets. You can sign up for their "Poem a Day" program and get a poem sent to your in-box daily. (Favorite Poem Project, *www.favoritepoem.org*, features both poetry text and videos.) Or pick up a poetry anthology at your local bookstore or library. Try the poetry jam with family or friends.

New Findings

Some observers thought the 2010 State-of-the-Science report understated the case on the prospects of staving off Alzheimer's and other dementias. A year later, optimism found its way into the Alzheimer's Association International Conference on Alzheimer's disease in Paris. University of California, San Francisco, researchers presented a mathematical model that predicted as many as half of all Alzheimer's cases could be associated with lifestyles and behaviors. That meant many people could potentially lower their risk by changing their lives. According to the model, the most important predictive variables for Alzheimer's, in descending order of importance, were low education, smoking habits, sedentary lifestyle, depression, high blood pressure in middle age, diabetes, and obesity.

Studies at the same conference in 2012, in Vancouver, added to growing hopes. Two new early indicators of the onset of

A HANDFUL OF HOPE
Fifteen days' worth of pills rest in the hands of a patient with Alzheimer's in San Diego. New drug tests show hope of slowing the disease.

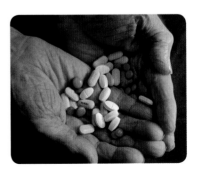

Alzheimer's were revealed to be changes in walking gait and sleep habits. And although no drug has been shown to reverse Alzheimer's, a new medication called Gammagard stabilized the disease in four patients for three years, scientists revealed at the conference. The size of the test group is too small to be significant, but much hope rests on further studies.

LIMITATIONS

Experts list various steps to improve memory. Some, such as doing specific mental puzzles to stimulate memory, strengthen the ability to perform particular tasks but have yet to demonstrate "generalizability," meaning improvement to all kinds of memory. Nowhere was this demonstrated more concretely, and humorously,

A LEAP FORWARD
Vigorous exercise, such as dancing or getting a cardiovascular workout in the park, is a great way to begin improving brain function, including memory.

than in Foer's book, *Moonwalking With Einstein*. Foer trained himself to become a world-class memory expert in narrow categories of competition, such as memorizing random numbers, cards, and names. Shortly after attending the world championships, Foer went to dinner with friends and then went home on the subway. As he walked through the front door, he realized he had driven his car to dinner. He had blanked not only where he had parked it, but also that he had driven it at all.

"That was the paradox," he wrote. "For all of the memory stunts I could now perform, I was still stuck with the same old shoddy memory that misplaced car keys and cars."

Stay Active and Stay Sharp

For everyday results, the first, and perhaps foremost, way to strengthen memory is to regularly engage in vigorous exercise and eat well. Cardiovascular exercise gets the blood pumping oxygen to the brain, and a diet rich in antioxidants, high in fiber, and low in fat provides the nutrition the brain needs. Dance appears to be a particularly good workout. Not only is it beneficial for the brain because increased respiration and heartbeat bathes the brain in oxygen, but also because learning new dance steps challenges the memory. But neuroscientists have yet to find clear, clean links between particular exercises, in particular amounts, and memory improvement.

"Right now, we can't say to somebody, 'We know that if you walk a mile every day for the next six months, your memory's going to be better,'" said Dr. Marilyn Albert, director of Johns Hopkins University Alzheimer's Disease Research Center in Baltimore.

Cardiovascular exercise gets the blood pumping OXYGEN to the brain.

[FACT: Treatments to lift depression usually improve memory. One reason is that depression reduces attention.]

CHAPTER 12

Mood and Creativity

Your brain wants to avoid pain and cultivate pleasure. No surprise there—it shuns the sticks and courts the carrots.

But it does not grant them equal weight. Your brain has a negativity bias, placing greater emphasis on bad things than on good ones.

Blame evolution. In the distant past, our human ancestors struggled to survive. They had to avoid becoming lunch for predators while working hard to hunt and gather enough food to keep them alive—at least long enough to bear and raise children. If someone missed an opportunity for food, chances were good he or she could find some another day. But if a person missed the signs of an approaching wolf pack or saber-toothed tiger, they likely wouldn't have a second opportunity to amend the error. People whose brains were marginally sharper in their perception of potential threats survived and passed their genes for superior threat detection to their offspring.

No longer do most humans have to worry about becoming a predator's lunch. Modern threats are usually less tangible. They include war, disease, personal security (including threats to home and career), and risky social and political situations. Nevertheless, the modern brain follows its evolutionary hard wiring. People work harder to avoid a loss than to obtain a gain of equal size.

BLUE SKY THINKING
(Opposite) Self-expression and mood not only color one's view of the world, but they also shape the brain.

TOUGH TIMES
(Below) Humans' negativity bias emerged in prehistoric times, including the Neolithic period, when a mistake could mean disaster or death.

ACCENTUATE THE NEGATIVE

This difference appears concretely in the brain. Bad news depresses mood more than good news elevates it. Experiencing a single bad social interaction causes such mental anguish that it takes about five positive ones to counterbalance it and restore equilibrium. As neuropsychologist Rick Hanson writes in *Buddha's Brain,* "Your brain is like Velcro for negative experiences and Teflon for positive ones—even though most of your experiences are probably neutral or positive."

This bias toward all things negative can cause a host of problems. It generates anxiety as a kind of background noise for everyday experience. It intensifies feelings such as depression, sadness, and anger. And it can create a self-image distorted like a fun house mirror:

> Bad news depresses **MOOD** more than good news elevates it.

BRAIN BOOSTER

LIST TEN WAYS YOUR BRAIN IS GREAT

It's easy to accentuate the positive when you really think about your brain

Take a few minutes and list ten ways in which your brain is totally awesome.

THINK ABOUT IT
Why take the time to reflect on our brain's strengths? As we grow older and worry more about memory loss and other possible problems, we tend to lose sight of all the really amazing things our brains do on a daily basis. Our brains are responsible for a whole range of remarkable feats, including:

➲ Keeping us awake (and getting us to sleep)

➲ Maintaining our senses

➲ Helping us speak

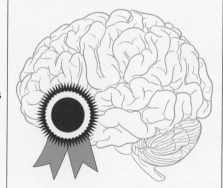

➲ Letting us love

➲ Giving us pleasure in the experience of new things, each and every day.

When we look at how much our brain does well instead of harping on small slips we all may experience from time to time, it can really change our perspective on our brain's health.

So it's important to take the time and think about what our brains do well, for a change—and I bet that you will quickly complete that list of ten items.

FUN HOUSE MIRROR
Like distortions in curved glass, twisted self-images can emerge from the brain's emphasis on the bad in life.

good characteristics shrunken and twisted, bad ones inflated until they dominate.

Furthermore, evolution has vastly enlarged the prefrontal cortex of human beings compared with other animals. This region is particularly vulnerable to the negativity bias. Among other functions, the prefrontal cortex draws on remembered experiences to envision the future. It runs simulations of how a person might choose to act in a variety of brain-devised virtual realities. That made sense from an evolutionary point of view; our ancestors' brains reviewed where they found good hunting and food gathering in previous years before deciding where to go looking anew. Today, after continual growth in the prefrontal cortex, the ability to simulate choices and their outcomes has increased. Choices have expanded in modern times: Which job, clothes, food, etc., are right for you? It can become overwhelming.

[FACT: Psychologist Martin Seligman lists three components of happiness: pleasure, engagement, and meaning. **]**

Daydream Believer

The modern human brain spends a lot of time both actively and passively playing out scenarios that pull attention away from the present moment and focus it somewhere else. A Harvard University study of 2,000 volunteers in 2010 found that people spend about 46 percent of their waking hours in daydreams, not actually thinking about tasks at hand. Researchers Matthew Killingsworth and Daniel Gilbert concluded that such undirected mental video clips aren't good things. "A human mind is a wandering mind, and a wandering mind is an unhappy mind," they said. Gilbert added, "Unlike other animals, human beings spend a lot of time thinking about what is not going on around them, contemplating events that happened in the past, might happen in the future, or will never happen at all."

DAYDREAM DIRECTIONS
It's normal for the mind to wander, but fixating on potential problems in the future is usually a waste of time and energy.

A lot of that mental rehearsal is channeled into visualizing negative outcomes—threats—in the future. Most of that energy is wasted. The majority of things people worry about never come to pass; meanwhile, most things envisioned as likely to bring great happiness deliver only a fraction of what the brain envisioned. But there's more impact than wasted time. Fixating on the future takes the brain out of the present moment—the here and how, where joy and love are the most real.

THE HERE AND NOW
Living in the joy of the moment, such as spending time with family and friends, helps reduce brain-debilitating stress and anxiety.

STRESS

Unfortunately, a great many people live in a nearly constant state of stress. Evolution once again may take much of the blame. When bad things happen, or even when you only have thoughts about bad things happening, your brain sets in motion a series of physical changes to prepare your body to deal with the consequences. If you hear a sound you recognize as signaling danger, such as the buzz of a rattlesnake's tail or the boom of a nearby lightning strike, your brain sends out a "fight-or-flight" signal to prepare your body for whatever comes your way. Something similar happens when you are rejected in response to asking someone out on a date, or when you worry about your financial future. Your brain keeps your body on edge—and that's a bad place to spend much time. In the business world, constant stress can lead to "burnout." For those exposed to stress all the time, such as combat pilots, the body adjusts and falls into a routine. But only for a while. Continual exposure tends to degrade performance.

People spend about 46 percent of their waking hours in **DAYDREAMS.**

THE AGE OF ANXIETY
(Above) A bit of stress stimulates the brain, but constant exposure overtaxes the brain. Continuous communication connections don't help.

FIGHT OR FLIGHT
(Below) Sensing a threat, from snake or enemy, bathes the brain in cortisol and suppresses reason.

A Jolt to the Body

Specifically, the brain activates the sympathetic nervous system and the hypothalamic-pituitary-adrenal axis of the endocrine system. The sympathetic nervous system jolts the major organ and muscle systems with an extra burst of energy and strength to prepare for fight or flight. Discrete brain regions also prompt the release of stress-related neurotransmitters and hormones. The thalamus, situated between the cerebral cortex and the brain stem, alerts the brain stem to release norepinephrine throughout the brain. This neurotransmitter has many functions, but its primary role in response to stress is to increase oxygen uptake in the brain and sharpen mental focus. Meanwhile, the hypothalamus prompts the adrenal glands atop the kidneys to release

BRAIN BOOSTER

COLOR YOUR WORLD
Pull out those colored pencils and enjoy yourself

Today's the day to bring out your inner artist (even if you haven't so much as scribbled since you were eight).

➜ REFRESHER COURSE
New or different activities such as coloring, even if we do them just briefly, refresh our attention, get us to try new (or rarely used) skills, and challenge us to see the world in a different way.

What do you need to fulfill today's tip? Just go get a set of crayons, markers, or colored pencils and spend some time doodling, drawing, or sketching. You can even purchase an abstract coloring book (you can find them online) to help you color away the minutes. Go ahead and color away at whatever comes to mind.

Have kids? Share this activity and have fun together.

stress hormones such as epinephrine (adrenaline) and cortisol into the bloodstream. Epinephrine increases the heart rate, speeds breathing, engorges the muscles with blood, dilates the pupils, and prompts the skin to start sweating to compensate for the increased body heat brought on by all of the other changes. Cortisol suppresses the immune system, preparing the body to minimize the impact of any physical injuries by lowering inflammation from wounds.

When all of these stress-related hormones and neurotransmitters are at work, they lower the strength of the executive function of the prefrontal cortex. It's as if the brain puts itself on autopilot, decreasing the higher cognitive functions to allow its basic survival circuits to reflexively handle any immediate danger. That's why when you're afraid or under stress, you don't think as clearly as when you're cool, calm, and collected.

[FACT: A study found that playing with dogs increased levels of joy-inducing hormones. **]**

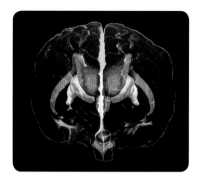

SENSORY PROCESSORS
The hypothalamus (green, center next to orange thalami), controls emotion and regulates release of hormones from the pituitary gland (green globe at bottom).

The Toll of Anxiety

Although it's good to have an occasional burst of stress-related brain activity in response to the once-in-a-while experience of driving on a dangerous road or facing an angry dog in the park, the human body wasn't designed for long-term exposure. Keeping the brain and body on constant alert, even at a low level, diverts energy from the immune system and the promotion of a positive mental attitude to the short-term energy requirements of facing threats. Unfortunately, a low-level burn seems to have become the normal stress level in the last few decades. Why this is so remains open for debate, but many observers point to the faster pace of life, including constant communication opportunities through email and handheld digital communication devices; increased time spent with television and video games; and less relaxation time with family and friends.

Long-term elevated stress levels can have severe physical consequences. These include a weakened immune system, which

BRAIN INSIGHT

TOO MUCH INFORMATION
The age of 24-hour news may be feeding our anxieties

The decade of the 1950s sometimes is remembered as the age of anxiety. Communism threatened from overseas, from space, and, if certain U.S. politicians were to be believed, from the halls of our own government. Cold War adversaries possessed thermonuclear warheads and the means to launch them. Racial tensions exploded in showdowns over Jim Crow laws.

So why is it that Americans reported higher rates of anxiety in the 1990s than the 1950s? Or that beginning in the 1980s, American children had higher anxiety levels than adult psychiatric patients in the 1950s?

Neurologist Richard Restak, who included those facts in his 2004 book *Poe's Heart and the Mountain Climber,* wonders whether the power of communication technology is at least partly to blame. Satellites, cable television, and the Internet constantly bathe media consumers in disturbing news from around the world. Professional communicators have capitalized on the motivating power of fear by creating advertising and marketing messages portraying a product or political candidate as an antidote. Political ads flooded TV in 2012 with scary visions of the future if the wrong candidate were elected.

INFORMATION OVERLOAD

"Because we are collectively feeling increasingly threatened, vulnerable, and helpless . . . our individual and communal anxiety levels are on the increase," Restak said. The brain adapts with various attitudes.

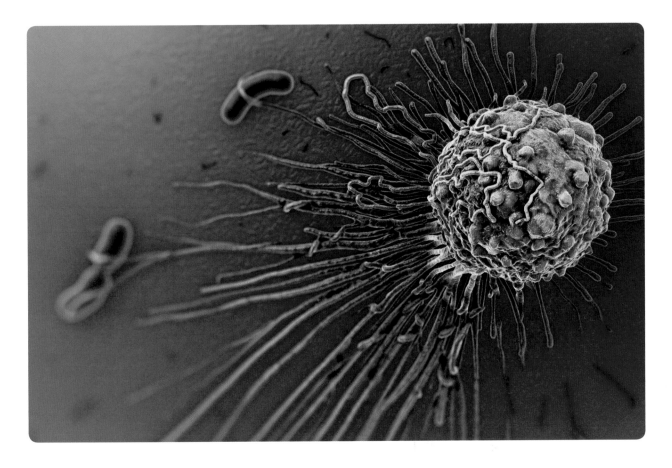

A macrophage cell attacks bacteria. The immune system, which protects the body from disease, grows weaker under stress.

brings higher susceptibility to colds, flus, and infections; heart disease, including hardening of the arteries; ulcers, diarrhea, and other gastrointestinal disorders; type II diabetes; and sexual dysfunctions including decreased libido.

Long-term exposure to heightened levels of the stress hormone cortisol produces many negative effects. It encourages the production of body fat by suppressing hormones associated with appetite. It also disrupts sleep, which affects mood and cognitive function, and increases patterns of negative thinking. And it shrinks the hippocampus, the most crucial brain region for memory formation. Researchers who produced a series of articles for the journal *Psychoneuroendocrinology* found memory impairment in all stages of the human life span when chronically high cortisol levels were present. Older adults with high cortisol levels during the three to six years

BRAIN BOOSTER

HUG FIVE

Fight stress by reinforcing those emotional ties

Here's an exercise that will move your mind and your heart. All you have to do is go and give five people a hug.

➲ SOCIAL AND HEALTHY
Why this tip about getting more huggable? Studies have shown that folks who are more socially engaged have an associated reduced risk for memory impairment. In one recent study, Harvard researchers found that participants who reported lower levels of social interaction were significantly more likely to show memory problems after six years than their more social peers. Maintaining our emotional ties can also reduce our risk for emotional distress, depression, and stress, all of which have been linked to an increase in daily memory problems and dementia risk.

So go out there and get your hugs going. Hopefully this one won't prove too hard for you to do! Just keep in mind that those hugs aren't only good for your soul, they're good for your brain.

of one study scored worse on memory tests than a control group of similar age. Among young adults, high levels of cortisol in the short term temporarily interfered with memory and other cognitive skills.

Cortisol levels were found to be higher among teenagers and younger children from lower socioeconomic classes than from higher ones. Given the relationship between cortisol and depressed thinking and memory skills, the study provides additional support for the idea that brain chemistry may be linked in part to environmental factors. And that likely contributes to the lowered cognitive performance scores recorded for children raised in poverty. Exposure to toxins and poor nutrition also may play a role. Brain regions showing the effects of chronic poverty included those associated with working memory, impulse control, and language.

[FACT: Exposure to oxytocin increases the level of trust people have for each other. **]**

ACHIEVING BALANCE

A healthy brain keeps the sympathetic nervous system in balance with the parasympathetic nervous system. If the former turns the screw, the latter loosens it. The parasympathetic nervous system, sometimes called the "rest and digest" system, is the portion of the brain's circuitry that slows the heart rate and increases glandular and intestinal activity. Stimulating this system brings on relaxation and a sense of well-being.

INNER PEACE
A senior monk sits in front of the Boudhanath Stupa in Kathmandu, Nepal. Himalayan monks and other meditators substantially change their gray matter.

BRAIN BOOSTER

MEDITATE

Let go of those intrusive, anxious thoughts for a while

This activity focuses on the "soul" side of brain health. You may not think of meditation as "brain healthy," but it may be one of the best things you can do for your gray matter.

FOCUS AND LET GO

Meditation offers many benefits. It is a perfect way to build attention, as it trains us to hold focus. It can also help us more effectively manage pain and emotional distress, all of which can detract from mental performance.

➡ To begin, sit in a quiet spot in your house. Get comfortably seated (on the floor or on a chair).

➡ Now, just be there, in that moment, observing your breath.

As anxious thoughts come to your mind (and they will), notice them and then just let them go. If you need help passing by those thoughts, here are two methods I have found helpful: First, just comment to yourself "everything passes," and then let the thought go. Or, as the thoughts come, think to yourself "blah, blah, blah" (which is really the noise those thoughts "make" after all), and let them go.

Meditation

Meditation, which may affect this system, has been found to create powerful, positive changes in the brain. Tibetan monks generate electrical pulses known as gamma brain waves, cycling 30 to 40 times a second, when they meditate. According to a study at the University of California, Los Angeles, the brains of experienced meditators exhibit more folding than those in control groups. They enjoy not only greater feelings of peace and relaxation, but also some physiological benefits, including lower rates of heart attacks and strokes.

Novices get benefits too. A 2011 study led by researchers at Massachusetts General Hospital documented measurable changes in gray matter in the brains of test subjects who participated in a mindful meditation program for eight weeks. The affected regions included memory, empathy, stress, and sense of self.

Meditators have long claimed that their practice provides cognitive and psychological benefits that persist throughout the day. According to researcher Sara Lazar, the Massachusetts study "demonstrates that changes in brain structure may underlie some of these reported improvements and that people are not just feeling better because they are spending time relaxing."

Any activity that focuses attention on the present brings some of the benefits of meditation. Walking, jogging, swimming, bicycling along a country road, or anything else that produces a feeling of calmness in the current moment will do. Try a low-impact exercise for five to ten minutes a day to see how your brain reacts. If your mind wanders back to stress-inducing thoughts, let those thoughts drift away so you can return your attention to the here and now. Don't keep talking or thinking about whatever it is that bothers you; fixating on the problem strengthens stress.

The brains of experienced meditators exhibit more **FOLDING** than those in control groups.

Combating Stress

Other methods to reduce stress include:

▸ **Visualization.** Picture a favorite place or thing that you associate with

A RELAXING RUN
Taking a walk or jog, whether in the Columbia Gorge or your neighborhood, puts you in the moment and acts as a form of meditation.

THE PERSONAL TOUCH
Physical contact, as between father and child in Spain, stimulates creativity and lowers blood pressure and stress.

happiness. It could be anything from a cabin in the woods to a fuzzy puppy from your childhood. If you can make it concrete in your mind, your brain will activate the sensory and emotional neural circuits associated with the experience when you formed the memory.

▶ **Changing the way you breathe.** Consciously taking slow, deep breaths stimulates the parasympathetic nervous system, spreading a surprisingly tangible feeling of calm. Focus your thoughts on the air going into and out of your lungs, as well as the changes in your chest and belly as you breathe.

▶ **Sharpening your senses.** Focus on the sensations striking your eyes, ears, skin, nose, and tongue. Try to identify the random noises of the office or backyard—the laugh of a loon, the chirrup of a squirrel, the whine of a distant jet engine. Anything that fixes your attention in the present moment detracts from stress (unless the present moment is full of stressful sensations, of course).

▶ **Expressing affection.** It could be a hug or kiss with your spouse, a tummy rub for a pet Labrador retriever, or just talking about good times with friends. Social interaction improves the brain's ability to find creative solutions to problems, and physical contact appears to lower stress hormone levels as well as blood pressure.

> Anything that fixes your attention in the present moment detracts from **STRESS.**

▶ **Limiting time with video games.** Be careful about how much you play video games, and what kinds of games they are. Games stimulate the basal ganglia, crucial to the brain's experience of pleasure. It's the same part of the brain that gets excited by addictive drugs, so it's possible for a game to feel addictive. Video games that put players in stressful roles cause stress. The brain's mirror neurons fire in response to what the player sees and hears on the video screen. Therefore, if a player swings an ax to kill a monster, mirror neurons fire in the brain just as if the player had reacted to seeing a real monster, and had swung the ax in real life.

Games that simulate violence may push the brain into neural changes that don't dissipate as soon as the game is over. But the jury is out on all of the effects generated by the wide range of video games. Some games appear to reduce stress. For example, test subjects in a recent study were less likely to develop symptoms of post-traumatic stress syndrome if they played Tetris or a similarly engaging video-spatial game shortly after witnessing something traumatic.

GETTING HELP

Decisions about treating negative mental states are best made in consultation with a doctor. Common options include prescription medications to restore neuro-chemical balance and therapy to adjust mental states. Both have advantages, and they are not mutually exclusive.

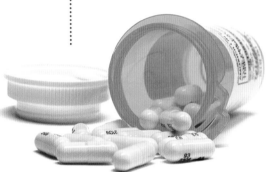

BRAIN BOOSTER

REACH OUT AND RECONNECT

Staying social is remarkably good for your health

All of us have friends from the past we have lost touch with over the years. Here's the chance to reconnect with one of those long-lost buddies.

➔ **YOUR SOCIAL WORKOUT**
Why rekindle that friendship? Higher levels of social engage-ment are associated with better mental health. Also, being with others gives us a great "skills" workout, as you really cannot be social without staying focused, thinking fast, and keeping your mind nimble.

Staying social also exposes us to different experiences or ways of thinking, which is great for our intellectual engagement.

Finally, our brain benefits from the "intangible" side of staying social, by lowering our risk for emotional distress.

➔ **WAYS TO CONNECT**
In our busy day-to-day lives, it is altogether too easy to lose track of friends whose company we really enjoy. So spend some time finding that long-lost pal. Use the Internet (Facebook and Google are great tools for this), or dig out an old phone book or alumni directory. Call or write, reconnect, and make a plan to stay in touch.

Medications

Prescription medicines aim to adjust neurotransmitter levels to enhance or suppress the firing of particular neural circuits. As inborn neural structure has been shown often to play a significant role in causing chemical imbalances in the brain, taking medication to restore mental balance makes sense. It's no different from taking an aspirin for a headache or wearing eyeglasses to correct vision. Nevertheless, it may be tempting for some to look upon medication as an easy fix. Use of antidepressants in the United States has increased significantly in the last two decades, making them the third most commonly prescribed class of medications. During the four inclusive years from 2005 to 2008, nearly 9 percent of Americans had at least one prescription for an antidepressant, according to the Centers for Disease Control. The vast majority of

BRAIN BOOSTER

BREATHE LIKE A LION

A classic yoga exercise can help you relax in record time

Feeling stressed? Often the stress we feel can lead to a constant state of feeling overwhelmed. This kind of chronic stress can affect our daily performance, making it harder for us to stay sharp and function effectively.

SAY "HA"

Here's a simple yoga breathing exercise called Lion's Breath that can help you keep stress in check in just a few minutes:

➲ Sit comfortably, with both feet on the floor and your hands resting in your lap or on your thighs.

➲ Start by taking a deep breath, breathing deep into your belly.

➲ As you exhale, stick out your tongue and exhale with a bit of force, feeling the air move out against the back of your throat. You may even make a bit of a sound as you force the air out along your throat, saying "ha" (assuming you have some privacy to do so).

➲ Repeat these steps for a few breaths.

When you are done, you will feel more alert, focused, and relaxed.

COGNITIVE THERAPY
U.S. Marines fill out research consent forms in 2009. Cognitive therapy has helped many veterans with post-traumatic stress disorder.

prescriptions were prescribed by doctors who were not psychiatrists for patients without a psychiatric diagnosis. That raises questions about whether that prescribed medication was always the best possible medical option.

Therapy

An alternative is cognitive behavioral therapy. It teaches people to think about their thoughts in a different way so that new thought patterns rewire the brain. In her book *Train Your Mind, Change Your Brain,* author Sharon Begley describes how it works. "In the case of depression, cognitive behavior therapy teaches you to basically

FACT: Women with depression outnumber men, but men are more likely to hide the condition's symptoms.

not catastrophize," she told National Public Radio. "So people who suffer from depression tend to take what [to] other people would be a minor setback—they had a lousy date, their roof leaks, something bad happens at work—and that gets parlayed or that avalanches into 'No one will ever love me, nothing will ever go right.' "

Cognitive behavioral therapy teaches people with depression to view such thoughts as false or as mere aberrations of the brain. The therapy patients' brain rewires itself as the patients learn to process thoughts and emotions in new ways. In the end, they have as much success bringing themselves out of their depression as those who take medication.

Begley said she has seen similar results with war veterans struggling with post-traumatic stress disorder. They may feel sharp fear or anxiety at a sudden sound, such as a door slamming, because their brains have learned to associate such sounds with danger, and those associations have formed strong neural connections over time. When the veterans received therapy in which they sensed a triggering sound or sight, but in a safe, relaxed setting, their brains conditioned themselves to quiet their fear circuits.

> Friends outrank family in their ability to **IMPROVE** an elderly person's mood.

DEPRESSION AND THE ELDERLY

Depression and other negative mental states strike the elderly more powerfully than the young. Unfortunately, depression is all too common among older adults. Friends and relatives die off with the passing years, leading to feelings of loneliness. In fact, neurologist Richard Restak considers loneliness "the greatest challenge of the mature years," as half of all men and women age 90 or older report feeling lonely all the time. On the other hand, elderly people become more accustomed to dealing with feelings

FACT: In the long run, lottery winners are no happier than anyone else. The brain stabilizes mood after a major jolt.

SOLITARY YEARS
Loneliness is "the greatest challenge of the mature years," according to neurologist Richard Restak. Losing friends and family challenges emotional health.

of loss, and many find emotional support in their circles of friends. (Surprisingly, perhaps, friends outrank family in the significance of their ability to improve an elderly person's mood. Speculation centers on the importance of confiding in friends more than family, and in the way time with friends breaks the monotony of daily life.)

Restak believes most depression among the elderly occurs because of chemical changes in the brain. As the brain ages, it produces smaller amounts of certain neurotransmitters, and the loss alters the neurochemical balance. Compounding the problem, elderly brains also are more prone to sleep disorders, including insomnia, sleep apnea (interruptions in breathing patterns), and frequent awakening. Sleep disturbances affect the strength of memories. Restoring the brain to healthy sleep patterns and a proper balance of neurotransmitters that combats depression, often accomplished with medication, may improve mental function, including memory.

CARVING OUT CHOICES
(Opposite) Being creative means making choices, and that energizes morale. Creativity can range from art and music to other intellectual pursuits.

THE POWER OF CREATIVITY

Creativity, in the form of the desire for self-expression and inner growth, promotes physical and mental health, and appears to be particularly important for mature and elderly adults. According to Gene D. Cohen in his book *The Creative Age: Awakening Human Potential in the Second Half of Life,* creativity improves life in a variety of ways. It strengthens morale in later life, he said, by altering the way the brain experiences problems. "No matter what our actual physical condition, we *feel better* when we are able to view our circumstances with some creativity," Cohen said. Furthermore, a creative outlook fosters a sense of well-being, which boosts the immune system and contributes to overall health. It does this through the promotion of positive emotions, the ally of the parasympathetic nervous system and enemy of negative moods.

The Chemicals of Creativity

Specifically, biophysics and physiology professor Candace Pert of Georgetown University Medical Center in Washington, D.C., has

BRAIN INSIGHT

THE VALUE OF FICTION
Fictional experiences take on a kind of reality in the brain

Want to navigate through life's rapids and eddies more smoothly? Maybe your prescription should be, "Take two novels and call me in the morning."

Research in 2008 by Canadian psychologists Raymond Mar and Keith Oatley found that people who read a lot of fiction develop better social skills than those primarily reading nonfiction.

"The function of fiction is the abstraction and simulation of social experience," they said. In other words, reading about fictitious events re-creates those events in the brain. When you read about a hero's quest, your brain makes you empathize with the hero's triumphs and tragedies.

That conclusion received corroboration a year later in brain-scan research by a team led by Nicole Speer, Jeremy Reynolds, Khena Swallow, and Jeffrey Zacks. They modified an fMRI scanner to image portions of the brain activated by reading. When a test subject read about a fictitious character performing an action, the brain regions associated with executing that action became active. If the character pulled a light cord, for example, the reader's brain region associated with grasping lit up.

Neural pathways activate to rehearse reactions to potential social situations too. The implication is that if you read enough fiction, your social abilities improve along with your words a minute.

THE DELANY SISTERS
Bessie Delany (left) was 102, and her
sister, Sadie, was 104, when they signed
copies of their book, *Having Our Say*.
They sought joy throughout their very
long lives.

studied the emotional impact of neuropeptides, which are released
by neurons to send signals along neural circuits, but are shorter-
chain molecules than neurotransmitters. Pert's study of more than
six dozen neuropeptides suggests a two-way communication link
between the brain and the immune system, with each influencing
the other. She believes that various body organs, including the
gastrointestinal tract, heart, and kidneys, contain receptor
sites for neuropeptides. Brain-stimulated neuropeptide
activity might account for "gut feelings" or "butter-
flies," she believes. Pert theorizes that the emotionally
charged state of being in a creative zone may cause the
brain and immune system to release specialized pep-
tides throughout the body that promote good health.
Creativity, lack of stress, and other hallmarks of a
healthy lifestyle may have contributed to the longevity of the
Delany sisters of New York City, Sadie and Bessie. They lived
well beyond 100 years and chronicled their century of living

together in the best seller *Having Our Say*. They ate plenty of vegetables, remained physically fit all of their lives, and insisted on living as stress-free as possible, to the point of refusing to put a telephone in their home. Analyzing her longevity, Bessie Delany said, "I'd say one of the most important qualities to have is the ability to create joy in your life. I love my garden so much that I would stay out there all day long if Sadie let me. That's what I mean about creating joy in your life. We all have to do it for ourselves."

Sadie said, "Life is short, and it's up to you to make it sweet."

When Bessie died, Sadie struggled with the burden of living alone for the first time. Although Sadie once said, "I would give myself two weeks without Bessie," she outlived her sister by more than three years. In the months after Bessie's death, Sadie coped with the devastating loss by channeling her energy into the creative outlet of writing another book, *On My Own*. Sadie Delany died peacefully in her sleep at 109.

> "Life is short, and it's up to you to make it **SWEET.**"

BRAIN BOOSTER

WRITE A SONG OF LOVE
Make every day Valentine's Day

It's time to expand your mind by singing a song of love.

➲ **HEART AND SOUL**
Chances are you haven't spent much time writing love songs. Yet, putting pen to paper and composing a tune for someone you adore is a wonderfully creative way to stretch your thinking.

Set aside some time, pull up a chair, and start composing.

Have fun as you let your imagination roam and the ideas form. Keep in mind that you don't necessarily have to perform your song. No matter how short or long, your love song is sure to be a great way to put your heart and soul into your Brain Booster.

Need some inspiration? Listen to some of the great love songs of the past. Or ask your loved ones to sing you their favorite love songs.

CHAPTER 13

Being the Boss of Your Brain

INFORMATION OVERLOAD
(Opposite) An overload of information—
which way to go, and why?—can prove
overwhelming and inhibit reason.

ARRIVALS AND DEPARTURES
(Below) Air traffic coordination requires
unflagging attention to a constant flow of
inbound and outbound planes.

F or a job that requires making important decisions under pressure, it's hard to beat air traffic controller.

Controllers must think and act quickly to keep a safe distance between planes that fly up to eight miles a minute. They must base decisions on complicated mental and physical maps in three dimensions, all the while keeping track of instrument readings and verbal and written communications. In difficult or dangerous situations, they have to parse information to focus on the most important details, and then communicate those details to pilots responsible for hundreds of lives. And although the job has its moments of boredom, controllers can never let their guard down. Studies have shown that most air traffic control errors occur during times of low or moderate activity, suggesting the dangers of failure to maintain attention.

Decades ago, when safety experts began developing air traffic control systems, they conducted an experiment simulating plane traffic. At the time, controllers gathered information from many channels at once, including visual data from video display screens, computers, and notepads, and auditory data from earphones and, if necessary, their neighbors in the room. As long as air traffic

TUCSON 2567

TOKYO 6706

DENVE

SIDNEY 10445

Sie

SEOUL

LHASA 7518 MILES

MOSCOW 50

BAN 7973

ATHENS 4111

HA

OSTON

RLIN 3806

remained at a normal level in the simulation, the controllers managed the multiple information streams without incident. If one of the channels broke down, there were others to fall back on. But when the simulation stepped up the traffic and placed more demands on the controllers' attention, their ability to make decisions got worse. Eventually, the controllers lost their cool. They shouted and banged on tables, and pointed and gestured, as they tried to visually communicate with pilots who could not see them. The controllers understood the problems, but they lost the ability to make and communicate smart decisions in a timely manner. No wonder the job can be stressful. There are many variables, including weather, equipment, traffic patterns, and occasional emergencies. Controllers must decide where to pay attention; how the situation may change; and how best to plan options, make choices, and execute the best action.

Eventually,
the air traffic
CONTROLLERS
lost their cool.

CROWDED AIRSPACE
An air traffic control monitor graphically reveals the multiple streams of information that controllers handle every moment.

DECISIONS, DECISIONS

Although the technology of air traffic control has improved and now places fewer demands on controllers' attention, it's still a job, like many, where decision making remains crucial. Angelika Dimoka, director of the Center for Neural Decision Making at Temple University, has scanned the brains of test subjects urged to make difficult decisions based on multiple variables. She chose an airport-related scenario, the purchase of landing slots. Her test subjects bid on slots that could be bought singly or in bundles, in a wide array of combinations. Bidders had to juggle not only

OPTIMUM AIR TRAFFIC
An air traffic controller watches a plane land. Controllers work best when traffic is neither too busy nor too quiet.

[**FACT:** Optimistic older people live longer than pessimists. The average difference is a bit more than seven years.]

prices—they aimed to get the best deals at the lowest cost—but also such variables as weather, the schedule of connecting flights, and passenger load. As the test subjects had to simultaneously weigh more and more information while making decisions, fMRI scans showed heightened activity in their dorsolateral prefrontal cortex. This brain region behind the forehead not only plays a key role in making decisions, but also helps regulate emotions and orchestrates other higher-cognitive functions.

At some point, the addition of extra information acted like the straw that broke the camel's back, causing activity in the dorsolateral prefrontal cortex to drop dramatically. The test subjects couldn't make smart decisions, and they struggled to control their frustration. "With too much information, people's decisions make less and less sense," Dimoka said.

LOSING CONTROL
Activity drops in the prefrontal cortex, home of executive function, when the load of information it must process passes a critical point.

BRAIN BOOSTER

BRAIN GAME NIGHT

Join with friends to take on some brain challenges

Have you got game? You certainly should, it's good for your brain! Try a Brain Game Night to get your game going.

➜ GOOD COMPANY

We know that mental activity is a key ingredient in any brain fitness plan. In addition, staying social has been found to reduce your risk for memory loss over time. What better way to get a good dose of both than having a brain game night with family or friends?

You can play board games, do jigsaw puzzles, or play some old-fashioned charades or Pictionary. This is a time to put away electronics and engage in some real-world interactions. Brain Game Night can be a wonderful time to pass down the rules of some favorite, tried-and-true games, as well as to try some new ones. Or try holding your own college bowl (remember those?) and test your knowledge of facts in all sorts of categories. Enjoy the company while giving your brain a workout!

RELAXATION

Dimoka's findings are bad news for the millions of people continually and intimately connected with information streams, such as the words, numbers, pictures, videos, and more available on the Internet and digital handheld devices. Information overload is a reality that is only likely to get worse.

One way to fight back is to relax the mind.

The brain increases its ability to solve difficult puzzles when it shifts its attention away from a problem and turns inward. This can create a catch-22: If you've ever obsessed about finding the answer to a thorny issue at work or in your academic studies, you probably find it difficult to *force* your mind to relax by *ordering* it to do so. But relaxation often comes quietly on its own when the brain is cut off from an overload of sensations. A pleasant shower or comfortable period of meditation may subtly push the brain into a state that stops the aggravating sensations brought on by too much attentional focus. Psychologist Joydeep Bhattacharya at

CALMING THE STORM
It seems counterintuitive, but quieting the mind, as during a candlelit bath, improves its ability to solve problems.

BRAIN INSIGHT

DREAMING

Do dreams have a purpose? Scientists still aren't sure

Why do we dream? Everyone has dreams, although not everyone remembers them. And it's extremely difficult to keep people from dreaming. Those facts raise the question: What function do dreams serve?

Sigmund Freud, founder of psychoanalysis, believed the brain conjured dreams as a way to access repressed wishes and desires. It's an interesting idea, but a hard one to test in a laboratory: How does one scientifically examine a repressed mental state?

Modern observers are split on the role of dreams. Some, such as

ARE DREAM IMAGES RANDOM?

cognitive scientist Owen Flanagan, author of *Sleep, Dreams and the Evolution of the Conscious Mind*, believe

dreams have no function whatsoever. According to Flanagan, they are a side effect of sleep and its role of recharging the body—"nothing, nada, just noise," Flanagan said.

Others see dreams as the brain's way to process the day's information, including the sorting of data into memory's circuits. In this view, the act of dreaming contributes to the necessary function of forgetting. Still others believe dreams create a safe way for the brain to simulate life's many threats as a therapeutic way to deal with them.

the University of London, says, "That's why so many insights happen during warm showers."

Reaching an Alpha State

Bhattacharya discovered a link between the phenomenon of insight and a steady brain rhythm emanating in the right hemisphere, as registered on an electroencephalograph, or EEG. The EEG records brain activity in the form of electrical impulses. These impulses move through the brain in a variety of frequency ranges, like radio stations arrayed throughout the AM and FM radio bands. The lowest frequency, seen in delta waves, is most commonly found in brains in a state of deep sleep. In ascending order above the delta waves are theta waves, which occur during prayer, daydreaming, and some sleep stages; alpha waves, associated with feelings of calm and control; beta waves, common in active mental states such as analyzing problems and making decisions; and gamma waves, which occur all the time in nearly all brain states and may play a role in synthesizing various brain functions. What Bhattacharya found is that the onset of alpha waves in the right-hand lobes heralds the *aha!* moment when the brain solves a nagging problem. His tests have shown that people who cannot reach a threshold level of alpha waves cannot solve tricky word problems even when given heavy hints.

Small wonder, then, that in a German study involving word puzzles that required a flash of insight to solve, subjects who reported feeling happy—the positive, calm mood typical of alpha waves—outperformed those who reported negative moods. Cognitive neuroscientist Mark Beeman at Northwestern University even found that people performed better at solving insight puzzles after watching a

HAVING A BRAIN WAVE
Brain waves of happy people differ from those in dark or tense moods and encourage insightful thoughts.

video clip of comedian Robin Williams, which apparently lightened their mood and helped them relax. Beeman has linked insights to the relaxed period typically experienced in the first few moments after waking up. In its drowsy, discombobulated state, the morning brain is ideally suited for solving mental puzzles by not actively focusing on them.

This suggests a practical way to try to trick your brain into doing its best work. If your mornings typically are overloaded with tasks to get done before work or school, try setting your alarm clock to give yourself just a few minutes of quiet time before you have to begin your responsibilities. When the alarm bell rings, hit the snooze bar but don't go back to sleep. Try thinking in a half-awake state.

> The morning brain is ideally suited for solving mental **PUZZLES.**

WAKE UP TO INSIGHT
When is the best time for insight? Perhaps the very first moment of the day, when the brain is half asleep.

BRAIN BOOSTER

PRACTICE MINDFULNESS
Learn to live in the moment

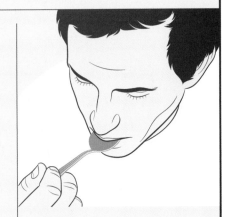

As we rush through our day, we often miss important details and meaningful moments. All this busy-ness takes a toll on our brain health. Wouldn't it be nice if we could just slow down, learn to be more focused, and give more attention to what we are doing?

➲ ACTIVE MEDITATION
The practice of mindfulness asks us to do just that. Becoming more mindful simply requires us to be more in the moment of our experience. Doing so regularly helps

us build focus and concentration, provides stress relief, and helps us capture more important moments that we might otherwise miss. In fact, mindfulness is an active meditation practice that carries the same benefits as meditation for our everyday intellectual functioning and long-term brain health.

➲ PICK A TARGET
Begin to practice mindfulness by targeting certain times or actions. Become more aware through all your senses of something in your daily life, such as the first bite of

each meal or your daily walk to work. Becoming more mindful will help both your mind and your spirit.

TAKING CONTROL

Making good decisions and taking control of your mind are important skills. Fortunately, your brain's cognitive control center, the prefrontal cortex, is not hard-wired. You have a strong measure of control over what you think, and what you think about it. In short, you can be the boss of your own brain.

The Power of Choice
Your ability to make choices is good for your health. People who are cared for by others often show concrete improvement if they are given the opportunity to make decisions affecting their lives.

[**FACT:** Charitable actions increase levels of happiness. They increase a sense of purpose and fulfillment.]

BRAIN BOOSTER

FIVE USES FOR MASKING TAPE

Think outside the box by finding new uses for familiar items

One measure of intellectual nimbleness is our ability to solve problems by thinking creatively, nimbly, and out of the box. So here's a little problem for you: What can you do with masking tape?

STRIVE FOR FIVE

Think of at least five uses for the tape. Clearly, masking tape can attach one object to another—can

you think of five other ways to employ it? Or even a few more?

If you like this exercise, try thinking of the many ways you can use the following household items:

➔ Paper clip

➔ Lemons

➔ Paintbrush

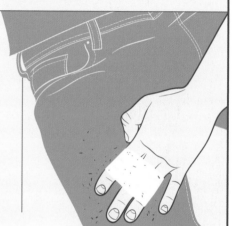

SUNNY BREAKFAST
Increasing your propensity toward optimism might begin with eating well, such as fresh berries, fruits, and muesli.

Even relatively insignificant decisions, such as which shirt to wear or when to eat, boost the health of residents in nursing homes and other care facilities. And people thrust into traumatic situations, such as a bad accident or a natural disaster, usually have less significant suffering in the long run if they made decisions at the time of the trauma and acted on them, such as the choice to comfort victims.

You can exercise control not only over how to act, but also about how to think and feel. If you choose to have positive feelings and attitudes, you'll be doing your health a favor.

Scientists at the Wageningen University in the Netherlands interviewed nearly 2,000 elderly men and women and classified them as optimists or pessimists by whether they agreed with statements such as "I still have many goals to strive for." The researchers followed up with their interviewees nine years later. Those who had expressed optimism in the initial interviews had far lower death rates than their more pessimistic peers—63 percent lower among the men, and 35 percent lower among the women.

The Dutch study controlled for other factors that could have influenced the subjects' longevity. These included whether the interviewees smoked or drank alcohol, as well as their weight, diet, and amount of physical activity. Researchers found a strong correlation between optimism and health-promoting behavior, such as eating and exercising well. It was as if the test subjects who felt good about their futures worked to ensure they would be there to enjoy them. Perhaps optimism increases the will to live. Another theory suggests that greater social interaction of optimists, as opposed to pessimists who wish to be left alone, promotes longevity by lowering levels of the stress hormone cortisol. The payoff at the end of life, according to University of California researchers: Optimists live about seven and a half years longer than pessimists.

CHEERS!
Gathering with friends for food and fun promotes a more positive take on life—and appears to extend it, too.

SECURE AT ANY AGE
Scientific studies indicate awareness of age affects cognitive performance. But if age doesn't define you, you don't let it rule you.

The Rewards of Positive Thinking

But optimists don't have to wait until old age to enjoy benefits. Being optimistic brings immediate returns. According to researchers at Carnegie Mellon University in Pittsburgh, optimism strengthens the ability of the body's immune system to fight off disease and also offers protection against the negative effects of stress. Other studies have shown that optimists suffer less chronic pain and have fewer disabilities than pessimists.

A general sense of well-being also improves cognitive function. Attitudes sometimes can become self-fulfilling prophecies. For example, if you believe you will do well on a test, you will perform better than if you believe you will do poorly. This was demonstrated by a North Carolina State University study of adults ages 60 to 82. The researchers gave the same mathematical and memory tests to the entire group, but before beginning, they dropped hints among members of one subset that their age might negatively affect their performance: They said the test measured how age

[FACT: Memories of an experience rely on the moment of peak intensity and the final moment. **]**

affected memory, and asked them to write their age just before taking the test. Group members reminded of their age and the likelihood of it affecting test results performed worse than those who simply took the test. The difference was more pronounced for the youngest members of the group, as well as those who had the highest education levels. The researchers speculated that the oldest test subjects showed less impact from the experimental treatment because they felt secure in who they were and cared less how others defined them.

These findings prove true the words of the Stoic Greek philosopher Epictetus, who lived nearly 2,000 years ago: "Men are disturbed not by things but by the views which they take of them," he said. But if you're not an optimist and want to become one, what can you do? Changing a core component of one's personality isn't as easy as flipping a switch.

Attitudes sometimes can become **SELF-FULFILLING** prophecies.

BRAIN INSIGHT

GOING TO THE NEXT LEVEL
Constant challenge will keep you on top of your game

If you want to improve a skill such as playing guitar, choose to get out of your comfort zone.

Most practiced physical actions, such as hitting a golf ball or shooting a free throw, occur as the brain is in or near a state resembling autopilot. The first time you shot a free throw, fingered the notes in a G chord, or swung a seven iron, you probably used your frontal lobes to concentrate on the required motions. As you made mistakes, you kept your level of concentration and made adjustments. But at some point, you likely became satisfied, and your improvement stopped. The neural processes associated with the skill then migrated from the front of the brain to the back, to the cerebellum.

To achieve your potential, move the skill back up front, to the frontal lobes. Try challenging yourself. If you're a musician, practice the toughest part of a song until you've mastered it. If you play sports, try to swish those free throws or drop your tee shot into a small circle. Analyze the motions that comprise the skill and adjust. And don't just do it one day. True experts practice both deliberately and continually.

PRACTICE ISN'T ENOUGH.

Neural pathways fire more easily after they have been fired often because synaptic connections grow strong for routines. So, if you have lived for years reacting with anxiety, stress, doubt, and cynicism to whatever comes your way, your neural pathways have figuratively become four-lane interstate highways for negative mental states.

COGNITIVE PRINCIPLES

The tools of cognitive therapy, introduced in Chapter 12, can help switch attitudes from negative to positive by injecting the concept of choice, or decision making, into mental states. Cognitive therapy rests on a foundation of three principles. First is to agree with Epictetus: The way you choose to view events in your life is crucial to your mental states. Second is the close relationship between moods and thoughts: Altering one alters the other. And

TAKE YOUR PICK
Cognitive therapy posits that you can control how you view an event, as positive or negative, for example.

third is that by manipulating thoughts, which can be managed to a degree, you can manipulate your moods.

The First Principle

The first principle suggests that you have a choice in how to view what happens to you. Although it may not seem true at times, it always is. Thus, when something bad happens to you, you can choose to try to recast it by looking at it in a new way that emphasizes potential good. If you're underperform-

ing at work, it might be because you devote so much time to family, children, church, or something you rank even more important. If you lose your job, it might be the opportunity to seek a new career that you have wondered about, but never had the courage (or time) to explore. If you cannot afford an expensive vacation far away, you might learn to better appreciate the attractions in your own county or state. And if your car needs to be in the repair shop for a couple of weeks, you might discover that you like to bike, walk, or carpool. This is not the same as being a Pollyanna. Sometimes there is no bright side. But there are always other perspectives, and it's beneficial to seek them out.

The Second Principle

The second principle probably calls to mind examples from your own life. If you've been in a bad mood, you likely recalled memories of bad things that happened in your life. Or, if you get a piece of bad news, such as a phone call telling you of a loved one who has been hospitalized, your mood probably went dark in a hurry. That bad mood may have triggered more negative thoughts, because moods and thoughts reinforce each other, like a feedback loop in an amplifier. For example, if you think you performed poorly on a college exam, you might feel depressed or angry. That might trigger

THE BRIGHT SIDE
Every event has two sides. A downturn at work may free you for more time with family, for example.

PERSPECTIVE
Ever struggle with an exam? Sure.
But it's only a test. Fight the temptation
to inflate small setbacks into crises.

thoughts that you don't belong in a particular college class, or that you're not as smart as your classmates. That could eventually lead to thoughts such as, "I'm no good at anything." That blanket statement is a long way from getting a less-than-desired grade on a single test, but that's a common neural pathway that some brains have established over time.

The Third Principle

The third principle is the key to healthy mental states. Recasting how you think about something sets off a new chain of thought–mood–thought reinforcement. If you get a bad grade, for example, don't think, "I'm stupid." Instead, embrace the perspective, "Everyone makes mistakes. Everyone bombs a test once in a while."

BRAIN BOOSTER

HONORABLE OPPOSITION

Shake up your mental routine by taking a fresh point of view

This tip asks you to open your mind. Often we fall into the rut of listening only to information and opinions that affirm the beliefs we already hold, be they in our political, philosophical, or personal lives. Listening to the opposite point of view can help us to rethink our positions (though not necessarily change them!), giving us a chance to engage our minds in a way we may not have done in quite a while and perhaps even see things from another's point of view.

LEAVE THE COMFORT ZONE
Spend some time today tuning in to TV or radio stations or reading articles that hold the opposite point of view from your own. Try talking about what you read with friends or family, seeing if you can even hold the counter position in your discussions.

Negative thoughts to be avoided arise in common categories. These include:

▶ Black-and-white thinking. Few things are wholly good or bad, but it can be easy to see them that way. And no relationship is without occasional problems.

▶ Exaggerating and overgeneralizing, which are similar to black-and-white thinking. Don't say, "I never have any fun," or "You never listen to me."

▶ Predicting worst-case scenarios that aren't likely to come true. Don't misinterpret a sneeze as anything more than a sneeze, unless you really are sick. Don't believe one mistake will forever change your relationships.

▶ Rationalizing good things that happen as if they weren't truly good. Don't try to read other people's minds when they interact with you, looking for selfish motives for good deeds. Accept good deeds with good cheer.

▶ Personalizing problems that aren't the fault of any one individual. Nobody is the center of the universe.

BLACK-AND-WHITE THINKING
Feedback loops of negativity in the brain can polarize experiences. Few things are entirely good or bad. See the gray.

Rules of Perspective

Cognitive therapist Gillian Butler and psychiatrist Tony Hope, authors of *Managing Your Mind: The Mental Fitness Guide,* offer four "rules of perspective" to help you skirt destructive thoughts that set off the feedback loop of negativity. First is the so-called "100-year rule." When something bad happens, ask yourself whether it will matter in a century. The exercise forces the new perspective of seeing events from a great distance—which almost always makes them look small.

Second is the "measuring rod rule," which invites you to ask yourself whether something bad in your life truly is the most important thing in your life. So what if you wrecked your car—you can get another one, and you have other things that are more important.

THE BIG PICTURE
Recasting events into proper perspective may be as easy as seeing them on a sunny day, or from the vantage point of great distance or time.

Third is the "middle of the night" rule. It suggests that dark moods and thoughts flourish in the nighttime, but the clarity of daylight often brings another view.

And the final rule is the "statute of limitations." Don't worry about things long after they could possibly continue to have substantial impact. Stop punishing yourself. One way to let go of old problems is to reimagine them as if they belonged to somebody else.

RECASTING MEMORIES

This ability to choose affects not only the brain's view of what's happening now, but also how the brain handles memories. Even old memories can be recast in a more positive light.

When a memory forms, your brain stores some significant details and trashes the rest. Along with those details, emotional colors are stored as well. Thus, your memories of a childhood picnic may include not only where your family gathered and what they ate, but also how you felt at the time.

Memories are fluid, not fixed. When you recall something from long-term memory, your brain reconstructs the memory from scattered neural circuits associated with sensations and facts. That memory, held anew in the brain, then gets associated with whatever else resides in your mind at the same time. Old memories are mixed with new thoughts. When the memory returns to long-term storage, the brain sends with it any new thoughts that it held at the same time. These new associations adhere to the memory. The next time the brain recalls the original memory, the added details are retrieved as well; the brain treats them all as if they were part of the same memory file. Thus, many things you believe you know for certain likely turn out to be at least partly false upon examination. That's why the

REFRAME DARK THOUGHTS
Fixating on a negative memory only implants it more concretely. Recast the memory and it changes as it returns to storage.

[**FACT**: Experiences make people happier than possessions. Memories last, while the thrill of ownership fades.]

BRAIN BOOSTER

WHAT'S IN THE CLOUDS?

A childhood pastime is still enjoyable and good for your brain, too

Remember this game from childhood? It's still fun, and even offers your brain a bit of recharge by helping you to flex your abstract reasoning skills.

LOOKING UP

Go outside on a partly cloudy (or partly sunny) day. Pick a nice spot where you have a good view of the sky and passing clouds. Next, take some time to see how many different things you can find in the clouds. You can look for shapes, objects, faces, animals, or even clouds that remind you of someone you know. Challenge yourself to find new things in the same formation as the clouds shift over time.

Want to make it more fun? Go ahead and do it with someone else.

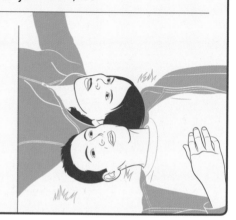

power of suggestion can change memories or even create false ones, and why some eyewitnesses crumble under cross-examination in court or provide credible testimony that later proves to be mistaken.

If you create negative mental states such as sadness or anxiety whenever you call up a memory from long-term storage, those dark feelings slowly become glued into the memory. For example, if recalling a date in high school leaves you sad, the neural circuits encoding that sadness grow stronger. Do it often enough, and you will physically change the power of the synaptic connections in your neural circuits.

Change Your Wiring

Fortunately, deciding to rewire your brain in a more positive way works just as well. It won't happen overnight. Instead, you can gradually replace negative memory associations with positive ones by choosing to bring good things to mind when you call up bad memories. If a childhood memory makes you feel unloved, focus on the love around you today. If a memory brings on feelings of inadequacy, think about something you're proud to have accomplished, and let it sink in. Then, over the next hour or so, try to repeat the connection between positive associations and the original memory. Research by behavioral neuroscientist Marie Monfils at the University of Texas suggests that in the moments after recalling a memory, the brain has greater power to change negative ones than positive ones.

In addition to thinking good thoughts, it helps to overtly state positive things to yourself out loud or in your mind. You don't have to be the goofy, saccharine character Stuart Smalley from *Saturday Night Live* ("I'm good enough. I'm smart enough. And doggone it, people like me."), but it wouldn't hurt to emulate Fred Rogers, the soft-spoken educator and Presbyterian minister beloved by two generations of children for his years on the Public Broadcasting Service program *Mister Rogers' Neighborhood*. He nurtured self-worth, telling children, "You always make it special for me by just your being you. I like you just the way you are. You know that, don't you?" And then he told children he would see them the next day, a promise that no matter what, his relationship with them would continue.

GOOD MEMORIES CAST OUT BAD
(Above) Deliberately recalling good times as bad memories arise can rewire the original memory. Love does conquer all.

HELLO, NEIGHBOR
(Left) "I like you just the way you are," said Fred Rogers, with toy trolley and King Friday XIII, as he cultivated self-worth among children.

CHAPTER 14

Whole Brain Health

Much of the advice of this book has focused on specific tasks or challenges you can use to improve the health of your brain or those of your loved ones. These range from learning to speak a second language or play a musical instrument, to training your memory with the method of loci, to doing word and number puzzles. Although these exercises all have value, research suggests they may not be as important as the simple, everyday care and feeding of body and brain through proper diet, exercise, sleep, and protective measures against brain injury. These may seem like small steps. But they add up. Nothing is better for your long-term brain health than having a strong body shaped by eating the right foods, following a regular exercise routine, and otherwise ensuring that your brain gets what it needs and avoids what it doesn't. Specific nutrients are absolutely key to keeping the brain in good shape, but too much of a good thing is bad. A balanced diet should include a wide variety of foods yet limit sugar, caffeine, alcohol, and other substances beneficial in small amounts but harmful in large ones.

FEED YOUR HEAD

The brain is a furnace burning energy, consuming about a quarter of all the body's blood sugar and oxygen. Yet the brain has no way to store extra fuel when supplies run low. Without proper nutrition and ample water, the brain grows sluggish and eventually begins to shut down.

FRUIT AND VEG
(Opposite) A strong brain starts with a healthy body, built on a variety of foods (right), especially fruits and vegetables of many colors.

HEALTHY LIVING
(Below) No matter your age, it's not too late to sharpen your brain by exercising, getting proper sleep, and avoiding harmful habits.

WAKE-UP CALL
Starting the day with the right kind of meal (right) gives the brain the glucose it needs for optimal functioning.

WAKE-UP CALL
Starting the day with the right kind of meal (right) gives the brain the glucose it needs for optimal functioning.

The Pros and Cons of Glucose

The brain's main fuel is glucose, also known as blood sugar. Not enough glucose in the bloodstream impairs mental focus, the ability to learn new information, and the ability to retain it. So, your mother was right—you should eat a good breakfast before heading to school in order to raise your glucose level. But if your breakfast, day after day, contains abundant sugar on your cereal or in your coffee, your body will compensate for the overdose by pumping out more insulin. Too much in the blood stream subjects the brain to oxidative stress and inflammation, aging the brain prematurely. Meanwhile, elevated glucose levels not only add to the likelihood of increased body fat, but may

also shrink the hippocampus, which regulates the functions of memory. According to recent research at Columbia University Medical Center, even moderately high levels of blood sugar can reduce blood flow to the hippocampus and contribute to cognitive deficiencies.

The calorie-rich lifestyle in the United States adds not only to the growing incidence of obesity but probably also to the increase in mental disorders in old age, when the brain loses some of its ability to regulate glucose levels. That's bad news for those with a Santa Claus-like physique. Belly fat doesn't

HOLD THE FRIES
Body fat, encouraged by a diet rich in calories such as fried foods, appears to be linked with the onset of dementia.

[**FACT**: Every year the average American eats 66 pounds of refined sugar, and nearly as much corn-based sweetener.]

just benignly jiggle; it actively releases streams of damaging inflammatory cells and hormones into the bloodstream. A 2008 study by Kaiser Permanente in California indicated that these fat-brewed chemicals play a role in the onset of some dementias. The Kaiser Permanente researchers dug into the medical records of people who were in their 40s in the 1960s and 1970s, and then tracked their health three decades later. In their 70s, at the time of the follow-up, people in the original group who had large waistlines and were obese, an indicator of the presence of abdominal fat, were more than three times as likely to have been diagnosed with dementia than those who had maintained a slim physique.

READ THE LABEL
Check the labels on food products. Your body and brain not only need the right calories, but also the right nutrients.

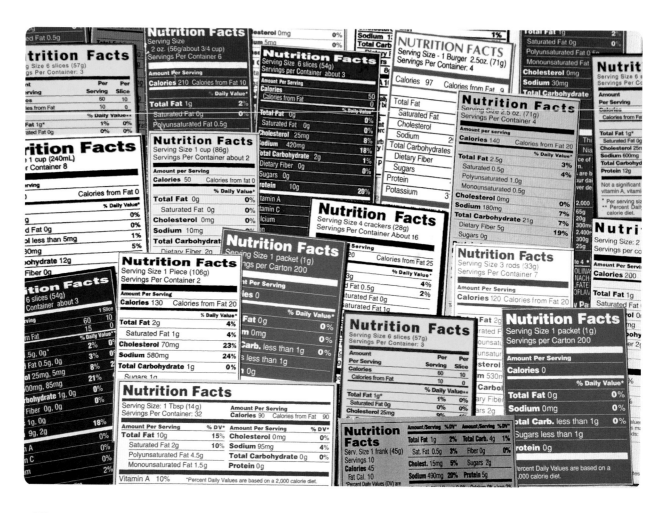

BRAIN BOOSTER

ALCOHOL CHECK

Drinking can make it harder for you to learn and remember new facts

At a family reunion or business event, and want to make sure you remember new names and faces? Try limiting how much alcohol you drink.

➲ **THINK BEFORE YOU DRINK**
Alcohol is known to impair the ability to learn new information. In addition, as you grow older, you become more vulnerable to the effects of substances like alcohol,

because your body doesn't process such substances as quickly as when you were younger.

Keep an eye on how well you balance your alcohol intake, especially at times when remembering new information, such as names, is critical. Increase your awareness of how drinking may be making it harder for you to remember, and control your consumption.

DIET

You should consume not only the proper amount of calories, but also get the right kind. Nutrients provide the molecular building blocks to create and replenish the brain's stocks of neurotransmitters, the chemicals that carry electrical signals between neurons. Deficiencies can cause mood changes, confusion, memory loss, and other mental disturbances. At times, mental problems that appear to be associated with dementia or other diseases are merely temporary manifestations of poor diet or lack of proper blood circulation.

Consider mood. The neurotransmitter serotonin prompts feelings of serenity and fights depression, anxiety, and inability to sleep. Eating carbohydrates such as pasta causes an amino acid called tryptophan, which the body needs to make serotonin, to enter the bloodstream via the gastrointestinal tract. Failing to get enough tryptophan into the

> You should not only consume the proper amount of **CALORIES,** but also get the right kind.

SUPER LUNCH
A lunch of whole-grain bagel, sliced low-fat turkey breast, fruits, and vegetables meets nutritional guidelines.

bloodstream can lower mood significantly, and can contribute to chronic depression if the condition persists. Equally crucial to keeping mood elevated are vitamins and minerals. Psychiatric patients often have lowered levels of vitamin C and B-complex vitamins, including folic acid, which the body uses to make oxygen-carrying red blood cells.

Eating for Health

Diets that support overall health and are good for your heart will also be good for your brain. They would include the following practices:

▶ **Eating a variety of foods to cover the spectrum of nutrients.**
There is no one "perfect" food. Perfection comes from eating many kinds of foods. Consider a "Mediterranean diet"—with a

focus on plant-based foods, fish and poultry, olive or canola oils instead of butter, and herbs and spices instead of salt. Try to cover half of your plate at every meal with vegetables of different colors to get not only fiber but also vitamins and minerals. Also eat fruits and nuts, the latter of which provide a good source of protein. Meat has plenty of protein, but like sugar, it should be eaten in small amounts—or avoided entirely, if you can manage to become a vegetarian. A diet rich in meat, particularly fatty red meat, has been linked in multiple studies to higher incidence of heart disease and cancer.

▶ **Eating foods rich in antioxidants.** These chemicals soak up bandit molecules called free radicals. Natural by-products of oxidation, the body's metabolism of oxygen, free radicals have at least one unpaired electron in the shells of their atoms. This creates an imbalance in electrical charge. Free radicals seek to achieve balance by stealing electrons from other molecules. If they grab electrons from neurons, the brain cells typically suffer DNA or other cellular

> Try to cover half of your plate at every meal with **VEGETABLES** of different colors.

ALLERGENS
Know your food. Soybeans and tofu (left) provide protein but are also common allergens.

FISH IS FINE
Fish oil, available in capsules (above), appears to promote emotional health. The fish-loving people of Iceland, below, have little depression.

damage but don't die. Damage to neural DNA, if widespread, has been linked to a host of brain disorders, including dementia.

Antioxidants act like an open bank vault offering free electrons for the roving antioxidants. Free radicals steal ample and easily available electrons from antioxidants in the bloodstream instead of targeting neural tissues. Good sources of antioxidants include blueberries, blackberries, and other complex berries, walnuts, artichokes, cranberries, and coffee.

▶ **Restricting the intake of sugar.** Especially try to skip the refined kind, found abundantly in widely advertised sugary drinks, as well as in cookies and cakes.

BRAIN INSIGHT

THE TEMPERATE LIFE

The benefits of a moderate diet have been known for centuries

ALVISE "LUIGI" CORNARO

In middle age, Venetian nobleman Alvise "Luigi" Cornaro faced the prospect of an early death because of his poor health. He examined his life and blamed his gluttony and hedonistic lifestyle. So, on his doctor's advice, he set about making changes.

Cornaro reduced his diet to bread, eggs in broth, a little meat, and new wine. His health returned so completely that he lived to be 98, dying in 1566.

When Cornaro was 83, friends urged him to record his story, not only because he had lived so long, but also because he maintained mental clarity. Cornaro's book, *Discorsi della Vita Sobria (Discourses on the Sober Life),* became a Renaissance best seller all over Europe, not only in his own day but also in the years that followed. Printers produced dozens of editions in England in the 18th and 19th centuries, and the book still goes through reprints in the United States.

Readers found much common sense in Cornaro's cardinal rule of temperance: "Whosoever wishes to eat much must eat little," meaning that abstaining from gluttony promotes longevity. Modern science has added its own voice in support of Cornaro's enthusiasm for eating less with studies linking severely reduced caloric intake to greater longevity in rats.

▶ **Eating the right kinds of carbohydrates.** Fruits, vegetables, and whole grains—as opposed to the processed grain flour of many commercially baked breads—provide carbohydrates and fiber without excess calories. Fiber helps the body regulate blood sugar levels and reduces cravings for fattier foods.

▶ **Drinking very moderate amounts of caffeine and alcohol.** Caffeine, found in coffee, cocoa, tea, cola, and chocolate, stimulates the brain. Americans consume about 200 milligrams a day, or roughly the equivalent of about one to two cups of coffee. Caffeine works by blocking the neurotransmitter adenosine, which induces sedation and eases pain and anxiety. By dampening adenosine, caffeine not only encourages the jitters but also raises a sense of alertness by arousing the cerebral cortex. In small amounts, such as two cups of coffee or less taken in the morning, caffeine accelerates thinking, boosts energy levels, and briefly

BRAIN BOOSTER

BE MINDFUL OF YOUR CAFFEINE
A little caffeine boost goes a long way

How much caffeine do you use each day? Caffeine is a stimulant, which in modest amounts can boost alertness and enhance learning and memory. However, too much caffeine can have the opposite effect, lowering memory performance as it leaves us jittery, and unable to focus and learn.

➡ Caffeine sources in our diet include coffee, black or green tea, caffeinated sodas, and chocolate. The recent popularity of energy drinks and caffeine as an additive has made us all more vulnerable to getting higher doses of caffeine in our diet than we might have intended.

➡ Caffeine affects each of us differently. Spend some time this week figuring out where you get your caffeine (don't forget the chocolate!), and how to best balance your use of it.

increases physical performance. It may even lower depression enough to lessen suicide levels. Too much caffeine, however, raises stress and blood pressure levels and interferes with sleep, which the brain needs to rejuvenate itself.

Likewise, a little bit of alcohol, such as one glass once in a while in the evening, has been shown to have health benefits, but alcohol is toxic to brain functions—hence the origin of the word *intoxication*. More than a little bit in the short run interferes with basic cognitive functions, such as memory, by blocking neural firing and the flow of oxygen, and in the long run can shrink the brain and also damage the liver in ways that affect mood, sleep, and attention span. Yet, alcohol in small amounts is believed to encourage the body to reduce the concentration of bad forms of cholesterol in the

JUMPIN' JAVA
A cup or so of coffee a day is great, as it stimulates the brain. Too much—no surprise here—causes harmful overstimulation.

bloodstream. If you're going to drink alcohol, try limiting your-self to a glass of red wine with dinner. Red wine contains resvera-trol, an antioxidant and anti-inflammatory chemical.

▶ **Drinking plenty of water.** The brain is 80 percent water, and it needs to stay wet. Dehydration impairs mental function, and in extreme cases, can cause a person to hallucinate or even die. Ohio University researchers found that mental functions become compromised long before dehydration becomes severe. They subjected healthy men and women in their 60s to tests of brain functions, including examinations of memory, eye-hand coordination, and attention. They also gathered data on test

[FACT: International studies show that waist circumfer-ence is a good indicator of cardiovascular health. **]**

GOOD ALL AROUND
(Opposite) Working your body also works your brain by requiring it to fire neural networks in tandem and sequence.

subjects' hydration levels. Those whose bodies contained a proper amount of water posted significantly higher scores on the cognitive tests.

▶ **Swallowing a daily multivitamin and mineral supplement.** B-complex vitamins are crucial for brain health, and although you likely will get all the vitamins you need in a balanced, vegetable-rich diet, it doesn't hurt to take out a little dietary insurance.

▶ **Taking omega-3 fatty acids regularly.** These acids, also called DHA (docosahexaenoic acid) and EPA (eicosapentaenoic acid), occur naturally in fish oil; you can get them by eating the fish themselves, or by taking them as pill supplements containing 500 milligrams of DHA and EPA. Vegetarians can skip the fish oil and substitute flaxseed oil, either in pill form or as a salad dressing.

The brain draws upon these fatty acids to grow neurons and elevate mood. Evidence of the link between eating fish and feeling contented comes from Iceland. Residents of that North Atlantic island country eat five times as much seafood each year as Americans, yet despite Iceland's long, dark winters, its people suffer extremely low rates of depression. Some research suggests benefits from omega-3s in fighting against dementia.

Doctors often prescribe
EXERCISE
as part of the therapy for patients with depression.

EXERCISE—AND REST

Regular exercise is good not only for the heart and muscles, but also for the brain. Movement of arms, legs, trunk, and head occurs because of coordinated firing of neural networks in the brain's motor cortex, cerebellum, and other regions. And anything that increases blood flow to the brain, such as a heart-stimulating run or weight lifting in the gym, improves every brain function because all neurons devour oxygen. Other brain benefits of exercise include greater control of blood sugar levels, which damage blood vessels in the brain when they're too high, and stronger heart muscle to pump blood more efficiently. And, of course, vigorous exercise encourages deep, natural sleep.

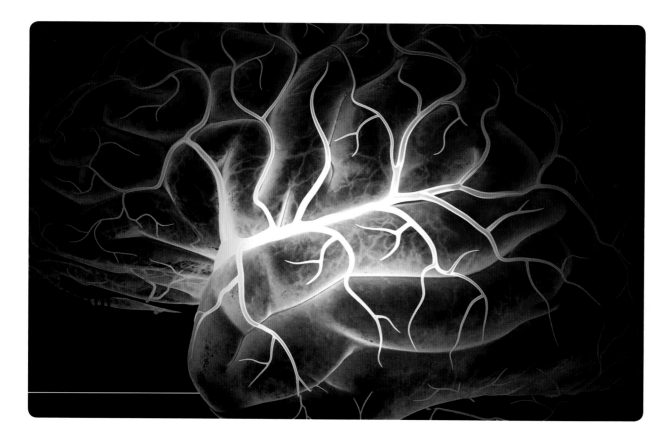

VITAL VESSELS
A lateral brain view reveals the middle cerebral artery. A study of Japanese Americans suggests exercise, which boosts blood to the brain, reduces dementia risk.

Physical exercise has also been linked to the growth of new cells, blood vessels, and neural connections in the brain. It boosts mood, so much so that doctors often prescribe exercise as part of the therapy for patients with depression. And it guards against brain shrinkage among the elderly.

The scientific studies that back up those conclusions are growing, and becoming more expansive every day. A study of 1,740 people by the Group Health Cooperative in Seattle found that those in the group who did some form of exercise at least three times a week cut their risk for dementia by 38 percent compared to their sedentary peers. A Hawaiian study of more than 2,220 Japanese Americans age 71 and older revealed that those who exercised the most over a six-year period halved their risk of developing dementia. A 1994 Harvard study concluded that men who burned more than 2,500 calories a day in aerobic exercise were substantially less likely to develop clinical depression than men who were less active. And in another study, published in 2007 by a University of Illinois research team, physically fit third and fifth graders at four elementary schools academically outperformed their peers who were not physically fit. Those results, found in examining 239 children, held true regardless of the pupils' race, sex, or socioeconomic background.

Get Your Heart and Arms Pumping

Good forms of physical exercise include ones that work your heart and lungs, as well as those that make your large muscle tissues burn with exertion. Aerobic exercise, such as jogging or swimming, get the heart pumping and growing stronger. But weight-bearing exercises, such as pressing iron at the gym, also are important, and particularly so as the body and brain grow older. Greater strength and flexibility in the limbs and trunk, along with improved balance, help prevent the devastating falls common with the elderly.

SWIMMING
It's a low-impact exercise that nevertheless gets the heart pumping and the muscles loose and warm.

BRAIN BOOSTER

GET PHYSICAL!
Simple aerobic exercise does wonders for your brain

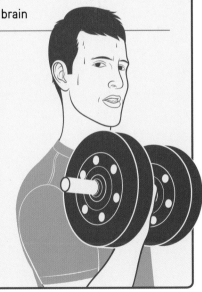

It's time to try one of the most "tried-and-true" things you can do to boost your brain's well-being—aerobic exercise. Recent research shows that regular aerobic exercise can:

➲ Improve your memory and other skills, such as attention, processing speed, and executive control, which matter to daily intellectual performance.

➲ Significantly decrease your risk for dementia.

➲ Significantly reduce your risk for or be an important part of managing medical conditions, such as obesity, diabetes, and hypertension.

Start today on the road to better brain health by boosting your exercise time. Get at least 30 minutes of exercise several days a week. Even brisk walking is beneficial to brain health. Make it easier to stick with your exercise plan by penciling in time to work out, finding an exercise buddy, or setting clear exercise goals with built-in rewards.

The best workout for you is one that you'll enjoy doing again and again, because it has to be part of a continuing routine. The exercise should challenge your body, but not pose a threat to it. And it should challenge your brain; new forms of exercise, or new twists on old ones, provide the novelty that helps foster and strengthen neural connections.

STROKE

It's not enough to eat well and exercise. Keeping your brain healthy requires that you keep it safe from injury. Two of the most common brain hazards are stroke and concussion.

Stroke suddenly restricts blood flow in the vessels leading to the brain, or in the brain itself. When brain cells are cut off from the oxygen in red blood cells, they die in a few minutes. Ischemic strokes involve blockage of blood vessels servicing a particular part of the brain. This can occur through formation of a blood clot in the brain, or by a clot traveling to the brain after forming in another part of the body, breaking free, and traveling through the bloodstream. Another type of stroke, called hemorrhagic, occurs when a blood vessel breaks and fills a brain region with blood.

Strokes are all too common. They are the fourth leading cause of death in the United States and the primary cause of disability. The types of brain damage caused by localized strokes depend upon the function of the affected neural networks. Strokes in the motor control regions restrict motion. Strokes in language-processing regions affect production and understanding of speech and writing. Strokes can also affect memory, mood, analytical abilities, and other cognitive functions. In vital areas such as the brain stem, they can swiftly kill.

LIFELONG FITNESS
(Opposite) A 100-year-old water-skis near his home in Washington State. The best exercises are ones you'll want to do again and again.

Keeping your brain healthy requires that you keep it **SAFE** from injury.

[**FACT**: Someone in the United States has a stroke every 40 seconds. About 28 percent of strokes are fatal.]

Treating and Preventing Strokes

Ischemic strokes usually respond well to treatment if given within three hours of suffering an attack. Administration of a drug called tPA, for tissue plasminogen activator, can help save brain tissue within that three-hour window. (Hemorrhagic strokes, on the other hand, might be made worse by tPA; doctors need to establish the kind of stroke before treatment.) For ischemic strokes, it's important to recognize stroke risk factors and indicators of stroke's onset to get treatment within that 180-minute window. Quicker response is even better. According to a study published in 2010 in the British journal *Lancet*, patients given blood-thinning tPA within 90 minutes of a stroke were more than twice as likely to have a good recovery than those who did not receive the medication.

GRIM CONTRAST
A light micrograph of a section of the cerebellum shows tissue killed by stroke (left) and healthy tissue (right).

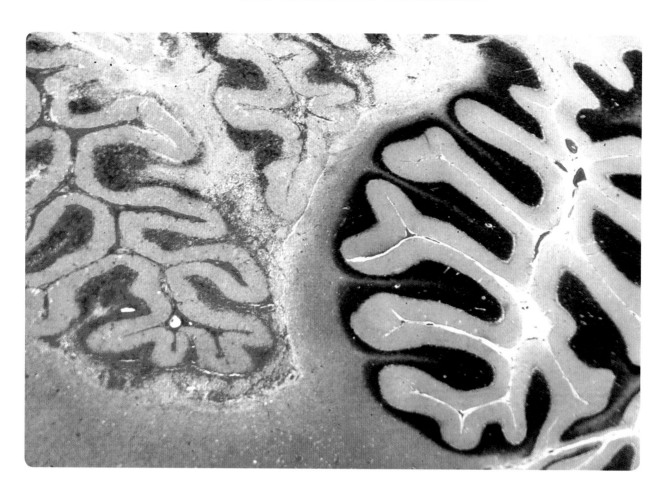

BRAIN BOOSTER

IS IT A STROKE?

This simple test can help you detect the warning signs

Stroke is a major cause of brain injury, the leading cause of adult disability, and the third leading cause of death in the United States. Recently, there have been tremendous advances in our ability to both prevent and treat for stroke. But you have to know what to look for and be ready to act quickly. I find that few folks really know the signs of a stroke—so let's learn them! This simple three-step test, developed by researchers, is highly effective in identifying a stroke. If you suspect that someone you know is having a stroke, try the following three things. If the person fails any of them, get to the ER as quickly as possible for an evaluation:

STEP 1: Smile
Ask the person to smile. Look for asymmetry (unevenness) in his or her expression. (For example, check to see if one corner of the mouth droops.)

STEP 2: Raise both arms
Ask the person to raise both arms. Look for asymmetry in the height of the hands.

STEP 3: Repeat a Simple Sentence
Ask the person to repeat a simple sentence, such as "No ifs, ands, or buts." Check for slurring or other disruption of speech.

Want to know more? Visit the National Stroke Association's website at *www.stroke.org.*

STEP 1

STEP 2

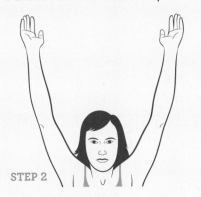

STEP 3

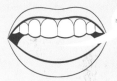

No ifs, ands, or buts

The highest risk factors for strokes are those that promote disorders in the blood vessels. These include high blood pressure, high cholesterol, hardening of the arteries, diabetes, and smoking, all of which restrict the flow of red blood cells. Warning signs commonly include sudden muscle or mental impairment, such as confusion, numbness, paralysis, and sudden headache.

CONCUSSION

The brain is soft, like gelatinous tofu. Evolution has encased it in the skull and surrounded it with a shock-absorbing cerebrospinal fluid to protect it from trauma. But that protection only

A BLOW TO THE HEAD
Violent sports such as boxing pose a risk of concussion, a brain injury that can have devastating, long-term effects. Strong blows to the head actually damage nerve cells, as shown below.

works for mild blows to the head. Strong blows slam the brain into the skull, causing impact trauma as well as tearing neural tissues where they bash into ridges on the underside of the skull's bony plates. Not every impact or concussion causes lasting injury; variations in the power of the blow and its location, as well as the genetics of the concussion sufferer, lead to unpredictable outcomes.

Concussion is a brain injury that can have short- and long-term effects ranging from dizziness to serious cognitive impairment. Concussions frequently occur to soldiers and athletes in sports where collisions are considered part of the game. Boxing and football probably come to mind as the most likely sources of concussion, but serious brain injuries can also occur in soccer, basketball, baseball, and other less brutal sports. For example, researchers at the University of Cincinnati found reduced amounts of gray matter in the brains of college soccer players compared with peers who did not play the game. They linked the damage to

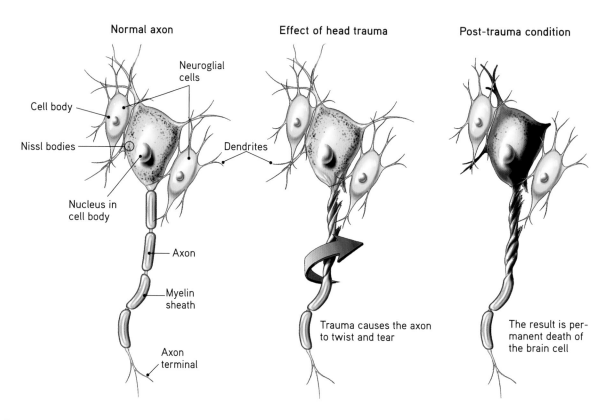

Normal axon

Effect of head trauma

Post-trauma condition

Neuroglial cells

Cell body

Nissl bodies

Dendrites

Nucleus in cell body

Axon

Myelin sheath

Axon terminal

Trauma causes the axon to twist and tear

The result is permanent death of the brain cell

BRAIN BOOSTER

CHECK YOUR BLOOD PRESSURE

Learn your numbers and reduce your risk of stroke

This tip comes right out of the medical textbooks: Take a few minutes today to check your blood pressure.

→ REDUCING YOUR RISK
Hypertension, or high blood pressure, when not controlled by lifestyle or medication, can seriously increase your risk for stroke, which in turn can cause disability, memory loss, or death.

You can have your blood pressure checked at most pharmacies,
many of which have a blood pressure machine available. If your pressure seems higher than usual, follow up with your doctor. Hypertension can readily be managed.

Want to reduce your risk for stroke? A 2008 study from the Harvard School of Public Health found that people could reduce their risk for stroke by up to 80 percent by leading a brain-healthy lifestyle, including regular exercise, a healthy diet, maintaining a healthy weight, and not smoking.

Now that's something to think about!

blows to the head, including the act of heading a ball in flight to redirect it toward the goal or another player. Falls in noncontact sports also can cause concussions.

The Effects of Early Damage

According to Daniel G. Amen, author of *Magnificent Mind at Any Age,* many people suffer a mild traumatic brain injury but don't realize it at the time. Therefore, they didn't realize that it might have caused lasting damage. Amen, who has performed thousands of brain scans, is quick to notice patterns of brain injury suggesting a history of impact trauma, such as concussions from violent sports. "Many people forget or they did not realize that they have had a serious brain injury," Amen wrote. "You would be amazed by

[FACT: Unconsciousness occurs 8 to 10 seconds after loss of blood supply to the brain. **]**

how many people after repeatedly saying no to this question suddenly get an 'aha' look on their face and say, 'Why yes, I fell out of a second-story window at age seven.' "

Amen notes that suffering a head injury increases later incidence of drug abuse, alcoholism, mood disorders, and other behavioral changes. This might be expected for damage to the frontal lobes, where the brain executes control over instinctive actions associated with the older and deeper portions of the mammalian brain. If a concussion weakens the brain's ability to reason, make good decisions, or override the circuitry that regulates pleasure seeking in favor of long-term benefits, it's no wonder that chronic concussion sufferers often exhibit self-destructive

> Chronic **CONCUSSION** sufferers often exhibit self-destructive behaviors.

BRAIN BOOSTER

PROTECT YOUR NOGGIN
Simple precautions can help to keep your brain from harm

Head injury, especially repeated head injury or concussion, can also mean brain injury. Recovery from such damage can take months, with symptoms including difficulty concentrating, double vision, and light sensitivity.

Even those of us who spend more time watching football than playing it can take steps to protect our heads. Here are some easy tips for taking care of your precious brain day in and day out:

➥ **WEAR A HELMET**
Everyone should wear a helmet when participating in a sport that carries a risk of head injury. Your helmet should fit snugly and comfortably, and should be strapped.

➥ **WEAR SEAT BELTS**
Wearing a seat belt is essential to restraining your head and the rest of your body in case of a car accident. In most states, it's also the law.

➥ AVOID RISK
Use your noggin to protect your head. Be thoughtful about what might increase your risk for a head injury: Look for tripping hazards on the floor or poor lighting in stairways.

➥ IN THE EVENT OF A CONCUSSION, GET EVALUATED AND TREATED
If you or a loved one suffers a concussion, see your doctor and follow his or her recommendations.

Want more information on concussion? Visit the Centers for Disease Control website at *www.cdc.gov/concussion* to learn more.

behaviors. Two high-profile cases in spring 2012 were the suicides of former NFL players Junior Seau and Ray Easterling, both of whom suffered brain trauma from playing the game.

Amen's advice is to teach children about the importance of the brain and insist that they take pains to protect it. Sports enthusiasts might choose competition with low levels of risk, or wear protective headgear before engaging in higher levels of risk. Helmets for bicyclists and motorcyclists are a must. So, too, are the right kinds of helmets for football players.

Football and Concussions

Football players as young as third graders experience blows to the head that would be considered high magnitude for college players, according to studies by

WEAR YOUR HELMET
Although young brains recover better than old ones from injury, it makes sense to protect children from trauma.

ALL AROUND PROTECTION
(Above) An x-ray reveals how a helmet cushions the head, above. Studies show that the best helmets generally are the priciest.

SPEED AND POWER
(Below) Marshall University tight end Eric Frohnapfel jumps for a pass against West Virginia University. Fierce tackles can register 100 Gs of force.

biomedical engineering professor Stefan Duma of the Virginia Tech University College of Engineering. Duma and his team of researchers provided helmets equipped with impact sensors to seven- and eight-year-old players and collected data on more than 750 blows to the boys' heads that occurred during games and practice. The most severe blow registered 100 Gs, or gravitational forces. One of the most surprising discoveries was that most of the worst blows to the head occurred during practice and not during the emotionally heightened contact of actual games. New kinds of impact sensors include high-tech mouth guards that record the severity of blows to the head and relay that information wirelessly to the sidelines.

Duma aims to take what he has learned from the studies to redesign football helmets to make them safer. Virginia Tech also published safety ratings for 15 brands of football helmets, with

BRAIN INSIGHT

NFL CONCUSSIONS

Professional football players are on the front lines of head injuries

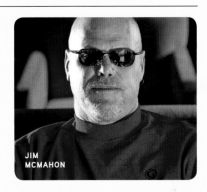

JIM
MCMAHON

Jim McMahon won a Super Bowl as quarterback of the 1985 Chicago Bears. Time and again in his career, McMahon bounced back from injuries, including bruised ribs, a lacerated kidney, a sore neck, bumps and bruises incurred by sliding headfirst to gain extra yards, and chronic concussions.

Today, McMahon is one of the highest profile litigants accusing the NFL of hiding vital information about concussions in order to keep players in the game. "We knew there was going to be a chance for injury," McMahon told ESPN. "But we didn't know about the head trauma. And they did, and that's the whole reason for this lawsuit."

Concussion occurs when a sudden jerk rams the brain into the skull, damaging brain tissue. Immediate effects may include dizziness, imbalance, and unconsciousness. Long-term effects vary greatly, but may include confusion, memory loss, depression, and suicidal thoughts. McMahon has trouble forming memories. Junior Seau, a former San Diego Chargers linebacker who took his life in 2012, suffered many concussions.

In 2011, the NFL changed its rules to better protect players showing signs of brain trauma. But it was too late to protect itself against scores of complaints that were consolidated into one big lawsuit against pro football in 2012.

several receiving top-end endorsements and one rated "not recommended." The key to creating an effective helmet is physics. Most helmets that are designed to handle high-impact blows contain layers of crushable foam. The foam absorbs the energy of collision as it flattens, shielding the brain from the worst potential damage. It probably comes as no surprise that, in general, the helmets that afford the most protection have higher price tags.

But isn't the brain worth the extra protection? Pinching pennies is a poor strategy for ensuring long-term brain health. If you do all you can to protect and nurture your brain, from eating and exercising right to shielding it from injury, you will give yourself the best odds of enjoying a long and brain-healthy life.

FACT: Concussions are often misdiagnosed in older adults. Many occur as a result of falls.

PART 3

The Brain of

the Future

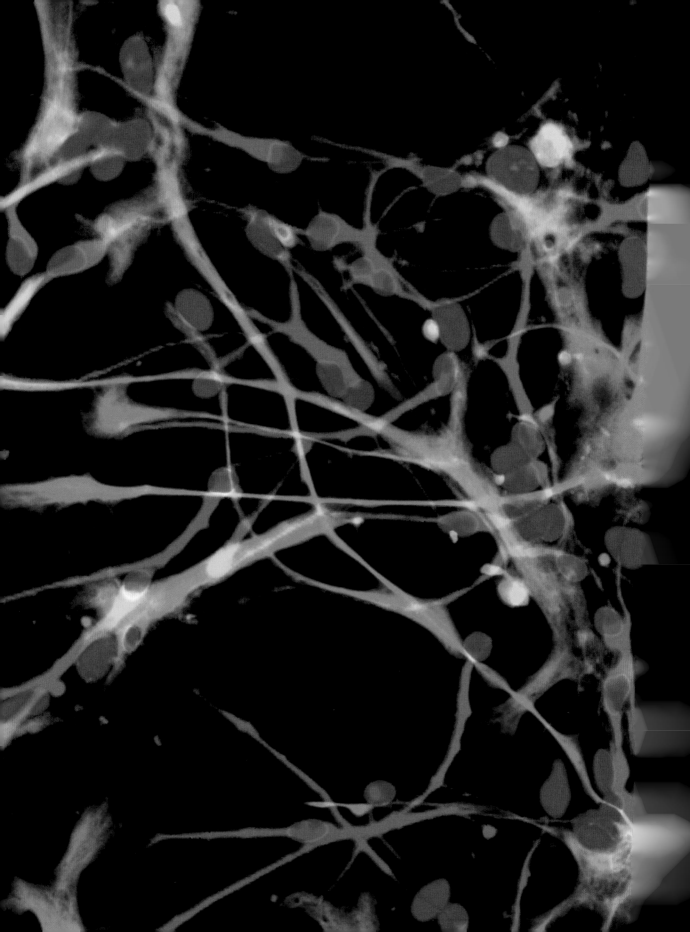

> *"The world of the future will be an ever more demanding
> struggle against the limitations of our intelligence,
> not a comfortable hammock in which we can lie down
> to be waited upon by our robot slaves."*
> NORBERT WIENER

HOPES AND QUESTIONS
Amazing advances may lead to tough decisions

Neuroscience has made fantastic breakthroughs in the last few decades. And the pace of discovery grows ever swifter as science begins to fill in the small details in its maps of the human brain. Visions of the future include new drugs and technologies. They may cure or prevent diseases, such as Alzheimer's, that long have challenged researchers. They may help modify memories of traumatic events to let healing begin. They may enhance particular functions, creating seemingly superhuman acts of intelligence and physical performance. They may open new forms of communication between humans and machines or even directly, via telepathy, between two minds; software connections to the "wetware" of neurons already have moved artificial limbs and converted mere thoughts to words on a screen. Some believe even death itself may fall to science. These possibilities raise big hopes—and big questions.

CHAPTER 15

Better Brains Through Chemistry

BRAIN CELLS FROM SCRATCH
(Preceding pages) Neurons (red) and astrocytes (green) can now be made from stem cells, one of many promising steps toward better brain medicine.

THE FINAL STEP
(Opposite) Some day, evolution of the human brain will extend intelligence beyond biology into things created by the brain. (Below) The 1960s-era optimism about robots hasn't yet panned out.

S
o, what comes next in the science of brain health?

It's notoriously difficult to predict the scientific future with accuracy. And the difficulties compound themselves with distance: The further into the future we seek to forecast, the greater the likelihood of missing the mark.

Nowhere is this more evident than in the predictions made for artificial intelligence by the creators of the first electronic computers in the years after World War II. Machines dazzled the public with their ability to solve mathematical problems and play simple games such as checkers. Scientists predicted that it wouldn't be long before the household robot maid or chef—like Rosie of the television cartoon *The Jetsons*—would become commonplace.

THE CLOUDY CRYSTAL BALL

In a small way, this has become true. Personal computers, introduced in the late 1970s, have become ubiquitous as word processors, information sources, and game players. But applications of artificial intelligence (AI) have yet to achieve the grandiose claims of AI pioneers. One of the top developers of early computing machines, Herbert Simon, famously predicted in 1965,

SILICON AVATAR
An android in female form touches electronic screens in an imagined future. Technological change rushes ever faster toward such a day.

"Machines will be capable, within 20 years, of doing any work a man can do." The reality: Computers are great at playing chess because the game follows rules. They're not so good at creative thinking, nor at performing physical tasks that humans take for granted. Decades must pass before computers can simulate the brains of small mammals. Decades more to simulate those of *Homo sapiens*.

It is argued that once science can make an artificial brain, it will better understand the workings of the natural kind. And that will open vast new possibilities.

[**FACT:** When exposed to the neurochemical arginine vasopressin, promiscuous voles became monogamous.]

A Blessing or a Curse?

The future of brain research, and its applications for brain health, appears extremely encouraging for the next few years. Beyond that, chaos theory takes over: We cannot see far into the future because, thanks to sensitive dependence on initial conditions, tomorrow's breakthroughs will have unforeseen consequences. Some visionaries paint a future that's bright, evolving into a world where new scientific knowledge leads to empowering the individual brain to learn and do more, with the aid of new medications and technological enhancements. In this world, mental and physical disease and disorder, and even death itself—defined as cessation of function in the brain—may be conquered. Others see a darker future as a possibility, where the quest to understand and replicate the human brain in silicon avatars leads to either a world of haves

> Computers are not so good at **CREATIVE** thinking.

BRAIN INSIGHT

ADDERALL ABUSE

Some brain-altering drugs may be reaching more than their target audience

Each year, 21 million prescriptions for medication to treat attention-deficit disorder are filled for Americans ages 10 to 19. Yet some of these prescriptions are going to students without a legitimate need. Many students abuse such drugs because they help focus attention, particularly while studying for and taking tests. In 2012, the *New York Times* reported that, according to interviews with doctors and students at more than 15 prestigious schools, 15 to 40 percent of students take stimulants to help them study.

Adderall, an amphetamine that treats attention deficit/hyperactivity

disorder, has become routinely abused, especially at highly competitive schools where excellent performance is a step toward admission to an elite college. A

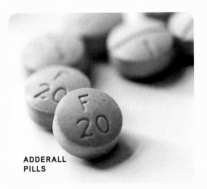

ADDERALL PILLS

federal drug enforcement agency said Adderall abuse exists throughout the United States.

Abuse can alter mood or lead to other drugs. And, as it was designed to do, Adderall affects brain function by interfering with neurons' ability to reabsorb dopamine from the synapses. Extended Adderall use lowers dopamine levels.

"Children have prefrontal cortexes that are not fully developed, and we're changing the chemistry of the brain. That's what these drugs do," Paul L. Hokemeyer, a family therapist in Manhattan, told the *Times*.

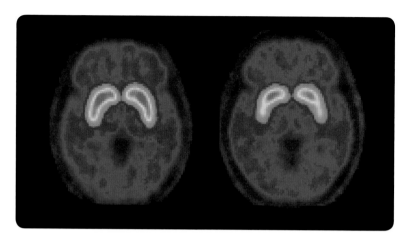

MODAFINIL IN THE BRAIN
Red regions in PET images of the brain indicate higher levels of dopamine release in people given modafinil (left) than a placebo (right).

and have-nots, or perhaps one in which robots move beyond serving humans to becoming their masters.

The short-term outlook, at least, is bright. Brain-boosting science is making advances on several fronts, including neuropharmacology, cognitive training, and technology, including surgically implanted prostheses, to improve brain function.

BRAIN DRUGS

Neuroscientists and psychologists foresee the development of a wave of new brain-enhancing drugs. That's a safe prediction, as many drugs already are marketed as tools to enhance cognition. Some, like caffeine, a mental stimulant, have been around for centuries. Others have been developed to treat specific medical issues, such as attention deficit/hyperactivity disorder (ADHD), and have been adopted, sometimes illicitly, by users seeking to enhance mental performance in areas not intended by the drugs' manufacturers or by the medical community. For example, some soldiers take modafinil, which targets the sleep disorder narcolepsy, because they believe it improves their memory and judgment. And college students often cadge or buy Ritalin, a treatment for ADHD, from friends because its attention-focusing properties seem to help them cram for tests.

Altering Memories

In the next few decades, more powerful brain-enhancing drugs are likely to become available. Patients with traumatic memories, such as witnessing or being a victim of terrible violence, might be able to take a pill to allow them to forget. Such medical treatment might also cause a person to delete an addictive craving from basic neural wiring.

Memory-easing and memory-erasing treatments are already in development. The principle behind them comes from the cycle of memory creation, storage, retrieval, and restorage. Memories take time to form in the brain. While they start to "solidify," like gelatin in a mold, they can become stronger or weaker depending on the presence or absence of adrenaline, a stress hormone associated with the so-called "flashbulb" memories of fear-inducing events, such as the attacks on New York's Twin Towers on September 11, 2001. Neurobiology professor James McGaugh of the University of California, Irvine, who discovered the memory link to adrenaline, went looking for a chemical that would block the effects of adrenaline on memory enhancement.

He found it in propranolol, a beta-blocker often used to treat the symptoms of a panic attack. McGaugh describes it as blocking the ability of adrenaline to dock with neurons, thus keeping it from making memories more pronounced. Scientists believe that giving

BURNING MEMORIES
The south tower of the World Trade Center collapsed on September 11, 2001. Drugs are in the works to treat memories of such traumatic events.

propranolol to someone who has just witnessed a traumatic event, such as a soldier in combat, will reduce the impact of the memory and perhaps aid in preventing or easing post-traumatic stress disorder.

But are such treatments ethically responsible? A council on bioethics that reported to President George W. Bush took issue with changing memories. "Rewriting" memories with drugs risks "undermining our true identity," the council said. Perhaps envisioning a dystopian version of novelist Aldous Huxley's *Brave New World,* the council said, "It risks making shameful acts seem less shameful or terrible acts less terrible than they really are." Although there is room for abuse in memory-altering drugs, such as the practice of taking them for trivial reasons, the council's report raises a fundamental question: Who *wouldn't* want to take away some of the pain associated with a rape or murder?

Scientists envision other drugs that could alter the effects of commonly used mind-altering substances. It may be possible to produce drugs that induce effects similar to alcohol or so-called recreational drugs, without their terrible side effects. Or, drugs might be created to block the effects of dangerous, but easily obtained, pharmaceuticals.

> There is room for abuse in memory-altering DRUGS.

INSIDE A BETA-BLOCKER
A polarized light micrograph brings to light the crystals of the beta-blocker drug propranolol, a medication that may aid in treating post-traumatic stress disorder.

BRAIN INSIGHT

THE DUBIOUS BENEFITS OF GINGKO BILOBA

So far, claims that gingko extracts can fight dementia have not held up

GINGKO LEAVES

In the mid-1990s, purveyors of alternative medicines began selling gingko leaf extracts as a way to combat memory loss, including disorders caused by dementia. Studies showed that ginkgo improved blood flow to the brain by dilating vessels and reducing the sticky properties of platelets. Those findings became evidence for broad claims about ginkgo fighting cognitive decline.

A study of more than 3,000 test subjects, ages 72 to 96, published in 2009 in the *Journal of the American Medical Association,* found no evidence to back up the claims. Ginkgo biloba did not slow the progress of cognitive disorders, nor did it prevent memory loss. The findings held true for test subjects who had mild cognitive problems and those who did not. A 2012 study published in *Lancet Neurology* also showed negative results.

Still, ginkgo remains popular, especially in Europe. A German manufacturer of ginkgo extracts protested the 2009 study as "methodologically so weak that it is of limited relevance," and continues to tout the leaves.

The Blood-Brain Barrier

Designers of new brain medications run into an old problem: the blood–brain barrier. This biological screen, formed by specialized cells making up the blood vessel network of the brain, acts like a sieve. It prevents molecules with more than 500 times the molecular weight of a hydrogen atom from reaching the central nervous system through the bloodstream. The barrier evolved to protect the brain from harmful chemicals, but it also prevents the delivery of potentially beneficial drugs that could treat a variety of disorders including brain cancer, multiple sclerosis, and Alzheimer's disease.

In 2011, researchers at Cornell University announced a discovery that might allow doctors to control the blood–brain barrier, opening and closing it at will. They focused on the adenosine molecule, which signals trauma to the brain and performs a variety of other physiological functions. The Cornell team found that when they activated adenosine receptors on the cells of the blood–brain barrier in the brains of mice, they could establish a "gateway"

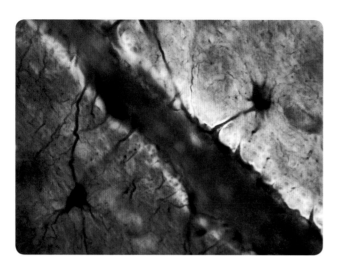

BLOOD-BRAIN BARRIER
Extensions of neuroglial cells, in contact with a brain capillary, may help form the barrier that keeps many drugs and antibiotics out of the brain.

Several existing chemical compounds show some promise toward boosting COGNITION.

across the barrier. Similar adenosine receptors have been found in human brains. Lexiscan, a drug already approved by the FDA for use in heart imaging, is based on adenosine and has been found to temporarily open the barrier.

Whereas the blood-brain barrier once allowed only small molecules such as water, oxygen, glucose, and amino acids into the brain, modifications could shepherd much larger and more complex molecules into neurons that need treatment. "The biggest hurdle for every neurological disease is that we are unable to treat these diseases because we cannot deliver drugs into the brain," said Cornell immunologist Margaret Bynoe. "Big pharmaceutical companies have been trying for 100 years to find out how to traverse the blood-brain barrier and still keep patients alive."

Among the large molecules the Cornell team successfully introduced into the brain were antibodies that targeted beta-amyloid plaques found in patients with Alzheimer's disease. For treatment of multiple sclerosis, the team hopes to find ways to tighten the holes in the blood-brain barrier to keep out destructive cells.

MEMORY ENHANCEMENT

If drugs can mute memory, how long will it be before medicines to enhance it, or at least slow its decline, become common?

Some are already on the market, but their value has yet to be proved. Ginkgo biloba, for example, has been shown to increase blood flow to the brain and thus boost neural activity, but enhancement beyond the temporary boost of oxygen has not been proved. Something truly powerful, with long-term effects, would no doubt be popular as well as lucrative.

Turning Back the Clock?

Nothing discovered so far comes close to the fictional drug NZT, featured in the 2011 movie *Limitless;* the drug bestows an immediate and astounding brain boost to the main character, who masters Mandarin, unravels the hidden trends of the stock market, and absorbs arcane information like a sponge. Several existing chemical compounds show some promise toward boosting cognition in general, and memory in particular, but results are limited and not entirely proved. These include carnitine, ampakines, and the peptide known as FGL.

A study in Italy found that people with Alzheimer's who took two grams of carnitine every day for a year demonstrated increases in long-term memory as well as in verbal ability. A similar study in 2002 at the University of California, Berkeley, showed that aging

RED MEAT
Acetyl-L-carnitine, found in red meat, worked with an antioxidant to increase the vigor and mental clarity of lab rats in a California study.

RODENTS REVIVED
Old laboratory rodents "did the Macarena" with youthful energy in tests of mitochondrial-energizing drugs.

lab rats improved their memories and achieved a youthful vigor after taking the amino acid acetyl-L-carnitine, found in red meat, and the antioxidant alpha-lipoic acid.

These two chemicals target mitochondria, the tiny organelles inside cells that supply them with energy. Bruce Ames, the lead researcher of the study, said that when the rats received the two drugs, which increase mitochondrial energy and neutralize the harmful by-products of metabolism, "those old rats got up and did the Macarena." The Berkeley team gave two-year-old rats the two drugs for a month, and then compared their physical and mental levels with adolescent rats as well as old but untreated rats. The treated rats improved their performance on memory tests. Controlled, long-term tests have yet to offer proof of the effect of acetyl-L-carnitine or suggest the optimal dose. Nevertheless, it is marketed as a supplement and used by those who claim it enhances memory, including Ron White, multiple winner of the U.S. National Memory Championships.

BRAIN INSIGHT

MARILU HENNER'S PERFECT MEMORY

The actress is one of a few people in the world with hyperthymesia

The idea of a pill to enhance your memory has long been a beautiful dream for many with weakened memory functions, as well as an opportunity for enterprising advertisers to make a fast buck.

But would you want perfect memory?

Actress Marilu Henner is one of a dozen or so people in the world diagnosed with hyperthymesia, an extraordinary memory that allows her to recall virtually everything she has ever experienced. She calls her condition a "gift."

MARILU HENNER

"I don't lose my parents," Henner told CBS. "I lost my parents a long time ago and it's [memory] insurance against loss. It's the strongest defense against meaninglessness that we have."

Asked once to recall the day she got a part on the network TV sitcom *Taxi,* she said, "It was June 4 of 1978. It was a Sunday and I found out at the *Grease* premiere party."

Her earliest memory is being baptized, she said. She likened her memory searches to scanning the scene-selection feature on a DVD.

Others with the condition, such as author Jill Price, note the dark side of super-memory: Bad personal experiences linger. Unpleasant memories haunt the present. Still, Price would not give up her skill even if she could.

The Promise of Smart Pills

Another group of chemical compounds, ampakines, has also shown results in enhancing memories of lab rats in a University of California, Irvine, study. Neuroscientist Gary Lynch injected ampakines into rats' brains and then watched them navigate mazes better than untreated rats. Lynch believes that if ampakines, which boost the presence of the neurotransmitter glutamate, are found to be safe for common human use, they may have shattering implications. Humans taking ampakines may be able to change their place in the intellectual hierarchy by revving their powers of memory.

Among drugs available today, the "smart drug" Provigil may be the closest to the ideal of a cognitive enhancer without serious side effects. It seems to promote attentiveness and mental function, although reported side effects, including insomnia and headaches, have caused some people to declare that the drawbacks outweigh the benefits.

A new drug on the horizon may consist of a small protein fragment, or peptide, that appears to strengthen synaptic connections in rats. The results were reported in 2012 by a team of researchers from the Centro de Biología Molecular Severo Ochoa in Spain, the Brain Mind Institute at the École Polytechnique Fédérale de Lausanne in Switzerland, and the Department of Neuroscience and Pharmacology at the Faculty of Health Sciences in Denmark. Rats fed the peptide, known as FGL, learned more easily and retained more spatial information. The study found that FGL tends to stimulate synapses of the hippocampus, a key brain area for the transformation of short-term memories into long-term ones.

THE NEXT BIG THING
Scientists at the Institute of Biomedical Research of Barcelona, Spain, and at other laboratories seek to make brain-enhancing drugs.

[**FACT**: High blood pressure, microwaves, and infections can open up the blood-brain barrier.]

CHAPTER 16

The Electric Brain

C ognitive training programs have exploded in popularity in the last few years. Most work by having users run a computer program targeting specific mental skills with the hope that enhancements developed on the computer screen will transfer into the real world, and will be more than just fleeting improvements. Training programs exist for storing auditory, visual, and spatial information and recalling it upon demand. Computer programs also have shown some success in treating attention deficit/hyperactivity disorder, and in helping the elderly regain the ability to drive.

It is not clear if the abilities that are enhanced by software, or by doing such low-tech puzzles as crosswords and Sudoku, translate to a more general environment. The transfer of skills is affected by a host of variables, including fatigue, motivation, mood, and the presence in the body of chemicals such as caffeine and nicotine. The strength of transfer appears to vary widely from one person to the next. Gaining an understanding of why this is so would allow the developers of cognitive training programs to tailor their products for individual brains.

THE MAGNETIC BRAIN

C ognitive enhancement also may become commonplace in the not-too-distant future through a procedure, already available in the United States, called transcranial magnetic stimulation, or TMS. It works by placing a powerful magnetic coil next to the skull,

AWAKE ALL NIGHT
(Opposite) Experimental subject David Poser of the University of Wisconsin is wired to register brain activity while going without sleep.

YOUNG BRAINS
(Below) Young brains are the most plastic, and perhaps most able to adapt to technological changes on the horizon.

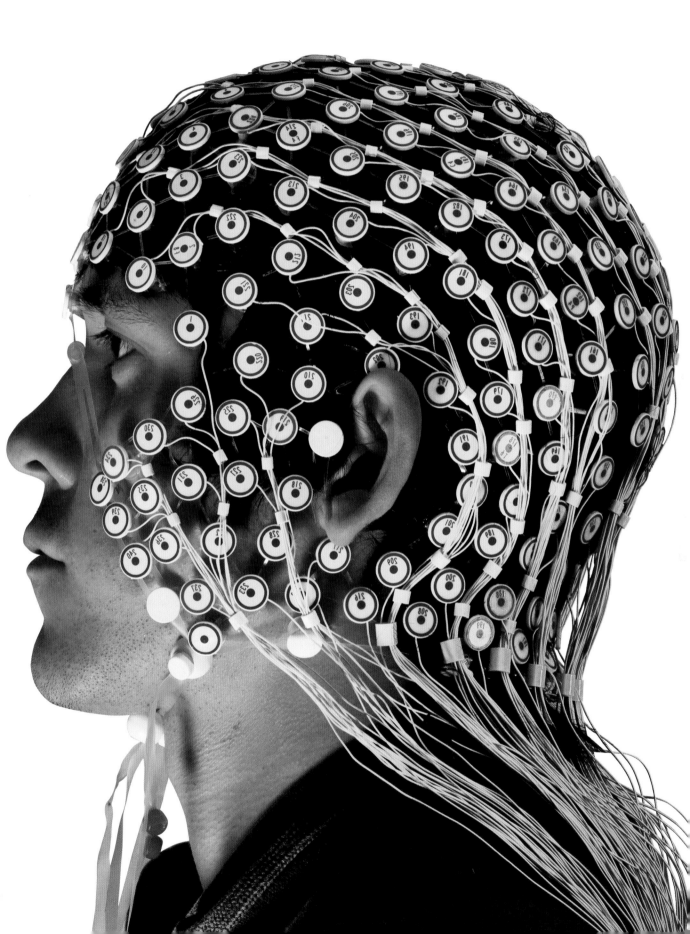

BRAIN INSIGHT

TELEPATHIC TWEETING

Your thoughts in 140 characters or fewer

In early April 2009, University of Wisconsin biomedical doctoral student Adam Wilson prepared to send the first message that could be described as telepathic.

Wired magazine likened the event to the moment when Alexander Graham Bell, inventor of the telephone, sent his assistant what Bell said was the first phone message: "Mr. Watson, come here. I want to see you."

Wilson's message was more a simple announcement of what he was doing, and could be seen by anyone with access to the Internet: "USING EEG TO SEND TWEET."

Wilson manipulated a computer program that recognized changes in his brain activity patterns when he concentrated on particular letters of the alphabet. His thoughts moved a cursor and selected letters to be posted to his microblogging Twitter account. The interface emerged from a software tool developed by Justin Williams of the University of Wisconsin's Neural Interface Technology Research Optimization Lab and Gerwin Schalk, a neural injury specialist at the Wadsworth Center, a public health laboratory in upstate New York.

Medical uses being explored for this program include opening avenues of

ADAM WILSON (RIGHT)

communication with patients who have "locked-in" syndrome and cannot move or speak. Wilson's subsequent brain-to-computer messages indicated other applications. "GO BADGERS," tweeted the University of Wisconsin football fan.

sending microvolts of an electromagnetic pulse into a nearby part of the brain. The pulse provokes a storm of activity, silencing the brain's rehearsed order of neural firing. A brief session with the TMS controller poised over the speech center of the brain temporarily interrupts a person's ability to vocalize words.

American doctors use the process to cut off stimulation to the circuits involved in obsessive-compulsive disorder and depression. The latter disorder has been targeted for some time with higher doses of electricity, as when electroconvulsive therapy shocks people with severe depression hard enough to push them into a seizure. The mechanism of their recovery isn't fully understood, but it's believed that the electroconvulsive therapy acts like a hard

FACT: The brain is an electromagnetic organ. It reacts, weakly, to the electromagnetic fields of cell phones.

reboot on a computer, resetting a part of the patient's brain crucial to regulation of mood.

Magnetic Stimulation

Repetitive transcranial magnetic stimulation, or rTMS, may hold the key to the development of a working "thinking cap" in the next decades. Magnetic brain stimulation might alter perception, raise creativity, reduce prejudice, and perform other beneficial functions, according to Professor Allan Snyder, director of the Centre for the Mind at the University of Sydney, Australia. Snyder told *Psychology Today* that he believes savants, otherwise ordinary humans who have enhanced cognitive abilities in certain areas such as in multiplying two huge numbers in their heads, possess the ability to tap information normally processed below the level of consciousness. That ability may potentially exist in any brain, just waiting for some spark to set it off. Stroke, some forms of dementia, and physical wounds sometimes lead to the emergence of previously unseen skills. That would suggest that these seemingly superhuman skills existed in the brain and just needed a way to come out.

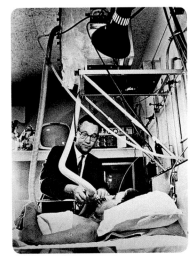

ELECTROCONVULSIVE THERAPY
(Above) An unconscious patient gets fitted with a respirator in a medical shock unit in 1970. The patient received electroconvulsive therapy to treat depression.

TRANSCRANIAL STIMULATION
(Left) A neuroscientist passes a key-shaped paddle over a targeted zone to perform transcranial magnetic stimulation.

Snyder has found that rTMS can often create temporary savant-like skills, including creativity, drawing ability, and number manipulation. The technology is still unproven and on the far edges of science. However, as savant-like abilities have been associated with the suppression of localized brain activity, it makes sense that rTMS, which also inhibits normal neural firing, might induce similar results. Inhibiting the left side of the brain, which usually names things and processes ideas, allows the right hemisphere to temporarily become dominant. Setting free the perceptual and holistic skills of the right side might improve drawing skills, for example, because the brain commands the hands to draw what the eyes see, rather than what the brain says must exist. The right hemisphere also is considered the home of intuition, so boosting its power might improve some forms of judgment.

THINKING CAP
Professor Allan Snyder (left) and graduate student Richard Chi (right) display their creativity-stimulating "thinking cap" on a glass head at the University of Sydney, Australia.

Boosting Creativity?

New York Times reporter Lawrence Osborne subjected himself to Snyder's rTMS treatments to see how it would affect his ability to draw. As Snyder hooked up Osborne to the machine, he described the technique as "a way of altering our states of mind without taking drugs like mescaline. You can make people see the raw data of the world as it is. As it is actually represented in the unconscious mind of all of us."

Osborne made four drawings of cats while undergoing the procedure. The first were "boxy and stiffly unconvincing," he wrote, but after ten minutes of magnetic stimulation to the left side of his brain, "their tails had grown more vibrant, more nervous; their faces were personable and convincing. They were even beginning to wear clever expressions. I could hardly recognize them as my own drawings, though I had watched myself render each one, in all its loving detail. Somehow over the course of a very few minutes, and with no additional instruction, I had gone from an incompetent draftsman to a very impressive artist of the feline form." Snyder said Leonardo da Vinci would have been proud of Osborne's cats.

Not everyone responds the same way, and some don't respond at all to repetitive transcranial stimulation. Snyder speculates that that's because different brains have different organizations and strengths. In addition, rTMS cannot focus its magnetic effects with great precision, making it hard to target, and hit, desired regions of the brain while leaving others unaffected. "For all these reasons," he said, "it's likely that we stimulate the 'sweet spot' (or network) in some people more successfully than in others."

Snyder's ultimate goal is to literally create a thinking cap. While the mind leaps with excitement at the possibility of enhancing intellectual or creative abilities, the successful invention of a portable and relatively cheap device that boosts brainpower raises many practical and ethical questions. Could students use such a

Snyder's ultimate goal is to literally create a **THINKING CAP.**

HELEN MAYBERG
The scientist's deep-brain stimulation of a region known as Area 25 has shown some promise in treating severe depression.

device to cheat on a college entrance exam, representing themselves as smarter than they normally are? Or gain an advantage in a music or art competition for a major cash prize? Or would that matter in a future where everyone might have access to transcranial magnetic stimulation? When the evil genius of *The Incredibles*, whose inventions allow him to levitate and unleash powerful bolts of energy, tells the film's genuine superheroes that one day he may sell his devices to the public, he laughs and says, "Everyone can be super! And when everyone's super . . . no one will be."

> Direct **STIMULATION** is believed to speed the processing of new material.

MEDICAL MIRACLES

Smaller doses of electricity applied directly to the skull through electrodes, in a process called transcranial direct current stimulation, are showing results for medical treatment of damaged brains, particularly from strokes. Unlike magnetic stimulation, transcranial direct current stimulation doesn't directly cause neurons to fire. Instead, it increases their *readiness* to fire.

When combined with learning, direct stimulation is believed to speed and enhance the absorption and processing of new material. Victims of stroke who have lost a measure of their language skills, for example, regain command of speech more quickly when traditional therapy is combined with the light application of electrical current.

Deep Brain Stimulation

Deep brain stimulation, which has already helped tens of thousands of people with Parkinson's disease, takes the application of electricity to the brain a step further. The disease is marked by the decline and eventual death of a group of neurons that produce the reward and addiction neurotransmitter dopamine inside the brain's substantia nigra. Surgically implanted electrodes directly stimulate the dopamine-producing region, electrically replacing the role formerly played by healthy neurons. It's serious surgery, and not for everyone; medication remains the most common Parkinson's treatment. However, deep stimulation could next be called upon to take on other disorders, including depression and obsessive-compulsive symptoms.

Groundbreaking researcher and neurologist Helen Mayberg has used deep brain stimulation to target a region of the brain known as Area 25 to treat patients with severe depression. One patient, Edi Guyton, experienced a remarkable turnaround after undergoing the procedure. When she was 19, Guyton tried to kill herself while depressed and had experienced ongoing depression. Mayberg drilled two holes in Guyton's skull and placed two battery-powered electrodes into Area 25, which has been identified as playing a key role in mood

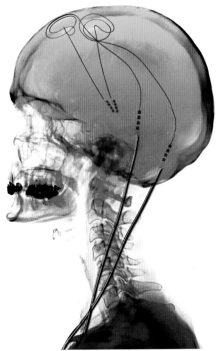

DEEP STIMULATION
A color-enhanced lateral x-ray of the head and neck reveals deep-brain stimulating electrodes implanted for treatment of symptoms of Parkinson's disease.

[**FACT:** Cochlear implants, used to improve hearing, are a form of human-machine interface.]

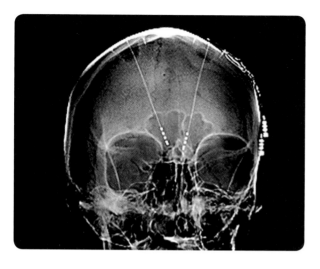

AREA 25
Insertion of electrodes into the so-called Area 25 of the brains of patients with depression could help to relieve their suffering.

regulation. The brain region appears to be overly active among those with chronic and severe depression; Mayberg believed that for those patients who fail to improve with other treatments, direct stimulation of Area 25 might electrically change the region and effectively alter the patient's mood. Mayberg tried direct stimulation of Area 25 in six patients in 2003. Some of the patients described immediate improvements after receiving the implants; one reported a new perception of her room being brighter and its colors more intense. Four of the six reported significant improvements after six months of treatments. More surgeries followed. Guyton's improvement appeared substantial.

Mayberg said researchers know a great deal about the brain circuits targeted by deep brain stimulation but don't know

---

BRAIN INSIGHT

THE BRAINPORT

An experimental device can train other body parts to take the place of the eye

A scientist rolls a ball toward a woman in a chair. She reaches out her hand and stops it.

Nothing remarkable there, except the woman is blind. And she "saw" the ball with her tongue.

The blind woman's tongue was wired to a device called a BrainPort, itself wired to a video camera capturing the movements of the scientist and ball. BrainPort, under development by the late Paul Bach-y-Rita of Wicab Inc., works by substituting electrical impulses for other sensory stimuli. In this case, it trades the visual system's processing of light for encoded bursts of electricity sent to the brain through the surface of the tongue. (The tongue's sensitivity makes it ideal for maximum data communication.) The brain teaches itself how to interpret tongue-borne electrical bursts as if they had been delivered through the eyes. Similar research is under way to substitute or augment sensory information lost in the skin and ears, as well as loss of balance. The vision centers of BrainPort users become active when processing electrical impulses from the skin.

Blind BrainPort operators, once

BRAINPORT V100 DEVICE

trained, perceive size, shape, depth, and other visual qualities. Letters of the alphabet become clear.

Wicab is working toward release of a commercial version of the product.

the general nature of how it works. However, there is growing evidence of changes in circuitry dynamics, with Area 25 being an important hub.

Implants

Beyond drugs and mental training programs lies the wide open future of implanted brain enhancements—the microchips or small motors that might compensate for disease or, in a *Matrix*-like world somewhere beyond the foreseeable future, act as a software–wetware interface, allowing the brain direct access to information encoded in metal. Such implants might stimulate, record, or block neural activity at a specific location, shutting off an epileptic seizure before it happens or releasing electrical impulses or small doses of medication to treat mood disorders at their first sign. Although this may

COMPULSIONS

Transcranial magnetic stimulation has targeted obsessive-compulsive behaviors to ease compulsions such as counting, sorting, cleaning, and checking.

sound pie-in-the-sky, some patients already have had tiny sensors injected into their brains to assist them in operating robotic limbs just by thinking; the sensors read neural firing patterns and translate them into movement commands for prostheses. And neural pattern detectors, in concert with computers, have allowed experimental subjects to move a computer cursor with their thoughts.

These technologies typically are developed and tested on people with brain injuries as a way to restore function and let them lead a more normal life. However, it's likely that they may make their way to broader markets after years of refinement. For example, a computer-brain interface that translated thoughts into words on a page would speed the task of writing and, if the author desired, create a true "stream of consciousness" novel.

CHIPS ON THE BRAIN
An imagined future implant, a microchip device in the brain, will be a significant step in merging technology and biology.

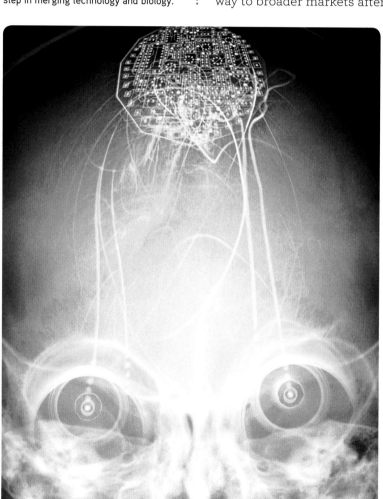

Mind Readers

Brain-reading devices are already coming onto the market, at prices most people can afford. Consider the $300 neuroheadset made by Emotiv, which can tap EEG brain waves to allow users to interact with some electronic games. It's not too much of a leap to imagine multiple users of a more sophisticated version of such software, with their minds linked together electronically. Imagine the next generations of such devices scanning the active brain, converting the electrochemical signals they discover into words or images, and transmitting them to a receiver that then places them directly into another person's

ROBOTIC ARMS

Sensors implanted in the brain can command electronic limbs

It's not much of a stretch to go from manipulating a computer cursor with a thought, accomplished in 1998 and depicted a few years later on the television drama *House M.D.*, to moving something more substantial.

In May 2012, a team of scientists announced that they had taught two quadriplegics to manipulate a robotic arm. The arm reached and grabbed, just like one of flesh and blood. One of the two people, a woman who had been unable to give herself a drink for 15 years, smiled broadly when she wrapped robotic fingers around a coffee cup and took a sip.

The arm receives electrical impulses from an aspirin-sized sensor implanted in the motor cortex. When the test subjects imagine making particular arm movements, the sensor picks up patterns of neural firing, translates them into signals that can be read by the arm, sends them along a wire, and sets the arm in motion.

The arm rests on a shoulder-height dolly and has yet to leave the lab. Researchers at Brown University, the Department of Veterans Affairs, and the German Institute of Robotics and

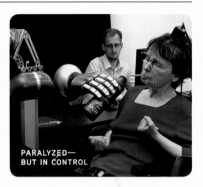

PARALYZED—
BUT IN CONTROL

Mechatronics hope to develop a wireless transmission system as well as lifelike limbs that are integrated into the body.

brain. Lovers could share intimate thoughts. Soldiers could coordinate an attack in the dark without ever having to make a sound.

Mind Thieves

Or thieves could steal ideas. That possibility already has been demonstrated with the Emotiv headset. Researchers at Oxford University, the University of California, Berkeley, and the University of Geneva published a paper in 2012 that laid out the privacy and security risks of such new technology. They asked students to put on Emotiv headsets and then showed them a variety of images, including pictures of automated teller machines and bank cards, that might spark them to think about secure information.

[FACT: Sensors implanted in the brain might one day be able to repair neurons. **]**

BRAIN-READING DEVICE
(Right) Hitachi researcher Akiko Obata uses headgear monitoring changes in blood flow in her brain to run a model train while colleague Kei Utsugi checks a monitor.

HANDS-FREE HEADSET
(Below) The Emotiv EPOC neuroheadset taps into the user's brain activity to operate electronic games.

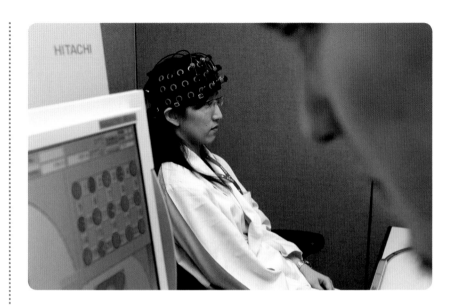

The researchers essentially "hacked" the users' thoughts, correctly guessing their bank and personal identification numbers to access their accounts on the first try about one time in five. More than half the time, the researchers correctly guessed the users' birth month.

The hacking worked because the researchers focused their attention on the so-called P300 signal, which the brain typically activates when it recognizes something meaningful, such as a very familiar person or thing. They found that the signal could be used as a sort of lie detector test, noting, "the P300 can be used as a discriminative feature in detecting whether or not the relevant information is stored in the subject's memory." It's unlikely that a person could unknowingly give up secrets through such an attack. The hackers would have to get their target to wear a headset, and then show random personal identification numbers or some other images to induce the P300 circuit to fire. However, a patsy might be induced into playing a game into which triggering images are embedded and made to look like part of the rules or protocols of the game. Such camouflage would make the sinister interrogation seem more benign.

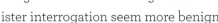

BRAIN INSIGHT

THE BRAIN FITNESS INDUSTRY

Brain fitness is a promising field, but it's still in its infancy

The brain fitness industry brings in about $265 million a year in the United States. In the next few years that number is expected to grow past a billion dollars as baby boomers who bought exercise programs to improve their cardiovascular fitness turn to maintaining their mental clarity.

The youth of the industry has clouded its future. Experts are uncertain whether the software industry for brain enhancement will follow the path of entertaining computer games produced by existing industry giants, with little or no solid evidence of cognitive

BRAIN AGE GAMER

improvement, or the path of smaller, more neurally focused companies such as NovaVision. The FDA has cleared this company's product as a way to improve vision compromised by stroke or traumatic brain injury.

Jonas Jendi, chief executive of Cogmed, the maker of a program that treats ADHD, believes clinical data to back up claims of cognitive improvement will be crucial to software companies that want to succeed.

"I think it will be very difficult to make money in the field of games, even though I think a lot of people will try," he told Reuters. "Our approach is to prove our product works through proper research." Cogmed uses clinicians to distribute its program.

It's not impossible to imagine a new industry of countermeasures, as seen in the movie *Inception,* that train the brain to recognize such attacks and to fight back. The researchers noted that just as other household appliances have improved dramatically with time, the quality of brain-hacking programs will most likely improve, and so will the likelihood of attacks. The researchers noted in describing their work that many open-ended questions must be answered before brain hacking becomes more of an exact science. For one, there must be a trade-off between obtrusiveness by the hackers, in order to get the subject to pay attention to the information the hackers seek to steal, and concealment designed to mask the thieves' true agenda. The researchers plan to explore the challenge of sorting truth from fiction when a subject attempts to "lie" during a brain-hacking attack.

> The researchers essentially "hacked" the users' THOUGHTS.

CHAPTER 17

Visions of Brains to Come

Robotic arms and telepathic tweeting already seem to be merging brain technology with science fiction. But longer-term advances in brain science and health, including stem cell implants and brain-machine interfaces, may someday allow us to regrow damaged areas of the brain or erase the distinction between human and artificial intelligence.

Research is in its infancy into the implantation of neural stem cells as a treatment for traumatic brain injury. However, scientists believe future study could lead to new methods of treatment and rehabilitation for patients with serious brain damage.

Neural stem cells are basic structures, found in adult neural tissue, that can develop into more specialized kinds of cells found in the central nervous system. Future stem cell research may open the door to cures for currently incurable brain diseases. One avenue of research explores the possibility of turning neural stem cells into the type of neurons that produce dopamine as a possible treatment for patients with Parkinson's syndrome. Another line examines the possibility of transforming neural stem cells into the particular type of brain cells that produce myelin, the fatty insulation surrounding axons that makes neural firing more efficient.

Psychiatric diseases are also being targeted for neural stem cell research. In 2012, scientists using cultures of neural stem cells identified molecules that caused some cells in the brains of people with schizophrenia to multiply more rapidly than those of people

INTERFACE
(Opposite) As technology advances, an imagined future includes virtual interfaces between brain and machine.

PARKINSON'S TREATMENT
(Below) A digital illustration compares the low dopamine level in a Parkinson's-affected neuron (left) with the level in a normal neuron.

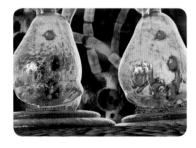

without the mental disorder. The study, led by Alan Mackay-Sim of the National Centre for Adult Stem Cell Research in Brisbane, Australia, revealed a correlation between schizophrenia and physical impairment of the regulatory mechanisms of brain cells. Neural stem cells might be coaxed into growing into cells that exhibit normal cell-cycle patterns, instead of the shortened cell cycles and other phenomena associated with schizophrenic brain cells.

BRAIN MONITORS

An IBM study in 2011 predicted a growing market for health-monitoring devices worn by people who are relatively healthy but want or need greater control over their lives. Such devices already exist, including ones that monitor blood sugar levels among people with diabetes, but future applications

ALZHEIMER'S CAREGIVER
Alexis McKenzie (right), executive director of an Alzheimer's assisted-living facility in Washington, D.C., laughs with a resident. Future devices may monitor patients' brains and call for help when needed.

are wide open to speculation. IBM sees a demand for more sophisticated machines that plan, predict, and monitor health-related information and send it directly to caregivers via wireless connections. These machines could be entirely new, or graft onto existing smartphones or gaming devices modified with new software. Not only could users communicate easily with medical professionals, potentially reducing the frequency of office visits, but also connect to online communities of people with similar health issues, such as the "virtual communities" that gather in cyberspace to discuss post-traumatic stress disorder, chronic pain, depression, and so on.

BODY MONITORS
A runner checks a health-monitoring bracelet that links to his smartphone to track his calories burned and steps taken.

Help for Impairments

Applications for brain health are intriguing. Many people with Alzheimer's disease live without around-the-clock supervision. Monitoring devices for such patients could remind the person when to take medication, and how much. If the Alzheimer's patient wanders away, the device would report the person's location to a primary caregiver or to authorities.

A personal mobility coach could **MONITOR** body movements.

For people with limited movement, new devices may provide coaching for exercises that improve mobility as well as warnings of physical decline that could lead to a fall or other setback. A personal mobility coach could monitor body movements and suggest exercises to boost stability, range of motion, and muscle coordination. The device would analyze potential problems with body

[FACT: Raymond Kurzweil has suggested that data could enter the brain via nanobots, microscopic robots. **]**

TELEPATHY
A rendering of communicative lines between two people suggests telepathic communication, perhaps possible with computer assistance.

Already, **BRAIN-MONITORING** devices have begun "reading" simple thoughts.

movements, such as difficulty in rising from a chair or wobbling while walking. Ideally, it could detect the signs of an oncoming fall and alert the device's user to rest for a while. If the user did fall, the device could send an automatic call for help.

Perhaps most exciting, brain monitors already being developed might learn to recognize electrical patterns in a person's neural networks and communicate that person's thoughts or feelings automatically to caregivers. A person unable to speak or move, for example, could communicate the results of medical treatment or ask for a doctor's attention. If such devices sound like a rudimentary form of telepathy, that's an appropriate description. Already, brain-monitoring devices connected to computers have begun "reading" simple thoughts, such as individual letters of the alphabet, and translated them to characters on a computer screen. Patients with "locked-in syndrome," such as the author of the 1997 memoir *The Diving Bell and the Butterfly,* would have access to forms of communication previously denied to them by their nearly total paralysis.

REVERSE ENGINEERING

No matter what the enhancement might be, it will not reach its full potential until science understands much more about how the brain functions at both a macro and micro level. Theoretical physicist Michio Kaku predicts that by the middle of the 21st century, science will be able to reverse engineer the human brain. "Scientists, frustrated that they have not been able to create a robot made of silicon and steel, are also trying the opposite approach: taking apart the brain, neuron by neuron—just like a mechanic might take apart a motor, screw by screw—and then running a simulation of these neurons on a huge computer," he wrote in *The Physics of the Future.* Tests will start with small animals, such as

---

BRAIN INSIGHT

LIFE IN 2100
Will brain-computer partnerships be the norm a hundred years from now?

Physicist Michio Kaku, extrapolating into the future, has plotted the acceleration of technology and devised a scenario of life in 2100, when computers and the human brain will communicate directly with one another.

As described in Kaku's book *Physics of the Future,* it's a sometimes dizzying world of starships, Martian colonies, and DNA manipulation. In daily life, computer-brain interfaces make life more comfortable, as he outlines in a description of a typical day.

In the morning, you telepathically tell servant computers to adjust room temperature, prepare breakfast, and play

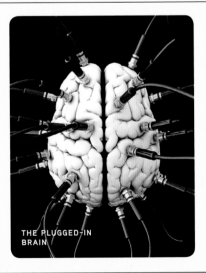

THE PLUGGED-IN BRAIN

music. You insert Internet-display contact lenses and scan the news without ever having to use your hands.

At the office, brains telepathically control robots doing difficult work—in Kaku's scenario, underwater construction.

Back home, you ask your computer assistant to help you shop. Your brain-computer interface calls up images of stores and goods.

The scenario progresses through dating, marriage, and parenthood. Then, as now, in Kaku's vision, you can always choose, including decisions about health and offspring. Brain never becomes slave to machine.

FLY CONTROL
(Above) Experiments have caused fruit flies' neurons to fire, and produce desired behavior, when exposed to laser light.

STOPPING THE SHAKES
(Below) A laser developed by Karl Deisseroth and colleagues at Stanford University has been shown to stop tremors in mice with Parkinson's disease.

mice and rats, and will eventually work their way up the evolutionary scale toward humans.

To get to that point requires understanding brain functions. Historically, brains could only be analyzed postmortem, or when damage to a particular brain region manifested itself in impaired memory, motor control, or some other function. Modern-day electronic and magnetic brain scans have allowed researchers to peer into the bioelectrical processes of living brain tissue. Kaku relates such macroscans to road maps that show interstates and major highways, but not the smaller thoroughfares or even the streets of your neighborhood.

Optogenetics

A new science called optogenetics, combining optics and genetics, is picking apart small neural pathways in animals. It may even allow scientists to control animal behavior by deciphering and then

stimulating behavior-initiating neural pathways. Optogenetic tests have been performed on fruit flies, which have about 150,000 neurons. The new science lets scientists activate particular neurons in the flies' brains associated with known behaviors. Stimulating two specific neurons, for example, prompts a fruit fly to try to escape by spreading its wings and taking off.

Understanding this connection allowed geneticists to breed a type of fruit fly whose escape-function neurons fired every time they fell under the light of a laser beam. Shine the laser light on the flies, and they fly away. More complex behaviors likely could be controlled with stimuli, and in larger animals too. How convenient it might be to snap your fingers and activate a set of neurons in your pet dog's brain that makes him immediately come to your side and sit, without you having to train him to do so. More sinister applications for human behavior no doubt could be imagined.

BRAIN INSIGHT

100 PERCENT BRAINPOWER?

Sorry, but you're already using all of your brain

In the 2011 movie *Limitless,* a character played by actor Bradley Cooper takes a pill that supposedly allows him to call on the cognitive power of his entire brain, rather than the 20 percent that the movie says humans normally access.

University of Minnesota physics professor James Kakalios, author of *The Amazing Story of Quantum Mechanics,* concedes that taking certain drugs can boost brainpower in the short run. However, he considers taking a pill to become a genius to be "crazy," far, far beyond current neurochemistry's boundaries.

The movie also perpetuates the myth that the human brain uses only a small percentage of its neurons. "We use all of our brains," Kakalios told NBC. "We don't understand a lot about how the brain works, but evolutionarily, everything in the three-pound hunk of meat on the top of your head is there for a reason."

Brain-imaging technology reveals no dead spots in a healthy brain. Although neural plasticity allows the brain to reroute the pathways for some functions around dead or damaged cells, demonstrating that some neural regions sometimes can be circumvented without complication, no neurons take a free ride inside the skull. Every brain cell has its function. Still, the urban myth about untapped brainpower has proved hard to kill.

NO DEAD SPOTS

MODELING THE BRAIN

Beyond optogenetics lies the enormous job of trying to model the entire human brain. This task, if successful, probably lies decades in the future. It might be accomplished either by modeling the entire brain at once, on some incredibly complex supercomputer, or by locating each of the billions of neurons in the brain and defining its function amid the brain's neural networks. A massive IBM computer called Blue Gene is already performing the former task in miniature by simulating a mouse brain. The mouse has about two million neurons, far fewer than a human. Yet simulating their interaction is very difficult, given each neuron's multiple connections to its neighbors.

Speaking in 2009, Henry Markram of the École Polytechnique Fédérale de Lausanne said it would not be impossible to "build" a human brain in ten years. However, the problem lies in power and scale. Achieving results would require a computer with 20,000 times more power than those currently available, and it would have to have memory storage capacity of about 500 times what's available on the Internet.

Realizing **RESULTS** in human terms may take many decades.

Learning the Brain, Cell by Cell

The other option, teasing apart the brain, neuron by neuron, already is under way, but realizing results in human terms may take many decades. Scientists have begun by slicing the brains of fruit flies into wafers about 150 atoms wide. Scanning electron microscopes then photograph each slice in detail, building up terabytes of data. Analyzing the many connections of the fruit fly brain by examining these photographs is likely to take years—perhaps 20, according to Gerry Rubin of the Howard Hughes Medical Institute. "After we

[**FACT:** Genes that produce light-sensitive proteins have been inserted in neurons, making them photoreactive.]

solve this, I'd say we're one-fifth of the way to understanding the human mind," Rubin said. That remaining four-fifths appears formidable, given the small size of the fruit fly brain compared with that of a human being.

Perhaps, by mid-century, the top-down and bottom-up approaches to understanding the brain will meet in the middle. When computer imaging of the whole joins with recognition of the roles of each individual part, science may understand the workings of the brain at a level that will make possible amazing advances in pharmacology, psychiatry, psychology, and biological and mechanical brain implants. Perhaps these will include drugs administered in precise doses in precise locations by implants or genetically engineered and grown tissues. Or stimulation of selected neural circuits to adjust mood. Maybe selection of memories to make them stronger or weaker—or even, in a nod to the movies *Total*

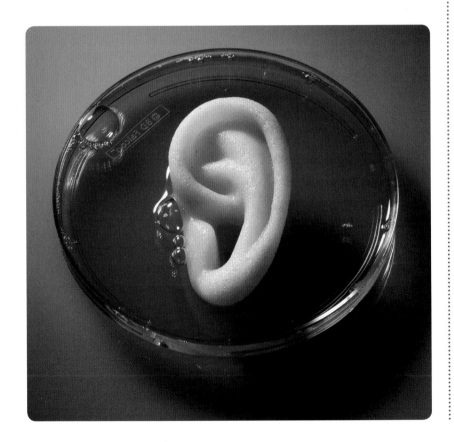

ENGINEERED TISSUE
A human ear is grown at the Wake Forest Institute for Regenerative Medicine. Might it be possible to build a brain from its parts?

TOTAL RECALL
Actor Colin Farrell stars in the remake of the 1990 movie *Total Recall,* which imagined implantation of memories.

Recall and *The Matrix,* the ability to plant ideas directly into the brain. Even enhancement to learning skills to improve performance, whether in mental or physical challenges. And seamless brain-machine interfaces, matching the software of the computer with the wetware of gray cells.

THE IMMORTAL BRAIN

Ray Kurzweil, one of the world's leading artificial-intelligence experts, believes the advent of reverse engineering the human brain may be only two decades in the future, far earlier than most scientists predict. Kurzweil deserves to be taken seriously, given his track record at accurately predicting the arc of technological development as well as his own technological skills. He invented the first print-to-speech machine to read for the blind, selling his first copy to the blind singer Stevie Wonder, and has improved speech recognition and music synthesizing machines. Microsoft founder

BRAIN INSIGHT

THE HOMER SIMPSON GENE
Could evolution have selected for a gene that makes us stupider?

Normally, when a gene is disabled or mutated, bad things result. However, knocking out a mouse gene known as RGS14 actually increases the mouse's ability to learn and remember information. A protein produced by the gene is believed to play a crucial role in the creation of memories, but strangely, when the gene is deleted in genetically altered mice, they get better at remembering and recognizing objects, easily recalling locations to help them speed more quickly through water mazes.

Pharmacologist John Hepler and colleagues at Emory University are

TESTING LAB MICE

so confident that RGS14, also found in humans, lowers brain performance that they have nicknamed it the "Homer Simpson gene," in honor of the cognitively challenged cartoon character. Mice without the gene

created long-term, strong connections among neurons in the CA2 region of the hippocampus.

This raises what Hepler calls a big question: Why would evolution select for a gene that makes the brain less smart?

"I believe that we are not really seeing the full picture," he said. "RGS14 may be a key control gene in a part of the brain that, when missing or disabled, knocks brain signals important for learning and memory out of balance."

Further in the future are potential studies of the gene's impact on performance of the human brain.

Bill Gates calls Kurzweil "the best person I know at predicting the future of artificial intelligence."

The End of Death?

In a *Time* magazine cover story in 2011, Kurzweil predicted that in less than 40 years, reverse engineering the brain and software-wetware interfaces will have become so powerful and so commonplace that they will erase death itself. Tiny medical machines inserted into the body could repair it in ways not currently possible, rearranging components of cells and fighting off the effects of disease and aging. Powerful computers could also copy the contents of the human brain to preserve it beyond even the limits of technologically extended life spans. The contents of the brain could be downloaded into the memory chips and circuits of a machine. Your personality, your memories, your creativity,

STEVIE WONDER
Performing in Las Vegas with Shirley Strawberry, the blind musician bought the first machine to turn text into speech.

your physical skills, transferred from an all-too-corruptible shell of flesh, blood, and bone to a metal avatar that could be repaired and replaced as its parts wear out. *Time* breathlessly headlined the article, "2045: The Year Man Becomes Immortal."

Kurzweil sees that moment, when machines become more intelligent than humans, and humans merge with machines, as the jumping-off point for a new era in evolution. *Time* calls that moment the end of human civilization. Kurzweil calls it "the singularity." The word comes from astrophysics and refers to a black hole, an infinitely tiny and infinitely dense point in space where the rules of normal physics don't hold true.

> The pace of technological **GROWTH** is not a straight line.

Kurzweil picked the year 2045 by computing rates of technological change. He started with a widely known scientific principle known as Moore's law, which observed, with surprising accuracy across many years, that the number of transistors that can occupy a given space on a microchip doubles every two years. Computers steadily get more powerful and smaller with advancing time, making the smallest laptops today more powerful than their room-sized ancestors. Kurzweil then turned to another technological arc, plotting increases in the number of millions of instructions per second (MIPS) that can be performed by a computer that costs $1,000. Like Moore's law, Kurzweil's graphed lines of MIPS computing power indicated a doubling every two years. When

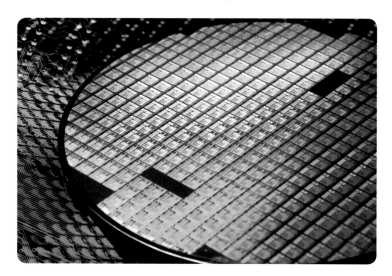

MOORE'S LAW
Moore's law says the amount of computing power on a given chip, such as this wafer, doubles every two years. That may lead to unknowable leaps forward.

he added the falling costs of DNA processing and other advances in biotechnology, he kept finding the same thing: The pace of technological growth is not a straight line. It shoots up like a rocket.

Which makes sense. Who hasn't sensed that the pace of change grows ever faster?

BRAIN INSIGHT

THE THREE LAWS

How realistic are Asimov's three laws of robotics?

If humanity perfects artificial intelligence and places it in steel robots, how might soft-bodied humans ensure their own safety?

ISAAC ASIMOV

Science fiction writer Isaac Asimov addressed that problem long before artificial intelligence became anything close to reality. Writing in 1942, he created the Three Laws of Robotics. They are:

❶ A robot may not injure a human being or, through inaction, allow a human being to come to harm.

❷ A robot must obey the orders given to it by human beings, except where such orders would conflict with the First Law.

❸ A robot must protect its own existence as long as such protection does not conflict with the First or Second Laws.

These laws, now commonly used in science fiction, appear to be common sense, but difficult to enact in the real world. "Most robots today can only work safely if segregated from humans, or if they move very slowly," said Antonio Bicchi of the University of Pisa's Faculty of Engineering. Bicchi is working on the Phriends project, funded by the European Union, to create robots that are safe and versatile enough to interact with humans. "The trade-off between safety and performance is the name of the game in physical human-machine interactions."

Forecasting where that accelerated technological change will take the human race, Kurzweil found the likely emergence of reverse engineering the brain in the middle of the 2020s, and the emergence of computers with brains equal to those of humans in 2045. Once computers achieve that level of intelligence, Kurzweil expects artificially intelligent beings to take over the design of artificial intelligence. When smart robots design even smarter robots, there's no telling where such technology will lead.

And that may include immortality, according to Kurzweil and others who follow emerging trends in science.

[**FACT**: Scientists trying to mimic creativity have programmed computers to paint and write jazz.]

FLESH OR SILICON?
Will brains of the future be gray matter, circuitry, or both?

Not everyone is happy with that idea. Kurzweil told *Time* he finds it surprising that so many people object to the possibility of fundamental changes in the human life cycle, including the end of mental and physical declines. "There are people who can accept computers being more intelligent than people, but the idea of significant changes to human longevity—that seems to be particularly controversial," he said. "People invested a lot of personal effort into certain philosophies dealing with issues of life and death. I mean, that's the major reason we have religion."

The Perils of Immortality

Critics of Kurzweil and his singularity doubt that any machine could ever duplicate the incredible artistry of the 100 billion neurons of the human brain, easily the most complicated object in the known universe. And ethicists raise red flags about immortality itself. Leonard Hayflick, who discovered the "Hayflick limit" that limits the longevity of cells by their number of cell divisions, outlined some of his cautions in his book *How and Why We Age*. Imagine, he said, that immortality could be achieved by downing a particular pill every day. "Who would get access to the pill if the cost were low, medium, or high? Who would have access to it if it was in short supply?" he asked. And if the pill were universally available, would that not create serious problems with overpopulation and strain scarce resources?

Perhaps human minds in silicon brains wouldn't tax the planet's resources the same way human bodies do when they require clean air and water, nourishing food, and shelter from heat and cold. But would immortal humans produce offspring? And if so, would there be the same problems of overcrowding and environmental strain that Hayflick mentioned? Immortality might not be all it's cracked up to be, if living forever means eventually living with unpleasant sensations, thoughts, or choices.

A Wealth of Choices

As this book has shown, the most distinguishing characteristic of the brain is its plasticity, its ability to change, adapt, and learn. Nobody can predict the future of brain science with any certainty. But it seems clear that neuroscience will provide not only breakthroughs to maintain and even improve brain health, but also lay out for ordinary people a smorgasbord of technology that could be used to open new levels of cognitive achievement, control states of mind, and generally make life more enjoyable—or, if misused, more difficult.

The future of brain health, both in the abstract and in the individual and concrete, is all about choice. And those choices can start today.

ETHICS OF IMMORTALITY
Leonard Hayflick, discoverer of a famous limit on cellular life, raises serious questions about the impact of life-extending technology.

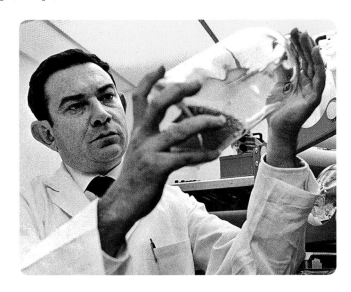

GLOSSARY

Agnosia. The inability to interpret sensory impressions.

Alzheimer's Disease. The most common cause of dementia, primarily affecting memory, thinking, and reasoning.

Amygdala. Structure in the brain's limbic system that plays an important role in emotional learning.

Antioxidant. Nutrient or chemical such as beta-carotene or vitamin C. Inhibits oxidation and may protect cells from damage caused by free radicals.

Aphasia. Neurodegenerative condition affecting the ability to understand or express language, generally as a result of stroke or similar brain trauma.

Autonomic Nervous System. The division of the peripheral nervous system that controls cardiac muscles, smooth muscles, and glands.

Axon. The hairlike extension of a neuron that sends out impulses.

Brain Stem. The portion of the brain just above the spinal cord, consisting of the midbrain, pons, and medulla.

Central Nervous System. The brain and spinal cord.

Cerebellum. Part of the brain behind the medulla and pons; governs coordinated muscle activity.

Cerebral Cortex. Outer layer of the cerebral hemispheres, responsible for conscious experience, thought, and planning.

Cerebrum. The two cerebral hemispheres that make up most of the brain.

Cortisol. A hormone released by the adrenal cortex in periods of extended stress.

Delirium. Temporary mental disturbance marked by hallucinations, disorganized speech, and confusion.

Dementia. A progressive mental condition, such as Alzheimer's disease, characterized by the development of many cognitive defects, such as disorientation and the inability to remember family members or make coherent plans.

Dendrite. The branching extension of the neuron cell body that receives electrical signals.

Diencephalon. Part of the forebrain that includes the thalamus, hypothalamus, and epithalamus.

Forebrain. The forward portion of the brain that includes the cerebrum and diencephalon.

Free Radicals. Atoms or groups of atoms with an odd number of electrons. Free radicals can start a chemical chain reaction within cells that can damage their DNA or other structures.

Frontal Lobe. One of four lobes in the front of the cerebral cortex responsible for movement and planning.

Ganglia (*singular, ganglion*). Groups of nerve cell bodies outside of the central nervous system.

Hayflick Limit. The natural limit that represents the highest number of times a cell can divide.

Hippocampus. Seahorse-shaped structure in the brain's limbic system that is involved in learning, memory, and emotion.

Hypothalamus. Structure in the brain's diencephalon that monitors the autonomic nervous system.

Insula. Region of the cerebral cortex linked to emotion and awareness of body states.

Life Expectancy. Expected number of years of life based on statistical probability that can be measured from birth or from any other age.

Limbic System. Part of the forebrain containing various structures involved in emotions and behavior.

Longevity. The length of life.

Medulla Oblongata. The lowest part of the brain stem.

Meninges. Protective coverings of the brain and spinal cord.

Method of Loci. A memory technique in which items to be remembered are associated with locations.

Midbrain. The brain stem between the pons and diencephalon.

Motor Neuron. Nerve that carries impulses from the brain and spinal cord to effectors, either muscles or glands.

Myelin Sheath. The multilayered fatty covering that insulates most nerve fibers.

Myopia. A condition in which images focus in front of the eye's retina, resulting in nearsightedness.

Neuroglia. Cells of the nervous system that support and protect neurons; also called glial cells.

Neuron. A nerve cell.

Neurotransmitter. Chemical released by a neuron at a synapse.

Optogenetics. A technology that allows users to control living systems using light.

Parasympathetic Division. Subdivision of the autonomic nervous system responsible for overseeing the conservation and restoration of the body's energy.

Parietal Lobe. A middle portion of each cerebral hemisphere that processes bodily sensations.

Peripheral Nervous System. The portion of the nervous system, consisting of nerves and ganglia, that lies outside the brain.

Pons. The bridge-like part of the brain stem between the medulla and midbrain.

Prefrontal Cortex. Brain region located in the anterior frontal lobe, responsible for reasoning, planning, empathy, and abstract ideas.

Presbycusis. Age-related hearing loss resulting from degenerative changes in the ear.

Presbyopia. Age-related changes in vision that lead to an inability to focus on close objects.

Proprioception. The perception of the position of the body in space.

Receptor. Specialized cell or portion of a nerve cell that responds to sensory input and converts it to an electrical signal.

Sensory Neuron. Nerve cell that carries sensory information into the brain and spinal cord.

Somatic Nervous System. The division of the peripheral nervous system that activates skeletal muscles.

Spinal Cord. The bundle of nervous tissue that runs down the center of the vertebral column, carrying messages to and from the brain.

Sympathetic Division. The subdivision of the autonomic nervous system responsible for overseeing activation of body systems in response to stress.

Synapse. The junction between two neurons or between a neuron and an effector, such as a gland or muscle.

Synesthesia. A condition in which the stimulation of one sense is simultaneously perceived by another sense or senses.

Temporal Lobe. A portion of the cerebral cortex, below the Sylvian fissure, that processes speech and memory.

Thalamus. A structure made of two egg-shaped masses of gray matter in the brain; acts as a relay station for sensory information flowing into the brain.

Ventricles. Large interior spaces in the forebrain and brain stem filled with cerebrospinal fluid.

Vestibular System. The portion of the inner ear responsible for balance and posture.

FURTHER READING

Amen, Daniel G. *Magnificent Mind at Any Age: Natural Ways to Unleash Your Brain's Maximum Potential.* New York: Three Rivers Press, 2008.

Begley, Sharon. *Train Your Mind, Change Your Brain: How a New Science Reveals Our Extraordinary Potential to Transform Ourselves.* New York: Ballantine Books, 2007.

Butler, Gillian, and Tony Hope. *Managing Your Mind: The Mental Fitness Guide,* 2nd ed. New York: Oxford University Press, 2007.

Cohen, Gene D. *The Creative Age: Awakening Human Potential in the Second Half of Life.* New York: Avon Books, 2000.

Eagleman, David. *Incognito: The Secret Lives of the Brain.* New York: Canongate, 2011.

Foer, Joshua. *Moonwalking With Einstein: The Art and Science of Remember Everything.* New York: Penguin Press, 2011.

Gottschall, Jonathan. *The Storytelling Animal: How Stories Make Us Human.* Boston: Houghton Mifflin Harcourt, 2012.

Green, C. R., and J. Beloff. *Through the Seasons: An Activity Book for Memory-Challenged Adults and Caregivers.* Baltimore, Md.: Johns Hopkins University Press, 2008.

Green, Cynthia R., and the editors of *Prevention. Brainpower Game Plan: Foods, Moves, and Games to Clear Brain Fog, Boost Memory, and Age-Proof Your Mind in 4 Weeks!* Emmaus, Pa.: Rodale, 2009.

Green, Cynthia R. *30 Days to Total Brain Health: A Whole Month's Worth of Daily Tips to Boost Your Memory and Build Better Brain Power.* Upper Montclair, N.J.: Memory Arts, 2011.

Green, C. R. *The Total Memory Workout: 8 Easy Steps to Maximum Memory Fitness.* New York: Bantam Books, 1999.

Hanson, Rick, with Richard Mendius. *Buddha's Brain: The Practical Neuroscience of Happiness, Love and Wisdom.* Oakland, Calif.: New Harbinger Publications, 2009.

Hayflick, Leonard. *How and Why We Age.* New York: Ballantine Books, 1994.

Higbee, K. L. *Your Memory: How It Works and How to Improve It.* New York: Marlowe and Company, 1996.

Hortstman, Judith. *The Scientific American Healthy Aging Brain: The Neuroscience of Making the Most of Your Mature Mind.* San Francisco: Jossey-Bass, 2012.

Johnson, Steven. *Everything Bad Is Good for You: How Today's Popular Culture is Actually Making Us Smarter.* New York: Riverhead Books, 2005.

Kaku, Michio. *The Physics of the Future: How Science Will Shape Human Destiny and Our Daily Lives by the Year 2100.* New York: Doubleday, 2011.

Katz, L. C. and M. Rubin. *Keep Your Brain Alive: 83 Neurobic Exercises to Help Prevent Memory Loss and Increase Mental Fitness.* New York: Workman Press, 1999.

Kurzweil, Ray. *The Singularity Is Near: When Humans Transcend Biology.* New York: Viking, 2005.

Michelon, Pascale. *Max Your Memory: The Complete Visual Program.* New York: DK Publishing, 2012.

Nordstrom, Nancy Merz. *Learning Later, Living Greater: The Secret for Making the Most of Your After-50 Years.* Boulder, Colo.: Sentient Publications, 2006.

Ramachandran, V. S. *The Tell-Tale Brain: A Neuroscientist's Quest for What Makes Us Human*. New York: W. W. Norton, 2011.

Ratey, John. *A User's Guide to the Brain: Perception, Attention, and the Four Theaters of the Brain*. New York: Random House, 2001.

Restak, Richard. *Mozart's Brain and the Fighter Pilot: Unleashing Your Brain's Potential*. New York: Harmony Books, 2001.

Restak, Richard. *Older and Wiser: How to Maintain Peak Mental Ability for as Long as You Live*. New York: Simon & Schuster, 1997.

Restak, Richard. *Poe's Heart and the Mountain Climber: Exploring the Effect of Anxiety on Our Brains and Our Culture*. New York: Harmony Books, 2004.

Rowe, J. W., and R. L. Kahn. *Successful Aging: The MacArthur Foundation Study*. New York: Pantheon Books, 1998.

Schacter, Daniel L. *The Seven Sins of Memory How the Mind Forgets and Remembers*. Boston: Houghton Mifflin, 2001.

Schwartz, Jeffrey M., and Sharon Begley. *The Mind and the Brain: Neuroplasticity and the Power of Mental Force*. New York: Regan Books/HarperCollins, 2002.

Snowdon, David. *Aging With Grace: What the Nun Study Teaches Us About Leading Longer, Healthier, and More Meaningful Lives*. New York: Bantam Books, 2001.

Sweeney, Michael S. *Brain: The Complete Mind: How It Develops, How It Works, and How to Keep It Sharp*. Washington, D.C.: National Geographic Press, 2009.

ABOUT THE AUTHOR

Michael S. Sweeney is a professor in the E. W. Scripps School of Journalism at Ohio University, where he heads the graduate program and teaches classes in reporting, writing, and editing. He has written several books for National Geographic, including *Brain: The Complete Mind* and *God Grew Tired of Us*. He lives in Athens, Ohio, with his wife, Carolyn.

ABOUT THE CONSULTANT

Cynthia R. Green, Ph.D., is a clinical psychologist, author, and leading expert on memory wellness and brain health. An assistant clinical professor of psychiatry at the Mount Sinai School of Medicine in New York, Dr. Green provides training, consultation, and keynote services on all things brain health to individuals, companies, and organizations through Memory Arts, LLC, and the Total Brain Health program (*www.totalbrain health.com*). Dr. Green appears frequently in the media as a contributor on brain wellness. A graduate of Smith College and New York University, Dr. Green lives with her family in New Jersey.

ILLUSTRATIONS CREDITS

All artwork by Jameson Simpson unless otherwise indicated.

2-3, EpicStockMedia/Shutterstock; 4, Konstantin Inozemtsev/iStockphoto; 5, Madlen/Shutterstock; 7, Karen Kasmauski/National Geographic Stock; 10 (LE), EpicStockMedia/Shutterstock; 10 (CTR), ATurner/Shutterstock; 10 (RT), Rodho/Shutterstock; 12, iDesign/Shutterstock; 14, Kitch Bain/Shutterstock; 15, Cultura/yellowdog/Getty Images; 16, Chris Leboe/chrisleboe.com/Getty Images; 17, Ian Cook/Time & Life Pictures/Getty Images; 18, Utekhina Anna/Shutterstock; 19, Felix Mizioznikov/Shutterstock; 20, hxdbzxy/Shutterstock.com; 21, Mike Price/Shutterstock; 22, Nicolas Hansen/iStockphoto; 23, Bob Riha, Jr./Nintendo via Getty Images; 24 (UP), Steshkin Yevgeniy/Shutterstock; 24 (CTR), Sascha Burkard/Shutterstock; 24 (LO), s_bukley/Shutterstock; 25, Ronnie Kaufman/Larry Hirshowitz/Getty Images; 26, Thomas Deerinck/Visuals Unlimited/Getty Images; 27, C.J. Guerin, PhD, MRC Toxicology Unit/Science Photo Library/Getty Images; 28, asharkyu/Shutterstock; 29 (UP), David Parker/Science Source; 29 (LO), Steve Gschmeissner/Science Photo Library/Getty Images; 30, Darren Hauck/Getty Images; 31, Bertl123/Shutterstock; 32, David Nevala/Aurora/Getty Images; 33, Ben Hider/Getty Images; 34, sai0112/Shutterstock; 35 (UP), Dusit/Shutterstock; 35 (LO), Hagit Berkovich/Shutterstock; 36, Mike Agliolo/Photo Researchers/Getty Images; 37, Willyam Bradberry/Shutterstock; 38 (UP), OZaiachin/Shutterstock; 38 (LO), Associates-Biophoto/Getty Images; 39, Oreon Strusinski/National Geographic My Shot; 40, Martin Valigursky/Shutterstock; 41 (UP), Bo Veisland, MI&I/Science Source; 41 (LO), Moodboard_Images/iStockphoto; 42, Brian Lawrence/Getty Images; 43, Photo by Allison Shelley/Getty Images for the International Committee of the Red Cross; 44, vhpfoto/Shutterstock; 46, Science Source/Photo Researchers, Inc.; 47, Art Wolfe/Getty Images; 48, AP Images/Gorilla Foundation; 49, lightpoet/Shutterstock; 50, John Darrell Van Horn and Carinna Torgerson, Laboratory of Neuro-Imaging at UCLA. Figure 1 from Van Horn JD, Irimia A, Torgerson CM, Chambers MC, Kikinis R, et al. (2012) Mapping Connectivity Damage in the Case of Phineas Gage. PLoS ONE 7(5): e37454. doi:10.1371/journal.pone.0037454; 51, AF archive/Alamy; 52, John Lund/Getty Images; 53, Alexandra Beier/Getty Images; 54, Dr. David E. Scott/Phototake, Inc.; 55, Ralph Hutchings/Visuals Unlimited/Getty Images; 56 (UP), ISM/Phototake, Inc.; 56 (LO), USGirl/iStockphoto; 57, Dorling Kindersley/Getty Images; 58, craftvision/Getty Images; 59 (UP), David Strick/Redux Pictures; 59 (LO), ZouZou/Shutterstock; 60, Sean Murphy/Getty Images; 61 (UP), E.A. Kennedy/The Image Works; 61 (LO), Howard J. Radzyner/Phototake, Inc.; 62, Theodore Robinson/The Bridgeman Art Library/Getty Images; 63 (UP), John Kelly/Getty Images; 63 (LO), Dionisvera/Shutterstock; 64 (LE), Pawel Gaul/iStockphoto; 64 (CTR), pukach/Shutterstock; 64 (RT), Mikael Damkier/Shutterstock; 66, Sebastian Kaulitzki/Shutterstock; 68, Scott Camazine/Photo Researchers/Getty Images; 69, Dusit/Shutterstock; 70, Scott Camazine/Photo Researchers/Getty Images; 71, suns07/Shutterstock; 72, Philip Lange/Shutterstock; 73, Christophe Testi/Shutterstock; 74, A Bello/Getty Images; 75 (UP), Picsfive/Shutterstock; 75 (LO), RelaxFoto.de/iStockphoto; 77, Steve Cole/iStockphoto; 78, Kim Pin Tan/Shutterstock; 79, Elena Gaak/Shutterstock; 80, PASIEKA/Science Photo Library/Getty Images; 81, Greg A Boiarsky/Shutterstock; 82, Norman Chan/Shutterstock; 83, criben/Shutterstock.com; 84, Kean Collection/Getty Images; 85, GWImages/Shutterstock; 86 (UP), Felixdesign/Shutterstock; 86 (LO), Steve Allen/Getty Images; 87, Composite image created using Shutterstock images: Stuart Monk/Shutterstock (NYC STREET SCENE), rangizzz/Shutterstock (HANDS HOLDING GLASSES); 89 (UP), Ralph Jr/Photo Researchers/Getty Images; 89 (LO), Cavan Images/Getty Images; 90 (UP), small_frog/iStockphoto; 90 (LO), Erik Von Weber/The Image Bank/Getty Images; 92 (UP), Yuri Arcurs/Shutterstock; 92 (LO), Anderson, George J., et al. Perceptual learning, aging, and improved visual performance in early stages of visual processing. Journal of Vision November 4, 2010 vol. 10 no. 13 article 4. doi: 10.1167/10.13.4; 95, Steven Wynn/iStockphoto; 96, Alex Luengo/Shutterstock; 98 (UP), restyler/Shutterstock; 98 (LO), s_bukley/Shutterstock.com; 99, Everett Collection/Shutterstock; 100, Lynn Watson/Shutterstock; 101, apixel/iStockphoto; 102 (UP), Graeme Dawes/Shutterstock; 102 (LO), Digital Vision/Getty Images; 104, Buero Monaco/Getty Images; 105, Omikron Omikron/Photo Researchers/Getty Images; 107 (UP), Dainis Derics/Shutterstock; 107 (LO), Marc Romanelli/Getty Images; 108, Don W. Fawcett/Science Source; 109, AYakovlev/Shutterstock; 110, technotr/iStockphoto; 112, BSIP/Science Source; 113, Tatiana Popova/Shutterstock; 114 (UP), sarsmis/Shutterstock; 114 (LO), Zia Soleil/Getty Images; 116, lightpoet/Shutterstock; 119 (UP), Matthew Stockman/Getty Images; 119 (LO), Paul Matthew Photography/Shutterstock; 120, Richard Heathcote/Getty Images; 121, AP Images/Frank Franklin II, File; 122, UIG via Getty Images; 124, STEVE GSCHMEISSNER/SPL/Getty Images; 125, ImagesBazaar/Getty Images; 126, juri/Shutterstock; 128, Electa/Leemage; 129, Maxim Tupikov/Shutterstock.com; 130, Stock Montage/Getty Images; 131, VLADGRIN/Shutterstock; 132, Aman Khan/iStockphoto; 134, F. D. Giddings/Phototake, Inc.; 135, marekuliasz/Shutterstock; 136 (UP), Jaguar PS/Shutterstock.com; 136 (LO), Chris Fortuna/Getty Images; 138, NoDerog/iStockphoto.com; 139, Taylor S. Kennedy/National Geographic/Getty Images; 141 (UP), rangizzz/Shutterstock; 141 (LO), Dan McCoy-Rainbow/Getty Images; 142, AFP/Getty Images; 143, Robyn Mackenzie/Shutterstock; 144, Niko Guido/iStockphoto.com; 145, Joe Raedle/Getty Images; 146, Don Bayley/Getty Images; 149, China Photos/Getty Images; 150, Brand X Pictures/Getty Images; 151, Andy Sacks/Getty Images; 152, Andrew Fox/Alamy; 153, Image Source/Getty Images; 154, Chris McGrath/Getty Images; 155, CoolR/Shutterstock; 156 (UP), Dulce Rubia/Shutterstock; 156 (LO), Thomas Northcut/Getty Images; 158, Jeff J. Mitchell/Getty Images; 159 (UP), Field Museum Library/Getty Images; 159 (LO), Benedict Campbell/Getty Images; 160, Purdue News Service photo/David Umberger; 162, Ivan Jekic/iStockphoto; 164, Pascal Goetgheluck/Science Source; 165, Zastol`skiy Victor Leonidovich/

Shutterstock; 166, piyato/Shutterstock; 167, Siri Stafford/Getty Images; 168, KEMAL BAŞ/iStockphoto; 171 (UP), Tara Moore/Getty Images; 171 (LO), Junko Kimura/Getty Images; 172 (UP), Gui Jun Peng/Shutterstock; 172 (LO), Arcady/Shutterstock; 174, Thomas Northcut/Getty Images; 175, LWA/The Image Bank/Getty Images; 176 (UP), Vasiliki Varvaki/Getty Images; 176 (LO), Tatiana Popova/Shutterstock; 178 (UP), MedicalRF.com/Getty Images; 178 (LO), Kuzmin Andrey/Shutterstock; 179, MarcelTB/Getty Images; 180, AP Images/Bruce Weaver, File; 181, Hulton Archive/Getty Images; 182, PhotoAlto/Ale Ventura/Getty Images; 183 Composite image created using iStockphoto images unless otherwise noted: (From L to R, Row 1) Steve Mann/Dreamstime.com, Jason Cheever, Timothy Large, Tony Lyons, (Row 2) Raf Croonen, stuartbur, Mary Catherine Brinkworth, Lance Bellers, (Row 3) Žiga Četrtič, Tobias Ott, Lisa-Blue, Andreas Nilsson, (Row 4) Nathan Watkins, Daniel Baumgartner, javarman3, Celso Pupo Rodrigues, (Row 5) Stuart Blackwell, Walter Harvey, Karl Martini, Taweesak Boonwirut; 184, Diego Cervo/Shutterstock; 185 (UP), Lasse Kristensen/Shutterstock; 185 (LO), Gray Mortimore/Getty Images; 186, Cornaile Photography/Getty Images; 188, Dan Kitwood/Getty Images; 189, Alex Potemkin/iStockphoto; 190, catnap72/iStockphoto; 191, matin/Shutterstock; 192, Tom England/iStockphoto.com; 193, Michael Hanson/Aurora/Getty Images; 194, Lawrence Migdale/Photo Researchers/Getty Images; 195 (UP), RIA Novosti/Alamy; 195 (LO), English School/The Bridgeman Art Library/Getty Images; 197, ZUMA Press/Newscom; 198, Science Source/Photo Researchers/Getty Images; 199 (UP), Chiyacat/Shutterstock; 199 (LO), Dan Tuffs; 200, Bloom Productions/Getty Images; 202, dundanim/Shutterstock; 205, stuartbur/iStockphoto; 206, PASIEKA/Science Photo Library/Getty Images; 207, Science Source/Photo Researchers, Inc.; 208 (UP), Living Art Enterprises/Getty Images; 208 (LO), Levent Konuk/Shutterstock; 209, George Mattei/Photo Researchers/Getty Images; 211, Spencer Grant/Getty Images; 212, Mat Denney/Getty Images; 213, Zhang Bo/iStockphoto; 214, Soren Svendsen/Getty Images; 215, Lynn Johnson/National Geographic/Getty Images; 216, Lobke Peers/Shutterstock; 217, Lasse Kristensen/Shutterstock; 218, akg-images/The Image Works; 219, MECKY/Getty Images; 221, Ashley Wiley/iStockphoto; 222, David Allan Brandt/Getty Images; 223, Karan Kapoor/Getty Images; 224 (UP), SVLuma/Shutterstock; 224 (LO), fivespots/Shutterstock; 226 (UP), ZEPHYR/Science Photo Library/Getty Images; 226 (LO), IvicaNS/Shutterstock; 227, Science Picture Co/Getty Images; 229, Buena Vista Images/The Image Bank/Getty Images; 231, Jordan Siemens/Getty Images; 232, Jekaterina Nikitina/Getty Images; 233, Stephen VanHorn/Shutterstock; 235, AP Images/Jae C. Hong; 237, Kyra Pfetzing/Shutterstock.com; 238, LanKS/Shutterstock; 239, John Burke/Getty Images; 240 (UP), Marianne Barcellona/Time & Life Pictures/Getty Images; 240 (LO), Africa Studio/Shutterstock; 242, Joao Virissimo/Shutterstock; 243, Jerry Horbert/Shutterstock; 244, t_kimura/iStockphoto; 245, Frank Hudec/Getty Images; 246, DrAfter123/iStockphoto; 247, Elena Schweitzer/Shutterstock; 248, Henrik Sorensen/Getty Images; 249, Andrea Michele Piacquadio/Shutterstock; 250, PaulPaladin/Shutterstock; 252, SerrNovik/Shutterstock; 253, Thomas Barwick/Getty Images; 254, Kin Images/The Image Bank/Getty Images; 255, Stephen Mcsweeny/Shutterstock; 256, DeiMosz/Shutterstock; 257, Cavan Images/The Image Bank/Getty Images; 258, Erik Isakson/Getty Images; 259, Balogh Tamas/Shutterstock; 260, Abel Mitja Varela/iStockphoto; 261, Maxim Malevich/iStockphoto; 263 (UP), Sollina Images/The Image Bank/Getty Images; 263 (LO), Fotos International/Getty Images; 264, ranplett/iStockphoto; 265, Anna Hoychuk/Shutterstock; 266 (UP), Lisovskaya Natalia/Shutterstock; 266 (LO), Nattika/Shutterstock; 267, Andrei Zarubaika/Shutterstock; 268, The Photo Works/Photo Researchers/Getty Images; 270, Hannamariah/Shutterstock; 271, Karen Sarraga/Shutterstock; 272 (UP), Brian A Jackson/Shutterstock; 272 (LO), Tuul/hemis.fr/Getty Images; 273, Alinari via Getty Images; 274, Valentyn Volkov/Shutterstock; 275, Zen Sekizawa/Getty Images; 277, Lacey Ann Johnson/Getty Images; 278, MedicalRF.com/Getty Images; 279, Heather Perry/National Geographic/Getty Images; 280, David McLain/National Geographic Stock; 282, Biophoto Associates/Science Source; 284 (UP), Jack Dagley Photography/Shutterstock.com; 284 (LO), Nucleus Medical Art, Inc/Phototake, Inc.; 287 (UP), YanLev/Shutterstock; 287 (LO), irin-k/Shutterstock; 288 (UP), Ted Kinsman/Getty Images; 288 (LO), Aspen Photo/Shutterstock.com; 289, Jay Drowns/Sporting News via Getty Images; 290 (LE), Lois & Bob Schlowsky/Getty Images; 290 (CTR), Yury Kuzmin/iStockphoto; 290 (RT), Djura Topalov/iStockphoto; 292, Photo by Institute for Stem Cell Research via Getty Images; 294, Keystone/Hulton Archive/Getty Images; 295, Alwyn Cooper/iStockphoto; 296, Henrik Jonsson/iStockphoto; 297, Chris Gallagher/Photo Researchers/Getty Images; 298, Courtesy Brookhaven National Laboratory. Figure 1 from Volkow ND, Fowler JS, Logan J, et al. Effects of Modafinil on Dopamine and Dopamine Transporters in the Male Human Brain: Clinical Implications. JAMA. 2009;301(11):1148-1154. doi:10.1001/jama.2009.351; 299, Thomas Nilsson/Getty Images; 300, Sidney Moulds/Science Source; 301, Peng Wu/iStockphoto; 302, Ed Reschke/Getty Images; 303, barbaradudzinska/Shutterstock; 304 (UP), Pakhnyushcha/Shutterstock; 304 (LO), Mark Sullivan/WireImage/Getty Images; 305, Javier Larrea/age fotostock/Getty Images; 306, VLADGRIN/Shutterstock; 307, Maggie Steber/National Geographic Stock; 308, Renee Meiller, University of Wisconsin-Madison College of Engineering; 309 (UP), Science Source/Photo Researchers, Inc.; 309 (LO), wunkley/Alamy; 310, TORSTEN BLACKWOOD/AFP/Getty Images; 311, Vitaly Korovin/Shutterstock; 312, Emory News Center; 313, Living Art Enterprises/Science Source; 314 (UP), © Helen Mayberg; 314 (LO), Wicab; 315, Omer Yurdakul Gundogdu/iStockphoto; 316, Zap Art/Getty Images; 317, braingate2.org; 318 (UP), AP Images/Shizuo Kambayashi; 318 (LO), Emotiv; 319, Ian Nicholson/PA Photos/Landov; 320, Carol and Mike Werner/Science Source; 321, Colin Anderson/Getty Images; 322, AP Images/Charles Dharapak; 323, Mike Harrington/Getty Images; 324, Ojo Images/Getty Images; 325, vasabii/Shutterstock; 326 (UP), Antagain/iStockphoto; 326 (LO), John B. Carnett/Popular Science via Getty Images; 327, Steven Hunt/Getty Images; 329, Rebecca Hale, NGP; 330 (UP), REKALL PRODUCTIONS/THE KOBAL COLLECTION/The Picture Desk; 330 (LO), FikMik/Shutterstock; 331, Isaac Brekken/WireImage/Getty Images; 332, Hui-Ju Chang/Shutterstock; 333, Mondadori via Getty Images; 334, Images.com/Corbis; 335, Stanford Medical History Center.

INDEX

Boldface indicates illustrations.

COMPLETE GUIDE TO
BRAIN
HEALTH

Michael S. Sweeney
Brain Boosters by Cynthia R. Green, Ph.D.

Published by the National Geographic Society

John M. Fahey, *Chairman of the Board and Chief Executive Officer*
Timothy T. Kelly, *President*
Declan Moore, *Executive Vice President; President, Publishing and Travel*
Melina Gerosa Bellows, *Executive Vice President; Chief Creative Officer, Books, Kids, and Family*

Prepared by the Book Division

Hector Sierra, *Senior Vice President and General Manager*
Janet Goldstein, *Senior Vice President and Editorial Director*
Jonathan Halling, *Design Director, Books and Children's Publishing*
Marianne R. Koszorus, *Design Director, Books*
Susan Tyler Hitchcock, *Senior Editor*
R. Gary Colbert, *Production Director*
Jennifer A. Thornton, *Director of Managing Editorial*
Susan S. Blair, *Director of Photography*
Meredith C. Wilcox, *Director, Administration and Rights Clearance*

Staff for This Book

Patricia Daniels, *Editor*
Elisa Gibson, *Art Director*
Kristin Sladen, *Illustrations Editor*
Linda Makarov, *Designer*
Marshall Kiker, *Associate Managing Editor*
Judith Klein, *Production Editor*
Lisa A. Walker, *Production Manager*
Galen Young, *Illustrations Specialist*
Katie Olsen, *Production Design Assistant*

Manufacturing and Quality Management

Phillip L. Schlosser, *Senior Vice President*
Chris Brown, *Vice President, NG Book Manufacturing*
George Bounelis, *Vice President, Production Services*
Nicole Elliott, *Manager*
Rachel Faulise, *Manager*
Robert L. Barr, *Manager*

The National Geographic Society is one of the world's largest nonprofit scientific and educational organizations. Founded in 1888 to "increase and diffuse geographic knowledge," the Society works to inspire people to care about the planet. National Geographic reflects the world through its magazines, television programs, films, music and radio, books, DVDs, maps, exhibitions, live events, school publishing programs, interactive media and merchandise. *National Geographic* magazine, the Society's official journal, published in English and 33 local-language editions, is read by more than 60 million people each month. The National Geographic Channel reaches 435 million households in 37 languages in 173 countries. National Geographic Digital Media receives more than 19 million visitors a month. National Geographic has funded more than 10,000 scientific research, conservation and exploration projects and supports an education program promoting geography literacy. For more information, visit www.nationalgeographic.com.

For more information, please call 1-800-NGS LINE (647-5463) or write to the following address:

National Geographic Society
1145 17th Street N.W.
Washington, D.C. 20036-4688 U.S.A.

For information about special discounts for bulk purchases, please contact National Geographic Books Special Sales: ngspecsales@ngs.org

For rights or permissions inquiries, please contact National Geographic Books Subsidiary Rights: ngbookrights@ngs.org

Copyright © 2013 National Geographic Society

Brain Boosters text copyright © 2013 Cynthia R. Green, Ph.D.

All rights reserved. Reproduction of the whole or any part of the contents without written permission from the publisher is prohibited.

ISBN: 978-1-4262-1244-4 (regular)
ISBN: 978-1-4262-1245-1 (deluxe)
ISBN: 978-1-4262-1671-8 (special sale edition)

Printed in the United States of America

15/QGT-QGL/1